D1571905

Polymer Adsorption
and Dispersion Stability

ACS SYMPOSIUM SERIES 240

Polymer Adsorption and Dispersion Stability

E. D. Goddard, EDITOR
Union Carbide Corporation

B. Vincent, EDITOR
University of Bristol, England

Based on a symposium sponsored by
the Division of Colloid and Surface Chemistry
at the 186th Meeting
of the American Chemical Society,
Washington, D.C.,
August 28–September 2, 1983

American Chemical Society, Washington, D.C. 1984

69865206

SEP/AE

CHEM

Library of Congress Cataloging in Publication Data

Polymer adsorption and dispersion stability.

(ACS symposium series, ISSN 0097–6156; 240)

Includes bibliographies and index.

1. Polymers and polymerization—Congresses.
2. Adsorption—Congresses. 3. Suspensions
(Chemistry)—Congresses.

I. Goddard, E. D. (Errol Desmond), 1926–
II. Vincent, B. (Brian). III. American Chemical Society.
Division of Colloid and Surface Chemistry. IV. Series.

QD380.P634   1984   547.8′40454   83–25787
ISBN 0–8412–0820–4

ACS Symposium Series

M. Joan Comstock, *Series Editor*

Advisory Board

FOREWORD

The ACS SYMPOSIUM SERIES was founded in 1974 to provide a medium for publishing symposia quickly in book form. The format of the Series parallels that of the continuing ADVANCES IN CHEMISTRY SERIES except that in order to save time the papers are not typeset but are reproduced as they are submitted by the authors in camera-ready form. Papers are reviewed under the supervision of the Editors with the assistance of the Series Advisory Board and are selected to maintain the integrity of the symposia; however, verbatim reproductions of previously published papers are not accepted. Both reviews and reports of research are acceptable since symposia may embrace both types of presentation.

CONTENTS

PREFACE

ALTHOUGH THE ABILITY OF A POLYMER in solution to act as either a stabilizer or a destabilizer of a particulate suspension has long been known— natural gums have been used for pigment particle stabilization since the days of antiquity, for example—the actual mechanisms involved have only recently received attention and clarification. Accurate description of the polymer adsorption process has evolved even more recently, and owes much to theories of interfaces and polymer solutions. During the last 20 years the technological importance of soluble polymers to areas such as mineral processing, oil production, fiber treatment, detergency, the personal care industry, flocculants, dispersants, lubricants, flow aids, antinucleating agents, reprographics, and so on has grown steadily; many of these areas are in the domain of the colloid chemist.

At the symposium on which this book is based, the various authors presented papers on the general topic of polymer adsorption and particle stabilization/destabilization. In this volume both aqueous and nonaqueous systems are included, comprising work on both natural and synthetic polymers. Together the chapters constitute a comprehensive update of research in progress on these topics and provide broad coverage of both experimental and theoretical aspects.

We would like to acknowledge the assistance of the Petroleum Research Fund in providing financial aid for the travel of several of the overseas academic participants, and also that of the many officers of the Division of Colloid and Surface Chemistry of the American Chemical Society who helped to make the symposium possible.

E. D. GODDARD
Union Carbide Corporation

BRIAN VINCENT
University of Bristol, England

November 10, 1983

OVERVIEW

Polymers in Disperse Systems: An Overview

B. VINCENT

School of Chemistry, University of Bristol, Cantock's Close, Bristol BS8 1TS, England

In this paper some of the current thinking in three closely-related areas is highlighted: polymer adsorption; the effect of polymer on the pairwise interaction between particles; and the effect of polymers on dispersion stability.

It would be an impossible task to summarize in one short review the many facets of this subject. This has been more than adequately attempted in several other recent reviews of the fields of polymer adsorption (1-4) and dispersion stability in the presence of polymers (1, 5-7). My objective, therefore, is primarily to set the scene for the papers that follow: to highlight current theoretical and experimental work, and to indicate where future research efforts might conceivably be directed.

It is convenient to divide this topic into three areas, which follow on from each other in a logical sequence:

i)   polymers at a single interface: adsorption and depletion
ii) interactions between two particles in the presence of polymer: establishment of the pair potential.
iii) dispersion stability in the presence of polymer: thermodynamic and kinetic considerations.

Polymers at a Single Interface

Our understanding of polymer adsorption has followed in the wake of developments in the theory of adsorption of small molecules and that of polymer solutions. It is useful, at the outset to introduce some of the ideas that have been developed in recent years, particularly with regard to the latter topic.

The characteristic feature of a macromolecule in solution is its high degree of conformational freedom. The simplest possible model for an isolated macromolecule is the random walk (or diffusion) model, in which a polymer chain is regarded as a series of r linear links, each of length 1, with no restriction on the angles between successive links. This leads to the well-known expression for the root-mean-square (r.m.s.) end-end distance, $<R_r^2>^{\frac{1}{2}}$,

$$<R_r^2>^{\frac{1}{2}} = r^{\frac{1}{2}}1 \qquad (1)$$

Such a model ignores restrictions on the bond angles and dihedral angles imposed by the local chemical structure. This may be taken care of empirically by defining a characteristic ratio, C_∞, where

$$C_\infty = \lim_{r \to \infty} \frac{<R_r^2>}{rl^2} \qquad (2)$$

where $<R_r^2>^{\frac{1}{2}}$ is calculated from experimental data (e.g. light scattering). C_∞ is essentially a flexibility parameter which may be calculated for certain classes of chains, using e.g. the rotational isomeric theory developed by Flory (8); values generally lie in the range 3-15.

A second problem with the random walk model concerns the interaction between segments far apart along the contour of the chain but which are close together in space. This is the so-called "excluded volume" effect. The inclusion of this effect gives rise to an expansion of the chain, and in three-dimensions, $<R_r^2>^{\frac{1}{2}} \sim r^{3/5}$ (9), rather than the $r^{\frac{1}{2}}$ dependence given in equation (1).

The effect of the solvent is a complex one, but can again be taken care of empirically. It is possible to define a solvent (a theta, θ, solvent) whereby the net effect of an unfavourable segment-solvent interaction is to reduce the dimensions of the chain so as to exactly compensate for the excluded volume effect. If we define $<R_r^2>_0^{\frac{1}{2}}$ as the r.m.s. end-end distance in a θ-solvent then we can introduce an expansion factor, α whereby

$$\alpha = <R_r^2>^{\frac{1}{2}}/<R_r^2>_o^{\frac{1}{2}} \qquad (3)$$

where $<R_r^2>^{\frac{1}{2}}$ is the value in the solvent under consideration. $\alpha > 1$ in a better-than-θ solvent, $\alpha < 1$ in a worse-than-θ solvent and $\alpha = 1$ in a θ-solvent (e.g. for polystyrene cyclohexane is a θ-solvent at 34.5°C, i.e. the θ-temperature).

The above considerations apply to isolated polymer chains in solution, i.e. at very low polymer concentrations or volume fractions, ϕ_p (i.e. in the limit $\phi_p \to 0$). As ϕ_p increases, interchain interactions become important. Indeed, at a critical polymer concentration, ϕ_p^*, interchain overlap begins, and beyond a second critical concentration, ϕ_p^{**}, the chains are so overlapped that the segment concentration is effectively uniform over the

whole solution. These conditions are illustrated schematically
in figure 1 for two interacting chains where the segment density
(ρ) profiles are shown; the individual profiles are Gaussian.
   Three concentration regions may be identified:

i) $0 < \phi_p < \phi_p^*$:   the dilute region.

ii) $\phi_p^* < \phi_p < \phi_p^{**}$: the semi-dilute region.

iii) $\phi_p^{**} < \phi_p < 1$:   the concentrated region.

   Edwards (10) has treated the concentrated region by considering a mean field approximation. The problem is to solve the
random flight or diffusion equation in a uniform field provided by
the segments (from all chains). This field is proportional to ϕ_p,
but is independent of position. It was shown that, under these
conditions, $<R_r^2>^{\frac{1}{2}}$ is again $\sim r^{\frac{1}{2}}$ (i.e. $\alpha = 1$, for all solvents).
   The problem of concentration effects has also been discussed
by des Cloisseaux, de Gennes and co-workers (11-13) using scaling
theory. Daoud and Jannink (14) have summarized the behaviour of
$<R_r^2>^{\frac{1}{2}}$ over the various regions of the temperature-composition
phase diagram for a polymer in a good (i.e. better-than-θ) solvent;
this is shown in figure 2, where τ is a relative temperature, i.e.
$\tau = (T - \theta)/\theta$. Region I corresponds to the dilute region, where
$<R_r^2>^{\frac{1}{2}} \sim r^{3/5} \tau^{1/5}$; region I' is the theta region, where $<R_r^2>^{\frac{1}{2}} \sim$
$r^{\frac{1}{2}}$; Region III is the concentrated region, where again
$<R_r^2>^{\frac{1}{2}} \sim r^{\frac{1}{2}}$ (i.e. as predicted by Edwards); Region II is the semi-
dilute region, where $<R_r^2>^{\frac{1}{2}} \sim r^{\frac{1}{2}}\phi^{-1/8}\tau^{1/8}$ (i.e. $<R_r^2>^{\frac{1}{2}}$ is temperature
and concentration, as well as chain length, dependent); Region IV
is the co-existing, two-phase region.
   The adsorption of chain molecules at the solid/solution
interface differs in many respects from that of small molecules.
Some of these differences are listed below.
i)   segments may be "adsorbed" although they are not in direct
      contact with the surface, i.e. in loops or tails rather than
      trains.
ii)   the nature of the adsorption isotherm; polymer adsorption
      leads in general to high affinity isotherms. The amount
      adsorbed rises very steeply at low concentrations, and then
      levels to a pseudo-plateau region. Unfortunately, practical
      difficulties inhibit the establishment of the isotherm beyond
      bulk polymer volume fractions, $\phi_p \sim 10^{-3}$ or so.
iii) it is difficult to desorb polymers by dilution (although they
      may be exchanged). This has sometimes led to the (mistaken)
      idea that polymer adsorption is "irreversible".
iv)   polymers are frequently polydisperse in chain length, r;
      this leads to fractionation on the surface, "rounded"
      isotherms and a dependence on the surface area/solution
      volume ratio.
v)   there may be problems in defining the relevant specific
      surface area, particularly for porous materials or when the
      adsorbent particle size is $\lesssim$ chain dimensions.

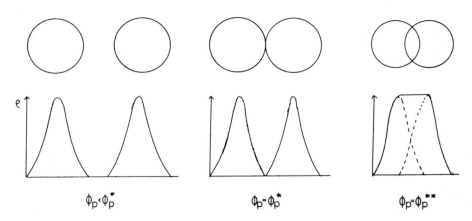

Figure 1.   Schematic illustration of the two critical concentrations in a polymer solution: ϕ_p^* and ϕ_p^{**}.

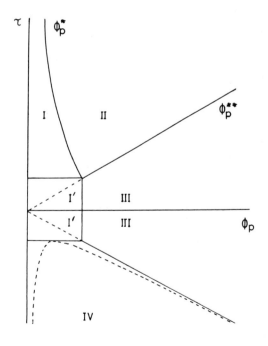

Figure 2.   Temperature-composition phase diagram for a polymer solution. $\tau = (T - \theta)/\theta$

vi) multilayer adsorption, per se, is rare, and restricted, in
general, to regions of the phase diagram (figure 2) close to
the phase separation boundary, or when aggregation is known
to occur in solution.

vii) adsorption rates are much slower, particularly in the case of
polydisperse chains.

There has been a plethora of theories of polymer adsorption
in recent years, at least for linear chains adsorbed on regular
surfaces: these have been adequately reviewed elsewhere (1-4).
Computer simulation and analytical methods have both been used,
based on diffusion equation, partition function and scaling theory
approaches. There are a number of parameters which are common to
most of these theories; some of these are also relevant to
theories of polymer solutions, i.e.

i)   the chain length, r, (i.e. the number of statistical elements
(segments) in a chain. This should be distinguished from the
number of monomer units in a chain, x (x = molar mass of
chain/molar mass of a monomer unit).

ii) the statistical segmental length, 1.

iii) the characteristic ratio C_∞ or some other flexibility
parameter

iv) the net solvent-segment interaction parameter, i.e. α, or
more explicitly χ, the Flory interaction parameter ($\chi = 0$ is
an athermal solvent; $\chi = \frac{1}{2}$ is a theta solvent).

v)   the polymer volume fraction, ϕ_p

For adsorbed polymers two other effects have to be considered:

vi) the surface is inpenetrable, i.e. z > 0, where z is the
distance normal to the surface.

vii) the net segment-surface interaction parameter, χ_s. A rigorous
definition of χ_s has been given by Fleer and Lyklema (4).

The objective of any theory is to predict how various parameters which characterise the adsorbed polymer vary with these
system variables. There are a number of parameters which characterise the adsorbed polymer, and which should, ideally, all be
measured for any given system:

i)   the adsorbed amount. This is best expressed as a dimensionless quantity, θ, the ratio of the total number of adsorbed segments/
maximum number of segments in a monolayer at the surface (i.e.
with every surface "site" filled). The exact correlation between
an adsorption site and the surface structure of the adsorbent is
not always obvious. If a lattice model is used, then considerable
difficulties also arise in correlating the size of the lattice
element with the structure of the polymer chain, the solvent
molecules and the surface structure of the adsorbent.

At high polymer concentrations, $\phi_p > \phi_p^*$, one also has to
distinguish between segments which are present in the adsorbed
layer region and belonging to chains which are actually adsorbed
(i.e. have at least one segment in contact with the surface), and
those segments which are present in this region but belong to free,

overlapping chains which have no segments in contact with the
surface. Scheutjens and Fleer (15,16) in their lattice model of
polymer adsorption have computed the relative contributions to
θ_{total} from these two types of segments. In figure 3, θ_{total} is
shown as a function of log r, together with the two contributions
θ_d (depletion) and θ_{ex} (excess) which are defined below, and interpreted in the inset

$$\theta_{ex} = \sum_i (\phi_i - \phi_p) \tag{4}$$

$$\theta_d = \sum_i (\phi_p - \phi_i^{n.a.}) \tag{5}$$

where ϕ_p is the bulk polymer (or segment) volume fraction
(Scheutjens and Fleer (15,16) use ϕ_* rather than ϕ_p as the symbol
for bulk polymer concentration), ϕ_i is the total volume fraction
of segments in layer i, and $\phi_i^{n.a.}$ is the volume fraction of
segments in layer i arising from non-adsorbed chains.
        From figure 3, where $\phi_p = 10^{-3}$, it can be seen that θ_{total}
exceeds θ_{ex} only for r $\gtrsim 10^5$, i.e. where $\phi_p > \phi_p^*$. For lower
values of r, $\theta \sim \ln r$.
        In figure 4, log θ is plotted as a function of log ϕ_p for two
values of χ ($\chi = 0$, athermal; $\chi = 0.5$, theta solvent) and fixed r
and χ_s. The log-log scale is used to highlight the main features.
The isotherm may be divided into three regions.
a)   the Henry's law region, where log θ increases steeply and
        linearly with log ϕ_p. Here adsorption occurs as individual
isolated chains.
b)   beyond some critical value of θ, chain overlap occurs on the
        surface and θ increases very much more slowly with ϕ_p. This
critical value, θ^* may be conveniently defined by the intersection
of the two straight lines as in figure 4. Clearly θ^* for the
surface has strong analogies with ϕ_p^* for bulk solution. Note that
θ^* occurs at inaccessibly low ϕ_p values. The experimental range
of ϕ_p values ($\sim 10^{-6}$ to $\sim 10^{-3}$) corresponds to the pseudo-plateau
region of the isotherm.
c)   beyond the limit of the dilute bulk solution region ($\phi_p > \phi_p^*$)
contributions from θ_d arise and θ increases rapidly up to the
value for $\phi_p = 1$.
        Experimentally, the adsorbed amount is usually expressed as Γ
i.e. mass polymer/area of surface. This is usually obtained from
a mass balance technique, after analysing the equilibrium solution.
$\Gamma \propto \theta_{ex}$, but an exact correlation is difficult to establish.
        Finally, in this section we consider the case where $\chi_s = 0$,
i.e. where no adsorption takes place. There is then a depletion of
segments in the region near the interface (figure 5). It is useful
to define an effective depletion zone of thickness, δ_d, defined
such that the two shaded areas are equal, and given by,

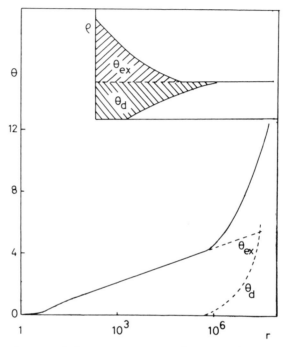

Figure 3. θ_{tot} and its components, θ_{ex} and θ_d, as a function of chain length, for $\phi_p = 10^{-3}$ (hexagonal lattice, $\chi_s = 1$, $\chi = 0.5$). The inset gives a quantitative picture of the segment concentration profile in the adsorbed layer. (Reproduced with permission from Ref. 16. Copyright 1982, Academic Press (London).)

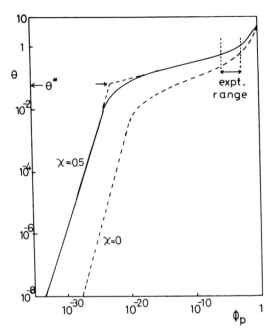

Figure 4.   log θ versus log ϕ_p for r = 100, χ_s = 1 at   the
two values of χ indicated.   (hexagonal lattice).
(Reproduced with permission from Ref. 16.   Copyright 1982,
Academic Press (London).)

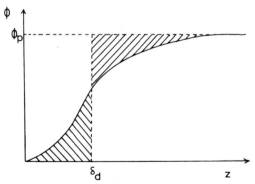

Figure 5.   Depletion near a surface where χ_s = 0.

$$\theta_d = \phi_p \, \delta_d \qquad\qquad (6)$$

ii) <u>the bound fraction of segments</u>. One may define the fraction
of segments in trains, p, by the relationship,

$$p = \theta_1/\theta \qquad\qquad (7)$$

where θ_1 is the fractional coverage in the first layer. In lattice
theories, $\theta_1 = \phi_1$. All theories predict (1) that p is a decreasing
function of ϕ_p and hence θ, at least beyond θ^*. χ_s is an important
parameter: there is a critical value of χ_s, χ_s^c, below which p = 0,
i.e. no segments are adsorbed. For $\chi_s > \chi_s^c$, p is an increasing
function of χ_s. p generally increases as χ decreases (i.e. as the
solvent "quality" is increased). For $\chi_s > \sim \chi_s^c$, fixed χ and θ, p
generally decreases as r increases.

p may be obtained (1-4) using spectroscopic (n.m.r., e.s.r. or
infrared), calorimetric or electrochemical techniques, either
directly or through the estimation of θ_1 (equation 7).
iii) <u>the extension of segments normal to the surface</u>. Ideally,
one would like to be able to predict theoretically and/or establish
experimentally $\phi(z)$ (or ϕ_i for a lattice model), i.e. the form of
the segment density profile normal to the surface. Clearly, this
only has real meaning for $\theta > \theta^*$, where a uniform distribution of
segments parallel to the surface may reasonably be assumed.
Although a number of recent theories are able to predict $\phi(z)$, the
Scheutjens-Fleer theory (15,16) is also able to predict the
separate contributions to ϕ_i from tails and loops.

Experimentally, the form of $\phi(z)$ has been recently established
for adsorbed homopolymers and terminally anchored tails by the
Bristol group (17,20). Knowing $\phi(z)$ one may then calculate the
r.m.s. thickness of the adsorbed layer. Previous measurements of
the "thickness" (1-4) have usually involved ellipsometry (flat
surfaces) or some hydrodynamic technique (particles). In neither
case can the calculated thickness be unambiguously related to $\phi(z)$,
although recent theoretical work by Cohen Stuart et al. (21), to be
discussed at this meeting, has made an attempt to relate the hydrodynamic thickness, δ_h, to $\phi(z)$.

The theoretical and (model) experimental work referred to
above has largely been concerned with linear homopolymers
adsorbed on regular surfaces. However, there is a vast literature
of experimental studies on more complex systems. Unfortunately,
in many cases the systems are either ill-defined and/or only
adsorption isotherms have been established; for drawing general
conclusions or comparison with theory such studies are of little
use. On the theoretical side, clearly the work needs to be
extended towards these more complex systems. In particular,
developments are required in the following areas (starts have
already been made in some cases):

a)   copolymers and branched polymers.
b)   polyelectrolytes (leading hopefully and eventually to
      bipolymers)
c)   polymer mixtures (fractionation)
d)   adsorption onto non-flat surfaces (especially spheres)
e)   adsorption onto heterogeneous surfaces
f)   adsorption at the liquid/liquid and liquid/vapour interfaces
g)   co-adsorption between plates or particles, and adsorption in
      cavities (pores).

Pairwise Interaction Between Particles in the Presence of Polymer

The starting point for any theory of particle interactions is the
D.L.V.O. theory (22), which considers the pair potential between
two charged particles across a continuous medium (solvent plus
ions, where appropriate). The total interaction free energy is
split into the contribution from the van der Waals (electrodynamic)
forces (G_A), and the electrostatic forces arising from the overlap
of the electrical double layers around the charged particles (G_E).
Both G_A and G_E are affected by the presence of adsorbed polymer
layers. Moreover, additional interactions are introduced. The
situation is complex even for neutral polymers, but may be conveniently rationalised in terms of figure 6. Two regions of interaction may be distinguished: (i) $h > 2\delta$; (ii) $h < 2\delta$.
      For $h > 2\delta$ (b > 0), the DLVO theory operates: one simply has
to investigate how the presence of the adsorbed polymer modifies
G_A and G_E. To attempt to do this exactly one would need to know
the form of $\phi(z)$ and also the charge distribution in the electrical
double layer. However, various simplifying approximations may be
made. For G_A (b) one may either assume that the average segment
concentration in the adsorbed layer is so small that G_A is not
perturbed by the adsorbed layer (valid for high M.W. polymers), or
use the Vold type of approach (23,24), which regards the particle
plus its adsorbed polymer sheath essentially as a composite
particle, assigned two Hamaker constants: one for the core and one
for the sheath.
      For G_E (b), a reasonable (although not strictly correct)
procedure is to replace the Stern potential in one of the standard
equations for G_E by the zeta potential of the polymer-coated
particles; this assumes that the plane of hydrodynamic shear
corresponds to the periphery of the adsorbed layer.
      For $h < 2\delta$, the situation is much more complex. One not only
needs to know $\phi(z)$ for each layer, but how $\phi(z)$ changes as the two
particles approach, i.e. $\phi(z,h)$; this may well depend on the time-
scale of the approach, i.e. the equilibrium path may not be
followed. Scheutjens and Fleer (25) in an extension of their model
for polymer adsorption have analysed the situation for two interacting uncharged parallel, flat plates carrying adsorbed, neutral
homopolymer, interacting under equilibrium conditions. Only a
semi-quantitative picture will be presented here.

One may divide the interactions into three contributions
(i.e. in addition to G_A)
a)   the elastic term (G_{el}): this arises from the loss in con-
      formational entropy of the chains. Depending on the coverage
(θ) and the configuration of the adsorbed chains, this may or may
not be a significant contribution for $\delta < h < 2\delta$, but clearly
becomes very important when $h < \delta$, since the chains are restricted
by the opposing surface and also polymer bridges form which have a
very low conformation entropy compared to loops or tails. Napper
(26) has given the following expression for G_{el} for two parallel
flat plates,

$$G_{el} = 2kT\Gamma \ln \frac{\Omega(h)}{\Omega(\infty)} = 2kT\Gamma\, R_{el}(h) \qquad (8)$$

where Γ is the number of adsorbed chains per unit area, and $\Omega(h)$
and $\Omega(\infty)$ are the number of conformations available to the adsorbed
chains at $h = h$ and $h = \infty$, respectively; R_{el} is a geometric
function which depends on the form of $\phi(z,h)$. G_{el} is always a
repulsive contribution.
b)   the mixing term (G_{mix}): this arises from the net segment/
      solvent interactions and the local changes in segment con-
centration in the interaction region between the particles. It
comes into play for all values of $h < 2\delta$. Napper (26) has also
derived an approximate expression for this term for two parallel
flat plates,

$$G_{mix} = \frac{2kT\, v_p^2\, \Gamma^2}{v_s} (\tfrac{1}{2} - \chi)R_{mix}(h) \qquad (9)$$

where v_p and v_s are the molar volumes of the polymer and solvent,
respectively. R_{mix} is again a geometric function which depends on
the form of $\phi(z,h)$. χ is the Flory interaction parameter. Clearly,
G_{mix} can be positive or negative (i.e. repulsive or attractive)
depending on the magnitude of χ. For a θ-solvent ($\chi = \tfrac{1}{2}$), $G_{mix}= 0$.
c)   the adsorption term (G_{ad}): this results from the change in
      the net number of surface/segment contacts, p, as h decreases.
G_{ad} (like G_{el}) may or may not be significant for $\delta < h < 2\delta$,
depending on the configurational changes that occur in this region
(i.e. whether changes in p occur) as h decreases, but clearly
becomes very important when $h < \delta$ since segments can now become
adsorbed on the surface of the opposing core particles or plates,
in addition to any changes in p at the original surface. One may
write the following expression for G_{ad} for parallel flat plates

$$G_{ad} = - 2kT\Gamma r \chi_s \cdot \Delta p(h) \qquad (10)$$

where $\Delta p(h)$ is the net change in p as a function of h. Since, in
general, as h decreases Δp will be positive, then G_{ad} will
constitute an attractive contribution.

Similar expressions to equations (8) to (10) may be derived for spherical particles. The form of the total interaction (i.e. $G_A + G_{el} + G_{mix} + G_{ad}$, assuming additivity) is clearly complex and depends very much on $\phi(z,h)$, which in turn depends on θ (or Γ). For simplicity and by way of illustration, we shall just consider two possible limiting cases: (i) at low θ ($\theta < \theta^*$); (ii) at high θ (psuedo-plateau region of the isotherm). These are illustrated in figure 7 for the case of a good solvent ($\chi < \frac{1}{2}$).

At low coverages (figure 7a), there is a significant minimum (G_{min}), resulting from the dominance of G_{ad} and G_A at $h < \sim \delta$, and G_s (= $G_{el} + G_{mix}$) for $h \ll \delta$. This results in so-called "bridging flocculation". At high coverages (figure 7b), on the other hand, $G_{ad} \sim 0$ and only a very shallow minimum exists at $h > \sim 2\delta$ due to the residual contribution from G_A at these distances. Clearly, provided G_{min} is small enough, the system will be stable to flocculation; this situation corresponds to so-called "steric stabilisation". The question of just how deep G_{min} has to be for flocculation to be observed will be discussed later in the paper.

The above analysis applies to the case of positive adsorption. What happens for example when $\chi_s = 0$, and depletion zones exist near the surface? This situation is dealt with in detail in a later paper (27) here. The first analysis was by Asakura and Oosawa (28,29), who showed that the overlap of the depletion zones (figure 5), results in a net attraction, and hence depletion flocculation. The origin of this attractive term may be viewed in terms of displacing solvent molecules from a region of higher chemical potential (in the depletion zone) to one of lower chemical potential (in the bulk polymer solution). There is a similarity here with the mixing term (G_{mix}) referred to above, where the reverse situation holds (in a good solvent), i.e. solvent is displaced from a region of lower chemical potential (the polymer sheaths) to high chemical potential (the bulk medium). Note, as we show in the later paper here (27), that as ϕ_p increases beyond ϕ_p^*, the thickness of the depletion zone, δ_d, decreases and hence the atraction term eventually decreases again, and the system is restabilised (depletion stabilisation).

The types of interaction that can occur between particles immersed in polymer solutions has been dealt with here on a rather ad hoc basis. Even for neutral systems, the situation is complex, although recent equilibrium analyses such as those given by Scheutjens and Fleer (25) for adsorbed homopolymers are beginning to shed some more light, but time-dependent effects need to be considered also. As with polymer adsorption per se, one expects the theories to be extended to deal with gradually more complex systems. In this respect, the introduction of charge effects (charged surfaces, polyelectrolytes) will be a major step forward; at best our understanding at present here is only qualitative. The ultimate goal must be to derive general equations for the pair potential, without the arbitrary (and possibly incorrect) separation into various terms.

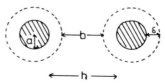

Figure 6. Two interacting particles carrying adsorbed polymer layers.

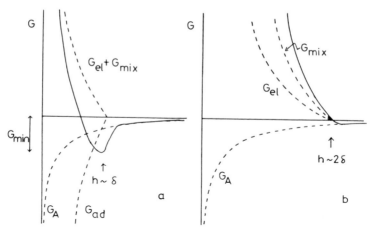

Figure 7. G(h) curves for two particles carrying adsorbed polymer layers: (a) low θ ($\theta < \theta^*$); (b) high θ (plateau region).

Dispersion Stability in the Presence of Polymer

"Stability" is a ubiqitous word as applied to colloidal dispersions; it may apply to more than one physical process (e.g. flocculation, settling, Ostwald ripening) and may be used in either the kinetic or thermodynamic senses. We restrict discussion here to flocculation and consider first the thermodynamic aspects.

Flocculation into a minimum of the type depicted in figure 7 will be opposed by the loss in configurational entropy of the particles. We may formally express this by the equation (30,31),

$$\Delta G_f = \Delta G_i - T.\Delta S_{hs} \qquad (11)$$

where ΔG_f is the net free energy of flocculation; ΔS_{hs} is the term associated with the loss in configurational entropy of a system of hard-sphere (non-interacting, i.e. other than in the sense that they are hard spheres and not points) particles; ΔG_i is the term associated with the interparticle interactions. ΔS_{hs} (positive) is essentially a function of the particle volume fraction ϕ_s: as ϕ_s increases so $|\Delta S_{hs}|$ decreases. ΔG_i (negative) is a function of G_{min}.

It is the subtle interplay of the two terms on the r.h.s. of equation (11) which determines the sign of ΔG_f. If ΔG_f is positive the dispersion will be thermodynamically stable. One can express this schematically in the form of figure 8, which shows the boundary between stability and (reversible) flocculation in a plot of log ϕ_s versus G_{min}. One may cross the boundary line either by increasing G_{min} at fixed ϕ_s, or by increasing ϕ_s at fixed G_{min}. The latter case gives rise to the concept of a critical particle volume fraction (c.f.ϕ) below which the dispersion is thermo-dynamically stable, but above which flocculation is observed. The former case may arise in several ways. The main variables which control G_{min} (at high θ) are:

i)   a and δ: in a good solvent ($\chi < \frac{1}{2}$) and ϕ_p small: $|G_{min}|$
    increases as a increases (fixed δ) or as δ decreases (fixed a)
ii) χ: $|G_{min}|$ increases as χ increases (solvency becomes worse).
There may be a dramatic increase in G_{min} beyond θ-conditions where G_{mix} changes sign (figure 7b). Note that δ may also decrease as χ increases. The situation here is complex and correlation between critical flocculation conditions and theta conditions may not always be observed, as is discussed in a later paper here(32).
iii) ϕ_p in the case of non-adsorbing polymers: as discussed above, an additional attraction may be introduced, due to depletion effects, leading to an increase in G_{min} which passes through a maximum with increasing ϕ_p.

The above analysis applies to those situations where the pairwise interaction curve is characterised by a free energy minimum (figure 7). If charges are present, then contributions

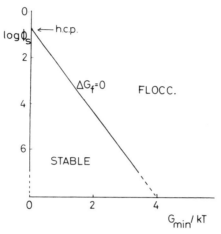

Figure 8. Stability/flocculation map, as a function of G_{min} and ϕ_s.

from G_E may give rise to a free energy maximum, as in classical
D.L.V.O. type systems. Such systems are kinetically stabilised
(i.e. metastable in the thermodynamic sense). Any change which
reduces the height of this maximum (e.g. pH, addition of electrolyte) increases the rate constant for the flocculation process.

The foundations of the theory of flocculation kinetics were
laid down early in this century by von Smoluchowski (33). He
considered the rate of (irreversible) flocculation of a system of
hard-sphere particles, i.e. in the absence of other interactions.
With dispersions containing polymers, as we have seen, one is
frequently dealing with reversible flocculation; this is a much
more difficult situation to analyse theoretically. Cowell and
Vincent (34) have recently proposed the following semi-empirical
equation for the effective flocculation rate constant, k_{eff},

$$k_{eff} \simeq k_o \left[1 - \exp(G_{min} - G^*_{min})/kT \right] \qquad (12)$$

where k_o is the Smoluchowski 'fast' (diffusion-controlled),
irreversible flocculation rate constant ($\sim$ 2-3 x 10^{-12} cm^3 s^{-1} for
aqueous dispersions at room temperature); G_{min} is the depth of
the minimum in the pairwise interaction curve and G^*_{min} is the
critical value for G_{min} (for a given value of ϕ_s) below which the
system is stable (figure 8). A reasonable fit of equation (12) to
experimental data was obtained (34).

As with experimental work on polymer adsorption, experiments
in the area of dispersion stability in the presence of polymers
require detailed characterisation of the systems under study and
the various controlling parameters (discussed above) to be varied
in a systematic way. One should seek the answer to several
questions. Is the system (thermodynamically) stable? If not,
what is the nature of the equilibrium state and what are the
kinetics of flocculation? If it is stable, under what critical
conditions (ϕ_s, T, χ, ϕ_p, etc.) can flocculation be induced?

One would like to see more experiments carried out with mixed
dispersions in the presence of polymers (leading to selective
flocculation?), and on the interaction of particles with macroscopic surfaces. Both of these areas have long-term implications
in biological studies. (Selective cell ahesion; adhesion of
microorganisms to surfaces.)

On the theoretical side, rigorous statistical mechanical
models describing equilibrium conditions in particle dispersions
are required; this, of course, awaits in turn more general
equations for the pair potential, at low ϕ_s, and possibly for
multibody interactions at high ϕ_s. Computer simulation may offer
one means of progressing here. Other experimental techniques,
such as light scattering and rheology, which reflect the form of
the pair potential, could also be carried out. For example,
angular light scattering gives the second virial coefficient,
which may also be computed for a system of interacting particles,
given the pair potential.

With regard to reversible flocculation kinetics, the problem is even more challenging. Detailed models for the deflocculation process as well as the flocculation process are required: computer simulation is probably going to be the only way forward here!

Literature Cited

1. Vincent, B.; Whittington, S.F. Surface Colloid Sci., Plenum Press, New York, Matijevic, E. Ed.; 1982, 12, 1.
2. Takahashi, A.; Kawaguchi, M. Adv. Polymer Sci. 1982, 46, 1.
3. Vincent, B. Chemistry and Technology of Water-Soluble Polymers Plenum Press, New York, Finch, C.A., Ed.; 1983, 215.
4. Fleer, G.J.; Lyklema, J. Adsorption from Solution at the Solid/Liquid Interface, Academic Press, New York, Parfitt, G.D. Ed.; 1983, 153.
5. Tadros, Th.F. The Effect of Polymers on Dispersion Properties Academic Press, London, Tadros, Th.F., Ed.; 1982, 1.
6. Napper, D.H. Colloidal Dispersions, Royal Soc. Chem. London, Goodwin, J.W., Ed.; 1982, 99.
7. Napper, D.H. Chemistry and Technology of Water-Soluble Polymers, Plenum Press, New York, Finch, C.A., Ed.; 1983, 273.
8. Flory, P.J. "Statistical Mechanics of Chain Molecules", Wiley-Interscience, New York, 1969.
9. Edwards, S.F. Proc. Phys. Soc. 1965, 85, 613.
10. Edwards, S.F. Proc. Phys. Soc. 1966, 88, 265.
11. Des Cloisseaux, J. J. Phys. 1975, 36, 281.
12. Daoud, M.; Cotton, J.P.; Farnoux, B.; Jannink, G.; Sarma, G.; Benoit, H.; Duplessix, R.; Picot, C.; de Gennes, P.G. Macromolecules 1975, 8, 804.
13. de Gennes, P.G. Polymer Letters 1977, 15, 623.
14. Daoud, D.; Jannink, G. J. Phys. 1976, 57, 973.
15. Scheutjens, J.M.H.M.; Fleer, G.J. J. Phys. Chem. 1979, 83, 1619; 1980, 84, 178.
16. Scheutjens, J.M.H.M.: Fleer, G.J. "The Effect of Polymers on Dispersion Properties", Academic Press, London, Tadros, Th.F., Ed.; 1982, 145.
17. Barnett, K.G.; Cosgrove, T.; Vincent, B.; Burgess, A.N.; Crowley, T.L. Polymer 1981, 22, 283.
18. Barnett, K.G.; Crowley, T.L.; Cosgrove, T.; Vincent, B.; Tadros, Th.F. "The Effect of Polymers on Dispersion Properties" Academic Press, London, Tadros, Th.F., Ed.; 1982, 183.
19. Cosgrove, T.; Crowley, T.L.; Vincent, B.; Barnett, K.G.; Tadros, Th.F. J. Chem. Soc. Faraday Symp. 1981, 16, 101.
20. Cosgrove, T.; Crowley, T.L.; Vincent, B. "Adsorption from Solution", Academic Press, London, Ottewill, R.H., Ed.; 1983 287.
21. Cosgrove, T.; Vincent, B.; Crowley, T.L.; Cohen-Stuart, R.M., this volume.

22.   See, e.g., review by Ottewill, R.H. Specialist Periodical
      Reports: Colloid Science, Chemical Society, London,
      Everett, D.H., Ed.; 1973, 1, 173.
23.   Vold, M.J. J. Colloid Interface Sci. 1961, 16, 1.
24.   Vincent, B. J. Colloid Interface Sci. 1973, 42, 270.
25.   Scheutjens, J.M.H.M.; Fleer, G.J. Adv. Colloid Interface Sci.
      1982, 16, 361.
26.   Napper, D.H. J. Colloid Interface Sci. 1977, 58, 390.
27.   Scheutjens, J.M.H.M.; Fleer, G.J.; Vincent, B., this volume.
28.   Asakura, S.; Oosawa, F. J. Chem. Phys. 1954, 22, 1255.
29.   Asakura, S.; Oosawa, F. J. Polymer Sci. 1958, 33, 183.
30.   Cowell, C.; Li-In-On, F.K.R.; Vincent, B. J. Chem. Soc.
      Faraday Trans.I 1978, 74, 337.
31.   Vincent, B.; Luckham, P.F.; Waite, F.A. J. Colloid Inter-
      face Sci. 1980, 73, 508
32.   Edwards, J.; Lenon, S.; Toussaint, A.F.; Vincent, B. this
      volume.
33.   Von Smulchowski, M. Z. Phys. Chem. 1917, 92, 129.
34.   Cowell, C.; Vincent, B. J. Colloid Interface Sci. 1983, in
      press.

RECEIVED October 7, 1983

ADSORPTION AND DESORPTION

Evaluation of a Macroscopic Model for Polymer Adsorption

R. HOGG

The Pennsylvania State University, University Park, PA 16802

An approximate analysis of polymer adsorption as a set of sequential reactions leads to a simple equation for the adsorption isotherm expressed in terms of three parameters. Comparison of the model with recently published statistical theories reveals remarkable agreement in both the general shape of the isotherms and the predicted effects of molecular weight. The problems of applying such models to experimental data are discussed.

The adsorption of soluble polymers at solid-liquid interfaces is a highly complex phenomenon with vast numbers of possible configurations of the molecules at the surface. Previous analyses of polymer adsorption have ranged in sophistication from very simple applications of "standard" models derived for small molecules, to detailed statistical mechanical treatments of the process. The use of the simplest models, such as the Langmuir isotherm, neglects variations in molecular configuration and assumes, in effect, that there is a single, "average" configuration of a molecule at the surface. In particular, the configuration is considered to be independent of the extent of coverage of the surface: a single molecule on an otherwise bare surface occupies the same area as an individual molecule on a surface saturated with polymer. Modern statistical models of polymer adsorption, on the other hand, emphasize the configurational aspects of the process and have provided considerable insight into the nature and structure of the adsorbed layers. The principal disadvantages of this approach arise from the complexity of the process itself. Mathematical treatments are necessarily very complicated, involving iterative solutions of complex sets of equations. Thus, while the statistical approach is invaluable in the description of adsorption processes, its applicability to the development of quantitative models for processes such as flocculation and steric stabilization is still somewhat limited.

0097–6156/84/0240–0023$06.00/0

In a recent paper (1), an attempt was made to develop an "intermediate" model which accounts for configurational effects in a simplified fashion but retains much of the simplicity of the "small molecule" models. The model is based on an approximate analysis of the thermodynamics of polymer adsorption in which it is assumed that the process occurs as a series of consecutive, reversible reactions between segments of the polymer molecules and sites on the solid surface. Clearly, this model represents a considerable over-simplification of the complex adsorption process. For example, no distinction is made between multiple adsorption of adjacent segments and that of segments from completely different locations in a molecule. Nevertheless, the model does appear to provide a reasonable description of the process and its predictions are in general agreement with observation. In the present paper, we will attempt to evaluate the general validity of the model by comparison with the statistical models. The problems of applying the model to experimental data and of parameter estimation will also be discussed.

The Basic Model

Details of the mathematical development of the model have been given elsewhere (1) and will not be repeated here. It is useful, however, to present a brief summary of the principal assumptions and approximations used in the description of the process. The basis of the model is the following set of assumptions:

  i)   Each polymer molecule consists of a fixed number of identical segments.

 ii)   Adsorption occurs at a fixed number of identical sites on the solid surface.

iii)   Individual polymer segments adsorb reversibly on the surface.

 iv)   Multiple adsorption of segments from the same molecule occurs sequentially. No distinction is made between which particular segments adsorb.

  v)   At any stage in the process, further adsorption can occur on any unoccupied site. There is no blocking of adjacent sites by adsorbed polymer segments, nor is there any appreciable interaction between adsorbed segments.

Assumptions (i) to (iii) are essentially the same as those used in the statistical treatments while (iv) and (v) are somewhat more restrictive.

The model is formulated by classifying the molecules in the system according to the number of adsorbed segments and writing down a set of simple mass-action relationships to describe the equilibrium conditions. The first step in the process consists of the attachment of one segment of a free molecule in solution to a site on the solid surface and the equilibrium condition can be written:

$$K_1 = \frac{\Gamma_1}{nc(1-\theta)} \tag{1}$$

where K_1 is the primary adsorption constant, Γ_1 is the adsorption density for molecules attached through one segment only, n is the number of segments per molecule, c is the concentration of free molecules in solution and θ is the fraction of surface sites occupied by adsorbed polymer segments. Any appropriate units can be used for Γ_1 and c while K_1 will have units of length. Thus, for Γ_1 in moles/cm² and c in moles/cm³, K_1 will be in cm.

Equilibrium conditions for the adsorption of second, third, fourth, etc., segments from molecules already attached to the surface can be written down in similar fashion and lead to the following expression for the ith step:

$$K_i = \frac{i\Gamma_i}{(n-i+1)\Gamma_{i-1}(1-\theta)} \tag{2}$$

where K_i is the adsorption constant for the ith step and Γ_i is the adsorption density for molecules adsorbed through i segments. For $i \neq 1$, K_i is dimensionless.

The overall adsorption density is given by

$$\Gamma = \sum_{i=1}^{n} \Gamma_i \tag{3}$$

and the fractional surface coverage by

$$\theta = \frac{1}{N_s} \sum_{i=1}^{n} i\Gamma_i \tag{4}$$

where N_s is the total number of sites per unit area of solid surface. The use of a further simplifying assumption, that all of the equilibrium constants for multiple adsorption (i>1) are the same, leads (1) to the following expressions for the overall process:

$$\theta = c^*(1-\theta)[1+K_s(1-\theta)]^{n-1} \tag{5}$$

$$G = \frac{c^*}{nK_s}\{[1+K_s(1-\theta)]^n - 1\} \tag{6}$$

Here, K_s is the multiple adsorption constant, c^* is a relative polymer concentration defined by

$$c^* = \frac{K_1 nc}{N_s} \tag{7}$$

and G is the relative adsorption density:

$$G = \frac{\Gamma}{N_s} \tag{8}$$

By means of Equations 5 and 6, the adsorption process can be described in terms of the parameters K_1 and K_s. Since the effective area of solid surface available to polymer adsorption is not generally known in practice, N_s is a third parameter which must be fitted from experiment and Equations 5 and 6 define a three-parameter model for the process.

Approximate Solutions

For the adsorption of polymers, the number of segments per molecule n is large which allows further simplification of the relationships. If the quantity $K_s(1-\theta) \ll 1$,

$$[1+K_s(1-\theta)]^n \simeq e^{nK_s(1-\theta)} \tag{9}$$

for all values for n, and for large n, Equation 6 reduces to

$$G \simeq c^* e^{nK_s(1-\theta)} \tag{10}$$

Elimination of c^* between Equations 5 and 6 leads to

$$G = \frac{\theta}{nK_s(1-\theta)} \{1+K_s(1-\theta) - \frac{1}{[1+K_s(1-\theta)]^{n-1}}\} \tag{11}$$

The last two terms on the right hand side of Equation 11 will generally be small and the expression can be approximated by

$$G \simeq \frac{\theta}{nK_s(1-\theta)} \tag{12}$$

which leads to

$$\theta \simeq \frac{nK_s G}{1+nK_s G} \tag{13}$$

Substitution in Equation 10 gives

$$c^* \simeq nK_s G \exp[-(\frac{nK_s}{1+nK_s G})] \tag{14}$$

Equation 14 is an approximate, single expression for the polymer adsorption isotherm. At very low concentrations, when G is very small, Equation 15 can be further reduced to

$$G \simeq \frac{C^*}{nK_s} e^{nK_s} \tag{15}$$

In other words, the model predicts a limiting form of a linear
(Henry's Law) type of isotherm as the polymer concentration tends
to zero.

   At very high surface coverage, the equations reduce formally
to the Langmuir form. However, it is very unlikely that the
required conditions (constant K_s etc.) would remain valid in such
cases.

   Some typical adsorption isotherms, calculated from Equation
14 (or from Equations 5 and 6) are shown in Figure 1 for $n=10^4$
with various values of K_s. In general, it can be seen that the
isotherms consist of three regions: a linear region at very low
concentration (described by Equation 15), a rather flat "plateau"
region at intermediate concentrations and another region of
increasing adsorption at very high concentrations. The extent of
the "plateau" region increases dramatically as K_s increases. It
should be noted that, according to Equation 14, the form of the
adsorption isotherm depends only on the product nK_s and not on the
individual values of these two quantities. Thus, the curves
shown in Figure 1 would also represent the effect of molecular
weight (which determines n) at fixed K_s. The other two parameters
of the model, K_1 and N_s are simply scaling factors for the bulk
concentration and the adsorption density respectively.

   It is clear from Figure 1 that the slope of the "plateau"
region is largely determined by the value of nK_s. Expressing
Equation 14 in logarithmic form:

$$\ln C^* = \ln nK_s + \ln G - \frac{nK_s}{1+nK_s G} \tag{16}$$

and differentiating, we obtain

$$\frac{d\ln G}{d\ln C^*} \simeq \frac{1}{1+G\left(\frac{nK_s}{1+nK_s G}\right)^2} \tag{17}$$

It can be shown that the "plateau" region occurs when the quantity
$nK_s G$ has a value close to unity. Then, approximating G by $1/nK_s$
in Equation 17 we obtain:

$$\frac{d\ln G}{d\ln C^*} \simeq \frac{1}{1+\frac{nK_s}{4}} \tag{18}$$

Thus, for experimental data obtained in the "plateau" region, the
slope of a log-log plot of Γ vs C can be used to obtain an initial
(rough) estimate of K_s.

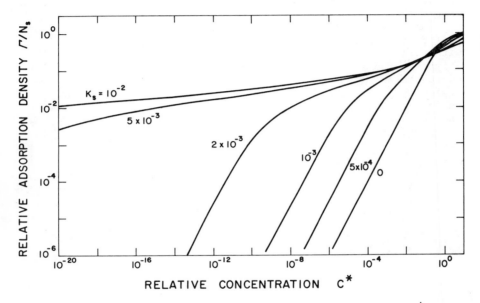

<u>Figure 1</u>. Typical polymer adsorption isotherms for n=10^4 with various values of K_s. Note the broad plateau regions for the larger K_s values.

Comparison with Statistical Models

Numerous statistical treatments of the adsorption of polymers at solid-liquid interfaces have been described in the literature. The earlier models (2-5) dealt primarily with the conformation of a single molecule at an interface and apply at very low adsorption densities. More recent treatments (6-10) take into account polymer-polymer and polymer-solvent interactions and have led to the emergence of a fairly consistent picture of the adsorption process. For details of the statistical theories of polymer adsorption, the reader is referred to publications by Lipatov (11), Tadros (12) and Fleer and Scheutjens (13).

It is of considerable interest to compare the present model with the predictions of the statistical theories. In particular, the results will be compared with the theories of Scheutjens and Fleer (9,10,13). These authors have pointed out that their results are in general agreement with other published models. Comparison of the adsorption isotherms shown in Figure 1 with those given by Scheutjens and Fleer (see, for example, Figure 5 of Reference 13) shows excellent qualitative agreement. In each case, the isotherms consist of three regions as described above. It is clear that good quantitative agreement should be possible by suitable choice of the parameters K_1 and K_s.

Some direct comparisons of the present model with the published results of Fleer and Scheutjens (13) are given in Figures 2 and 3. In the comparison of the adsorption isotherms, shown in Figure 2, the amount adsorbed is represented by the number of equivalent monolayers g (total number of segments in molecules bound to the surface) defined by

$$g = nG \tag{19}$$

The bulk polymer concentration is expressed as a volume fraction ϕ which is proportional to the total segment concentration nC. Thus, in this comparison, the relative concentration C^* is defined by

$$C^* = K_1' \phi \tag{20}$$

where K_1' is a modified primary adsorption constant which includes the segment volume and the surface site density N_s.

It can be seen from Figure 2 that the present model, with fixed K_s, is in substantial agreement with the statistical theory (for fixed values of the interaction parameters χ and χ_s) provided the parameter K_1' is allowed to vary with chain length. Some discrepancy can be seen at the higher chain length (n = 50 and 1000) with the statistical model predicting somewhat flatter plateau regions with generally lower adsorbed amounts. It should be noted, however, that the "transition concentration" ϕ^c, defined

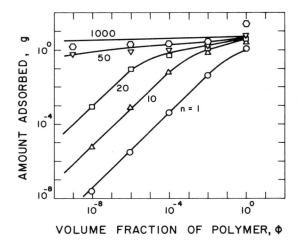

Figure 2. Comparison of adsorption isotherms based on the present model (solid lines) with the statistical theory of Scheutjens and Fleer (symbols). The following values of the parameters were used:

n	1	10	20	50	1000
K'_1	4.0	0.68	0.10	2.0×10^{-4}	10^{-87}
K_s	1.0	1.0	1.0	1.0	1.0

The values taken from Scheutjens and Fleer are for a 0-solvent $(\chi-0.5)$ and an adsorption energy parameter $\chi_s=1.0$.

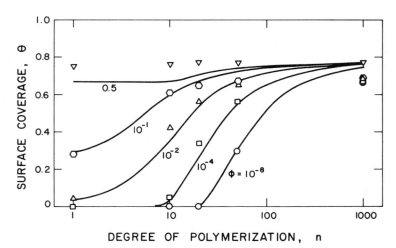

Figure 3. The effect of degree of polymerization on surface coverage (fractional site occupancy) at various polymer concentrations. The solid lines represent the present model and the symbols correspond to the theory of Scheutjens and Fleer. The parameter values are the same as in Figure 2.

by Fleer and Scheutjens (13), as the intersection of the extra-polated linear and plateau regions does agree very closely for these cases ($\phi^c \sim 10^{-12}$ for n=50 and $\phi_c \sim 10^{-235}$ for n=1000).

The predicted effects of molecular weight on surface coverage θ are compared in Figure 3. Again the agreement is generally good with some deviation at high concentrations ($\phi > 10^{-2}$) and for the higher chain lengths. It is clear from Figures 2 and 3 that the two approaches lead to very similar forms for the adsorption isotherms for bulk polymer concentrations less than about 10% by volume and values of the product nK_s less than about 50. It seems likely that these conditions are easily satisfied in systems involving the use of polymers as flocculants or dispersants where concentrations are typically of the order of parts per million and adsorption is probably relatively weak ($K_s \ll 1$).

The physical significance of the parameters K_1 (or K_1') and K_s is obviously of considerable interest. In the formulation of the model, these are simply arbitrary parameters which define, respectively, the extent of primary and multiple adsorption. For the particular case evaluated above (χ=0.5 and χ_s=1.0), K_s is approximately constant while K_1' appears to decrease exponentially with chain length n. It is expected that, for a given chain length, the parameters K_1' and K_s will both depend on χ and χ_s. Further comparisons, similar to that given here, will be required to establish the precise correspondence of the parameters used in the two approaches.

The good general agreement between the statistical and macroscopic models is not altogether surprising since both developments start from the same set of basic assumptions. The close correspondence does, however, indicate that the additional restrictions imposed on the present model (i.e. constant K_s and the lack of differentiation between the adsorption of adjacent, as opposed to more distant, segments of a molecule) has only minor effects on the form of the adsorption isotherms. The simple analytical form of the present model, especially as expressed by Equation 14, is especially attractive for the correlation and interpretation of experimental data and for incorporation into models for flocculation and dispersion processes. At the same time, it is important to recognize that the statistical approach provides a good deal of additional information, on the relative distributions of tails, loops and trains, in the adsorbed layers, for example. Such information cannot be obtained directly from the macroscopic approach. Nevertheless, one can envisage the use of a hybrid approach to the evaluation of polymer adsorption in which the simple model is used to characterize the process and evaluate parameters, after which the statistical theory can be used to provide a more detailed description of molecular conforma-tions etc. at the interface.

Application to Experimental Data

A major advantage of the simple model described in this paper
lies in its potential applicability to the direct evaluation of
experimental data. Unfortunately, it is clear from the form of
the typical isotherms, especially those for high polymers (large
n) that, even with a simple model, this presents considerable
difficulty. The problems can be seen clearly by consideration of
some typical polymer adsorption data. Experimental isotherms for
the adsorption of commercial polymer flocculants on a kaolin clay
are shown in Figure 4. These data were obtained, in the usual
way, by determination of residual polymer concentrations after
equilibration with the solid. In general, such methods are
limited at both extremes of the concentration scale. Serious
errors arise at low concentration due to loss in precision of the
analytical technique and at high concentration because the amount
adsorbed is determined by the difference between two large numbers.

Both sets of data show a very sharp increase in adsorption
at low concentration with a plateau region at higher concentrations. For comparison with the adsorption models, it is more
convenient to plot the data on logarithmic scales as shown in
Figure 4(b). From this plot, it can be seen that the results for
the cationic polymer fall essentially on a straight line indicating that this probably coresponds to part of the plateau region
of the isotherm. The results for the nonionic polymer appear to
indicate decreased adsorption at low concentration which may
correspond to the transition between the linear and plateau
regions. On the other hand, the apparent drop-off in adsorption
may simply reflect the uncertainty in the measurements at low
concentration.

The serious problems which can be encountered in fitting the
model to experimental data can be seen in Figure 5. In this
figure, a complete theoretical isotherm, using a reasonable value
for K_s is shown on the same relative scales as the actual data
for the cationic polymer. It is clear that there is a large
number of possible combinations of K_1 and N_s which would give
about the same "goodness of fit". It is obvious from the figure
that, in order to obtain reliable parameter estimates from such
systems, adsorption data are required over a very broad range of
concentrations. If possible, adsorption should be measured
directly (e.g. by radio-tracing techniques) rather than by difference. In this way, it should be possible to extend the range
of measurement and to reduce the errors at low and high concentration.

Application of this, or the equivalent statistical models,
to actual polymer adsorption processes is further complicated by
very imprecise knowledge of the solid surface area which is
actually available for polymer adsorption. Surface roughness etc.
can certainly be expected to have much more complex effects than
on the adsorption of small molecules due to restrictions on

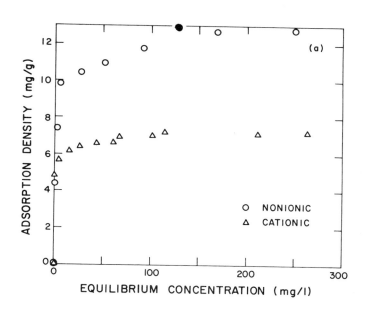

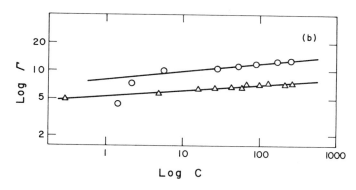

Figure 4. Data of Bensley (14) for the adsorption of commercial flocculants on a kaolin clay (BET surface area 15 m^2/g). Figure 4(a) shows the data plotted on linear scales while Figure 4(b) shows the same data plotted on logarithmic scales.

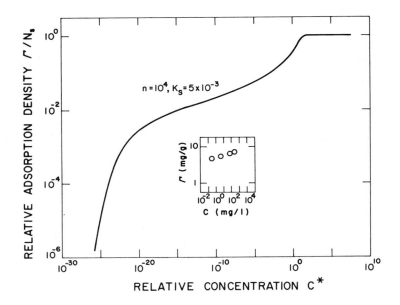

__Figure 5.__ Typical theoretical isotherm showing the experimental data for the cationic flocculant (see Figure 4) plotted on the same relative scales.

molecular configuration. Particle size can also be expected to
play a role since the opportunity for polymer bridging can lead
to an increase in the area available per adsorbed molecule, i.e.
to reduced adsorption (Γ) at the same surface coverage (θ) (15).
The extent of polymer bridging in any system is probably
influenced by factors such as solids concentration, particle size
and the frequency of particle-particle collisions due to Brownian
motion or mechanical agitation (16). Simultaneous flocculation
and adsorption can lead to changes in the effective surface area
due to the inability of polymer molecules to penetrate a growing
floc.

Summary and Conclusions

The equilibrium model for the adsorption of polymers at solid-
liquid interfaces recently presented by Hogg and Mirville (1) has
been evaluated at some length. It has been shown that, for
polymers consisting of a reasonably large number of segments, the
adsorption isotherms can be closely approximated by an expression
of the form:

$$C^* = nK_s G \, \exp[-(\frac{nK_s}{1+nK_s G})] \tag{14}$$

where C^* is the dimensionless polymer concentration, G is the
relative adsorption density, n is the number of segments per
molecule and K_s is a multiple adsorption constant (which characterizes the shape of the isotherm).
    Adsorption isotherms obtained from the model have been shown
to agree very closely with the predictions of recently published
statistical theories (9,13). While there can be no doubt that
the more sophisticated, statistical models provide more information on the nature of the adsorption process and the structure of
the adsorbed film, because of its simple form, the macroscopic
model can offer a powerful tool for the analysis, interpretation
and utilization of adsorption data.
    The problems associated with the application of this (or any
other) model have been discussed. Because of the form of the
typical isotherm, which exhibits a broad plateau region, fitting
of experimental results to the model requires that data be
obtained over a very broad range of concentrations. This is often
very difficult to accomplish in practice, especially when difference methods are used to determine the amount of polymer adsorbed.
Evaluation of adsorption in real systems is further complicated
by a lack of knowledge of the available solid surface area. The
latter may be affected by particle size, shape and surface
topography and by polymer bridging between particles.

Acknowledgments

The research described in this paper was supported in part by the National Science Foundation under Grant No. CPE-8121731 and by the Office of Surface Mining, U.S. Department of the Interior, under Grant No. G5115424. The author also wishes to thank Dr. Colin Bensley, Broken Hill Proprietary Company Limited, Wallsend, NSW, Australia for supplying the experimental data given in Figure 4 and for helpful discussions during the course of this research.

Legend of Symbols

C	Equilibrium polymer concentration
C^*	Relative polymer concentration defined by Equation 7
g	Amount adsorbed expressed as number of equivalent (segment) monolayers
G	Relative polymer adsorption density defined by Equation 8
i	An integer--the number of bound segments on a given molecule
K_1	Primary adsorption constant
K_i	Adsorption constant for attachment of the ith segment of a molecule
K_s	Multiple adsorption constant
n	Total number of segments per molecule
N_s	Surface site density (sites per unit area)
Γ	Overall adsorption density
Γ_i	Contribution to adsorption density by molecules with i segments bound to the surface
θ	Fraction of surface sites which have adsorbed polymer segments
ϕ	Volume fraction of polymer in bulk solution

Literature Cited

1. Hogg, R.; Mirville, R. J. "Adsorption of Macromolecules at Solid-Liquid Interfaces"; presented at 56th Colloid and Surface Science Symposium, Blacksburg, VA (1982).
2. Simha, R.; Frisch, H. L.; Eirich, F. R. J. Phys. Chem. 1953, 57, 584.
3. Silberberg, A. J. Phys. Chem. 1962, 60, 1872.
4. Hoeve, C. A. J.; Di Marzio, E. A.; Peyser, P. J. Chem. Phys. 1965, 42, 2558.
5. Roe, R. J. J. Chem. Phys. 1965, 43, 1591.
6. Silberberg, A. J. Chem. Phys. 1968, 48, 2835.
7. Hoeve, C. A. J. J. Polym. Sci. 1970, 30, 361.
8. Roe, R. J. J. Chem. Phys. 1974, 60, 4192.
9. Scheutjens, J. M. H. M.; Fleer, G. J. J. Phys. Chem. 1979, 83, 1619.
10. Scheutjens, J. M. H. M.; Fleer, G. J. J. Phys. Chem. 1980, 84, 178.

11. Lipatov, Y. S. "Adsorption of Polymers"; Keter Publishing House, Ltd.: Jerusalem, 1974.
12. Tadros, Th. F., Ed. "The Effect of Polymers on Dispersion Properties"; Academic Press, London, 1982.
13. Fleer, C. J.; Scheutjens, J. M. H. M. <u>Adv. Coll. Interf. Sci.</u> 1982, <u>16</u>, 341.
14. Bensley, C., unpublished data.
15. Scheutjens, J. M. H. M.; Fleer, G. J. <u>Adv. Coll. Interf. Sci.</u> 1982, <u>16</u>, 360.
16. Dirican, C. "The Structure and Growth of Aggregates in Flocculation"; M.S. Thesis, The Pennsylvania State University, University Park, PA, 1981.

RECEIVED October 7, 1983

Ellipsometric Study of Adsorption of Polyelectrolyte onto a Metal Surface

A. TAKAHASHI, M. KAWAGUCHI, K. HAYASHI, and T. KATO

Department of Industrial Chemistry, Faculty of Engineering, Mie University, Tsu, Mie 514, Japan

Adsorption of sodium poly(styrenesulfonate) from aqueous NaCl solutions onto a platinum plate at 25 °C was studied by ellipsometry as functions of molecular weight and concentration of NaCl. The plateau adsorbances at constant molecular weight increased linearly with the square root of NaCl concentration. For the same NaCl concentration the adsorbance was nearly independent of the molecular weight. The thickness of the adsorbed layer was approximately proportional to the square root of the molecular weight for the Theta solvent (4.17 M NaCl). For good solvents of lower NaCl concentrations the exponent of the molecular weight dependence of the thickness was less than 0.5. At the same adsorbance and molecular weight the cube of the expansion factor α_t, defined by the ratio of the thicknesses for good solvent and for Theta solvent, was proportional to the inverse square root of NaCl concentration.

Adsorption of polyelectrolyte on interfaces is concerned with various applications such as flocculation and steric-stabilization of colloidal particles in an aqueous phase, oil recovery, and soil conditioning. In these cases, both the adsorbance of polyelectrolytes and the conformation of the adsorbed polymer, which is connected with the thickness of the adsorbed layer, are very important.

Features of polyelectrolyte adsorption are that both the adsorbance and the thickness can be easily varied by changing the concentration of added salt as well as pH in bulk solution since such changes cause variation of the electrostatic repulsions of polyelectrolyte chains adsorbed, i.e., the excluded volume effect.

0097-6156/84/0240-0039$06.00/0

Hesselink attempted to calculate theoretical adsorption isotherms for flexible polyelectrolyte chains using one train and one tail conformation (1) and loop-train conformation (2) as functions of the surface charge, polyion charge density, ionic strength, as well as molecular weight.   His theoretical treatment led to extensive conclusions, which can be compared with the relevant experimental data.

Experimental studies of the adsorption of polyelectrolyte have been reported by several authors; Pefferkorn, Dejardin, and Varoqui (3) measured the hydrodynamic thickness of an alternating copolymer of maleic acid and ethyl vinyl ether adsorbed on the pore walls in cellulose ester filter as a function of the molecular weight and the concentration of NaCl.   Robb et al. (4) studied the adsorption of carboxy methyl cellulose and poly (acrylic acid) onto surfaces of insoluble inorganic salts. However, their studies are limited to the measurements of adsorbance and the fraction of adsorbed segments.

For homopolyelectrolyte, we first studied the ellipsometric measurement of the adsorption of sodium poly(acrylate) onto a platinum plate as a function of added sodium bromide concentration (5). We measured the effect of electrolyte on the thickness of the adsorbed layer and the adsorbances of the polyelectrolyte. It was assumed that the Donnan equilibrium existed between the adsorbed layer and the bulk phase.   The thickness was larger and the adsorbance of the polyelectrolyte was lower for the lower salt concentration.   However, the data on the molecular weight dependence of both the adsorbance and the thickness of the adsorbed polyelectrolyte have been lacking compared with the studies of adsorption of nonionic polymers onto metal surfaces (6-9).

The aim of this paper is to offer experimental results for the molecular weight dependence of adsorption of poly(styrenesulfonate) onto a platinum plate from aqueous NaCl solution at 25 °C.   Measurements of poly(styrenesulfonate) adsorption were carried out by ellipsometry.   The dependences of molecular weight and added salt concentration on the thickness of the adsorbed layer and also the adsorbances of polymer and salt are examined.

Experimental

Materials.   Four samples of sodium poly(styrenesulfonate) (NaPSS) prepared by sulfonation of polystyrenes with narrow molecular weight distribution were purchased from Pressure Chemical Co.   The characteristics of the samples, according to the manufacturer, are listed in Table I.   The intrinsic viscosities of NaPSS in aqueous NaCl solution were measured using an Ubbelhode viscometer at 25 °C.

Water was twice distilled using an all Pyrex apparatus. Analytical grade NaCl was used without further purification.

The platinum plate (Ishifuku Metal Co. Japan) was cleaned by soaking in a hot concentrated aqueous HNO_3-H_2SO_4 (1:1) mixture, washed thoroughly with distilled water, and then dried in a dust free box.

Table I. Characteristics of Sodium
Poly(styrenesulfonates)

Sample	$M \times 10^{-3}$	Degree of Sulfonation
NaPSS-1	88	0.89
NaPSS-2	177	0.81
NaPSS-3	354	0.99
NaPSS-4	1060	0.92

Ellipsometry. Adsorption measurements were performed with a Shimadzu P-10 Type ellipsometer at 25 $^{\circ}$C. The light source was a Nihon Denchi SH-85 Type high pressure mercury lamp. The wavelength of the incident light was 546 nm and incident angle was 70 $^{\circ}$.

Basic data of the thickness of the adsorbed layer, t, and the refractive index, n_f, of the adsorbed layer were calculated from the experimental data of the phase difference, Δ , and the azimuth angle, ψ, of the amplitude ratio by computer. The computer program proposed by McCrackin (10) was used.

Since the components in the adsorbed polyelectrolyte layer are considered to be the same as the bulk phase with a three component system which consists of polyelectrolyte, simple salt, and water, we calculate the adsorbances of polyelectrolyte and salt by assuming the Donnan equilibrium between the bulk phase and the adsorbed polyelectrolyte layer, as described previously (5).

To determine the adsorbances of polyelectrolyte and salt, the following relationships are used

$$\overline{R} = (n_f^2 - 1) \overline{M}/(n_f^2 + 2) d \tag{1}$$

where $\overline{R}$ is the mean molar refractivity, $\overline{M}$ the mean molecular weight, and d the density of the adsorbed layer. $\overline{R}$ and $\overline{M}$ are given by

$$\overline{R} = \Sigma(X_i R_i) \tag{2}$$

$$\overline{M} = \Sigma_i (X_i M_i) \tag{3}$$

where X_i denotes the mole fraction of component i. The density, d is expressed by

$$d = d_o + (M_+ - d_o V_+^{\,o}) C_+/1000 + (M_- - d_o V_-^{\,o}) C_-/1000$$

$$+ (M_p - d_o V_p^{\,o}) C_p/1000 \tag{4}$$

where d_o is the density of water, $V_+^{\,o}$, $V_-^{\,o}$, and $V_p^{\,o}$ are the apparent molar volumes, M_+, M_-, and M_p the molecular weights, and C_+, C_-, and C_p the molar concentrations of cation, anion, and polyion, respectively. The Donnan equilibrium gives

$$C_s^{\,o}(C_s^{\,o} + \nu \phi_p C_p^{\,o}) = [C_s^{\,o} + (\Gamma_s + \nu \phi_\sigma \Gamma_p/t)] (C_s^{\,o} + \Gamma_s/t) \tag{5}$$

where $C_s^{\,o}$ and $C_p^{\,o}$ are the molar concentrations of uni-univalent salt and polyelectrolyte in the bulk phase, respectively, ν is the number of charges per polyion, ϕ_p and ϕ_σ are the osmotic coefficients for the salt-free bulk polyelectrolyte phase and the adsorbed layer, and Γ_p and Γ_s are the adsorbances of poly-electrolyte and simple salt expressed in mol/cm^2. Equation 5 was first derived by Frommer and Miller (11) assuming the additivity rule for the osmotic factors.

From the measured refractive indices and densities for NaPSS in aqueous NaCl solution the molar refractivities and the apparent molar ion volumes were calculated. The following values were obtained; $R_{NaCl} = 9.23\ cm^3/mol$, $R_{H_2O} = 3.73\ cm^3/mol$,

$R_{NaPSS} = 71.23\ cm^3/mol$, $V^o_{Na^+} = -1.55\ cm^3/mol$, $V^o_{Cl^-} = 18.3$

cm^3/mol, and $V^o_{NaPSS} = 127.81\ cm^3/mol$. With $\phi_p = \phi_\sigma = 0.17$, which was reported previously (12), and the measured values of n_f, t, $C_p^{\,o}$, and $C_s^{\,o}$, Γ_p and Γ_s were calculated by solving Equations 1, 2, 3, 4, and 5.

Results

Adsorption Kinetics. Figure 1 shows the adsorbance, A_p, of NaPSS-3 as a function of adsorption time for two NaCl concentrations at the NaPSS concentration of 0.04 g/100ml. The A_p first increases with adsorption time and then the equilibrium adsorbance is attained after 1.5×10^3 minutes.

The thickness, t, of the adsorbed layer for NaPSS-3 is plotted against adsorption time as shown in Figure 2. The t also increases with increasing adsorption time and becomes a constant value. Similar time dependence was obtained in the other experiments. Therefore, both A_p and t determined after 1.5×10^3 minutes were taken as the equilibrium values.

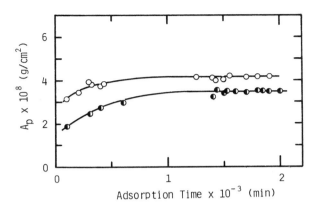

Figure 1. Adsorbance, A_p, of NaPSS-3 as a function of adsorption time: O , NaPSS concentration, C = 0.04 g/100ml, NaCl concentration, C_s^O = 4.17 M; ◐ , C = 0.04 g/100ml, C_s^O = 0.5 M.

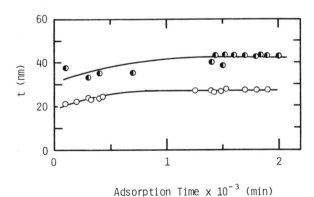

Figure 2. Thickness, t, of the adsorbed layer for NaPSS-3 as a function of adsorption time. Symbols are the same as in Figure 1.

In Figures 3 and 4, plots of A_p and t against the square root of adsorption time, T, are displayed, respectively. Before attainment of adsorption equilibrium both plots are linear within experimental error and therefore, adsorption process of NaPSS is governed by diffusion.

Adsorption Isotherm. Typical adsorption isotherms for NaPSS-3 in various NaCl concentrations are illustrated in Figure 5. The adsorbance, A_p, of NaPSS first rises with NaPSS concentration and levels off to a plateau value. The A_p value above the NaPSS concentration of 0.04 g/100ml is well in the plateau and increases with the NaCl concentration.

The adsorbance, A_s, of NaCl is *negative*, its absolute value increases with the NaPSS concentration, and reaches a constant value above the NaPSS concentration of 0.04 g/100ml for respective NaCl concentrations as shown in Figure 6. The plateau value of A_s decreases with increasing NaCl concentration.

The thickness, t, of the adsorbed layer increases with NaPSS concentration and becomes constant above 0.04 g/100ml for respective NaCl concentrations as illustrated in Figure 7. The t in the plateau rose with decreasing NaCl concentration. Similar isotherms for A_p, A_s, and t values were observed for the other samples. The plateau is established at the NaPSS concentration of 0.04 g/100ml irrespective of molecular weight.

The low adsorbance and the high thickness at low salt concentration are due to the electrostatic repulsion, i.e., the excluded volume between the charged groups of adsorbed polyions. As the ionic strength is increased, the intra- and inter-polyion interactions of adsorbed NaPSS chains diminish so that a larger adsorbance and smaller thickness should be obtained.

Molecular Weight Dependence. The aqueous 4.17 M NaCl solution at 25 ^{o}C was determined to be a theta solvent for NaPSS by Takahashi, Kato, and Nagasawa ([13]) from precipitation measurements. Though Table I shows that the degree of sulfonation of the NaPSS sample is less than unity, a linear plot between the intrinsic viscosities of NaPSS samples in aqueous 4.17 M solution at 25 ^{o}C and the square root of the molecular weight is obtained. Thus, we regard the aqueous 4.17 M NaCl solution at 25 ^{o}C as *a Theta solvent* for the present NaPSS samples. The molecular weights of the NaPSS samples given by the manufacturer were employed.

In Figure 8, the plateau adsorbance, A_p of NaPSS at the NaPSS concentration of 0.04 g/100ml is plotted against the molecular weight of NaPSS on a double-logarithmic plot for several NaCl concentrations. Though data points are somewhat scattered, the adsorbances are roughly independent of the molecular weight.

Figure 9 represents a double-logarithmic plot of the

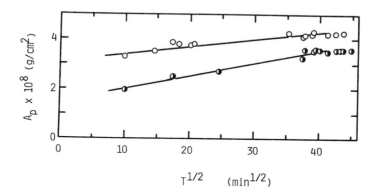

Figure 3. Plots of adsorbance, A_p, against the square root of adsorption time. Symbols are the same as in Figure 1.

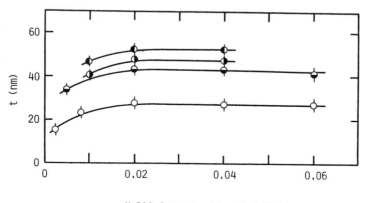

NaPSS Concentration (g/100ml)

Figure 4. Plots of thickness, t, against the square root of adsorption time. Symbols are the same as in Figure 1.

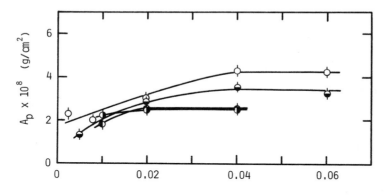

Figure 5. Adsorbance, A_p, vs. polymer concentration for
NaPSS-3. ○ , $C_s^o = 4.17$ M; ◕ , $C_s^o = 0.5$ M; ◑ ,
$C_s^o = 0.2$ M; ◖ , $C_s^o = 0.1$ M.

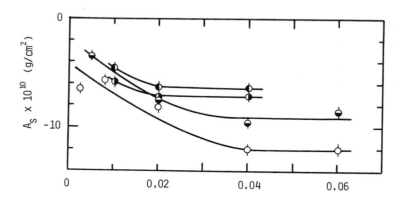

Figure 6. Adsorbance, A_s, of NaCl vs. polymer concentration for NaPSS-3. Symbols are the same as in Figure 5.

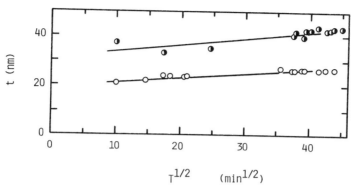

Figure 7. Thickness, t, of the adsorbed layer vs. polymer concentration for NaPSS-3. Symbols are the same as in Figure 5.

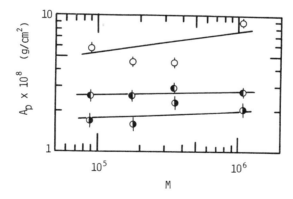

Figure 8. Adsorbance, A_p, at polymer concentration of 0.04 g/100ml vs. the molecular weight. ○ , $C_s{}^o$ = 4.17 M; ◑ , $C_s{}^o$ = 0.5 M; ◑ , $C_s{}^o$ = 0.1 M.

thickness, t, of the adsorbed layer at the NaPSS concentration of
0.04 g/100ml, against the molecular weight.   Log t is linear
with the logarithm of the molecular weight.   The slope of the
plot at the NaCl concentration of 4.17 M, which is the theta
point for the NaPSS sample, is nearly 0.5 but the slopes at the
lower NaCl concentration, namely, good solvent conditions are
less than 0.5.   The molecular weight dependences for the
thickness of the adsorbed NaPSS layer under Theta and good
solvent conditions agree with the case of a nonionic polymer (14).

Adsorbance of NaPSS, A_p.   Hesselink (1, 2) derived a linear
relationship between the amount of polyelectrolyte adsorbed in
the plateau region on an adsorbent with zero surface charge and
the square root of added salt concentration in bulk solution.
The typical plateau adsorbance for the NaPSS-3 sample at the
concentration of 0.04 g/100ml varies linearly with the square
root of the NaCl concentration as shown in Figure 10.

Expansion of Thickness of the Adsorbed Layer.   In the low
salt concentration the large thickness compared with the case of
the Theta solvent (4.17 M NaCl) is considered to be due to the
electrostatic repulsion, i.e., the excluded volume effect of the
adsorbed NaPSS chains.   Usually, the expansion factor α_t,
defined by the ratio of the thickness in good solvent and that in
the Theta solvent, is used to quantitatively evaluate the
excluded volume effect for the adsorbed polymers.
For adsorption of nonionic polymer, Hoeve (15) and Jones-
Richmond (16) attempted to incorporate the excluded-volume
effect into the expansion factor, respectively.   They suggested
that the thickness of the adsorbed layer in good and θ solvents
should be taken at *the same adsorbance and molecular weight,*
respectively.   We may calculate the expansion factor at the bulk
NaPSS concentration of 0.02 g/100ml, since the adsorbances are
almost the same for the respective NaCl concentrations, as seen
from Figure 5.
Experimentally the expansion factor α_s of a polyelectrolyte
chain in bulk solution is given as follows (17-19).   The α_s is
larger than α_t.

$$\alpha_s^3 - 1 \quad \sim \sqrt{1/C_s^o} \tag{6}$$

where C_s^o is the concentration of a uni-univalent salt.   In
Figure 11, the ($\alpha_t^3 - 1$) value for NaPSS-3 is plotted against
the inverse square root of NaCl concentration.   Figure 11
illustrates the linear proportionality of $\alpha_t^3 - 1$ to $\sqrt{1/C_s^o}$.

Conclusions

We studied the adsorption of sodium poly(styrenesulfonate)

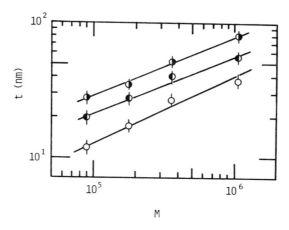

Figure 9.   Thickness, t, at polymer concentration of 0.04 g/100ml vs. the molecular weight.   Symbols are the same as in Figure 8.

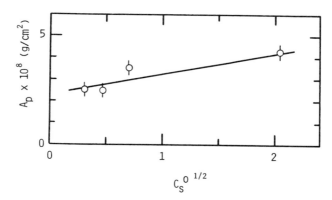

Figure 10.   Adsorbance, A_p, at polymer concentration of 0.04 g/100ml for NaPSS-3 vs. the square root of NaCl concentration.

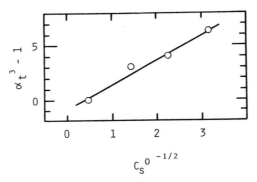

Figure 11. $\alpha_t^3 - 1$ vs. the inverse square root of NaCl concentration.

from aqueous NaCl solutions onto a platinum surface.   The adsorption isotherms are high affinity type and the adsorbance in the plateau region is proportional to the square root of salt concentration at constant molecular weight.

The thickness of the adsorbed layer, t, is approximately proportional to $M^{0.5}$ at the Theta point but in good solvent the exponent of the molecular weight dependence of t is less than 0.5.

Acknowledgments

We acknowledge the Grand-in-Aid for Scientific Research No. 56470079 from the Ministry of Education, Science, and Culture of Japan and the Asahi Glass Foundation of Industrial Technology for partial support of this work.

Literature Cited

1. Hesselink, F. Th. J. Electroanal. Chem. 1972, 37, 317.
2. Hesselink, F. Th. J. Colloid Interface Sci. 1977, 60, 448.
3. Pefferkorn, E.; Dejardin, P.; Varoqui, R. J. Colloid Interface Sci. 1978, 63, 353.
4. Williams, P. W.; Harrop, R.; Philips, G. O.; Pass, G.; Robb, I. D. J. Chem. Soc. Faraday Trans. I. 1982, 78, 1733; Cafe, M. C.; Robb, I. D. J. Colloid Interface Sci. 1982, 86, 411, Bain, D. R.; Cafe, M. C.; Robb, I. D.; Williams, P. A. J. Colloid Interface Sci. 1982, 88, 467; Robb, I. D.; Sharples, M. J. Colloid Interface Sci. 1982, 89, 301.
5. Takahashi, A.; Kawaguchi, M.; Kato, T. in "Adhesion and Adsorption of Polymers"; Lee, L-H., Ed.; Polymer Science and Technology Vol. 12B, Plenum: New York, 1980; p. 729.
6. Stromberg, R. R.; Tutas, D. J.; Passaglia, E.   J. Phys. Chem. 1965, 69, 3955.
7. Gebhard, H.; Killmann, E. Macromol. Chem. 1976, 53, 171.
8. Takahashi, A.; Kawaguchi, M.; Hirota, H.; Kato, T. Macromolecules 1980, 13, 884.
9. Kawaguchi, M.; Hayakawa, K.; Takahashi, A. Macromolecules 1983, 16, 631.
10. McCrackin, F. L. N. B. S. Tech, Note 1969, p. 749.
11. Frommer, M. A.; Miller, I. R. J. Phys. Chem. 1968, 72, 1834.
12. Takahashi, A.; Kato, N.; Nagasawa, M. J. Phys. Chem. 1970, 74, 944.
13. Takahashi, A.; Kato, T.; Nagasawa, M. J. Phys. Chem. 1967, 71, 2001.
14. Kawaguchi, M.; Takahashi, A. Macromolecules 1983, 16, in press.
15. Hoeve, C. A. J. J. Polymer Sci., Part C 1970, 30, 361.
16. Jones, I. S.; Richmond, R. J. Chem. Soc. Faraday Trans. II 1977, 73, 1062.
17. Takahashi, A.; Nagasawa, M. J. Am. Chem. Soc. 1964, 86, 543.

18.   Noda, I.; Tsuge, T.; Nagasawa, M. J. Phys. Chem. 1970, 74,
       710.
19.   Nagasawa, M.; Takahashi, A. in "Light Scattering from
       Polymer Solutions", Huglin, M. B. Ed.; Academic: New York,
       1972; Chap. 16.

RECEIVED October 7, 1983

The Role of the Solvent in Polymer Adsorption: Displacement and Solvency Effects

M. A. COHEN STUART, J. M. H. M. SCHEUTJENS, and G. J. FLEER

Laboratory for Physical and Colloid Chemistry, Agricultural University, De Dreijen 6, 6703 BC Wageningen, The Netherlands

In adsorption, the solvent always plays a double role, affecting both lateral interactions between the adsorbate molecules and determining the effective interaction between the surface and the adsorbate. For polymers, this means that they adsorb strongly from some solvents, whereas from others they do not at all. As a consequence, mixed solvents can give rise to an adsorption/desorption transition: the polymer is desorbed by a so-called displacer.

We investigate theoretically how the adsorption of the polymer varies with the displacer concentration. A simple analytical expression for the critical displacer concentration is derived, which is found to agree very well with numerical results from recent polymer adsorption theory. One of the applications of this expression is the determination of segmental adsorption energies from experimental desorption conditions and the adsorption energy of the displacer. Illustrative experiments and other applications are briefly discussed.

The role of the solvent in polymer adsorption has been the subject of much discussion. For example, theories have made predictions about the effect of the polymer/solvent interaction (i.e. Flory Huggins χ-parameter) on adsorption. For many systems, χ-parameters had already been tabulated so that a number of adsorption studies focused attention on this parameter. In spite of much effort, available data are ambiguous, sometimes verifying and sometimes contradicting the trends predicted by theory.

Of course, many investigators have realised that changes in solvent may not only affect the χ-parameter, but also the effective polymer/surface interaction, expressed by the adsorption energy parameter χ_s. In fact, it is almost impossible to vary these parameters independently and to obtain a clear picture of their separate effects in experimental situations.

An illustrative example is the work of Clark et al, on the conformation of poly(vinyl pyrrolidone) (PVP) adsorbed on silica (1). These authors determined bound fractions from magnetic resonance experiments. In one instance they added acetone to an aqueous solution of PVP in order to achieve theta conditions for this polymer. They expected to observe an increase in the bound fraction on the basis of solvency effects as predicted by all modern polymer adsorption theory (2-6), but found exactly the opposite effect. Their explanation was plausible, namely that acetone, with ability to adsorb strongly on silica due to its carbonyl group, would be able to partially displace the polymer by competing for the available surface sites.

Such displacement effects, although often very pronounced, have not yet been studied systematically. They will be the subject of the present paper. We will discuss the adsorption of polymer from a mixture of two solvents and we will see that in some cases drastic effects occur as a function of the mixture composition. Also, we explore some consequences and practical applications of displacement. It turns out that displacement studies not only increase our insight on the role of the solvent in polymer adsorption but can also be used to determine the segmental adsorption energy. So far, experimental data for this quantity were very scarce. Some illustrative experiments will be discussed briefly.

Theoretical

For adsorption from solution to occur, it is necessary that the exchange of solvent at the surface with adsorbate in solution results in a net decrease of the free energy. The exchange free energy, i.e. the difference in free energy between solvent/surface and adsorbate/surface contacts is a measure of the effective interaction between surface and adsorbate. Silberberg (2) introduced the dimensionless segmental adsorption energy parameter denoted as χ_s which refers to the afore-mentioned exchange process. Of course, for a given polymer and surface, χ_s may have both positive and negative values, depending on the solvent. If χ_s is negative, no adsorption of polymer occurs. For positive χ_s, adsorption is possible, provided that χ_s is larger than a critical adsorption energy χ_{sc}. The reason for a non-zero χ_{sc} (usually estimated as a few tenths of kT) is that the loss in conformational entropy experienced by an adsorbed segment must be outweighed by a net decrease in adsorption energy. Thus χ_{sc} separates two regimes; there are solvents for which $\chi_s > \chi_{sc}$ (adsorption) and solvents for which $\chi_s < \chi_{sc}$ (no adsorption). An obvious consequence is that in mixtures of solvents from either regime adsorption-desorption transitions occur when the composition of the mixture is varied. In dealing with binary solvent mixtures it is necessary to distinguish between the two components. We will denote the more strongly adsorbing component (for which usually $\chi_s < \chi_{sc}$) as the *displacer*, and the other one as the *solvent*.

An adsorption-desorption transition is illustrated schematically in Figure 1, where we plot a displacement isotherm, i.e. the adsorbed amount of a polymer as a function of the composition of a mixture of solvent and displacer. At the left in Figure 1, where the concentration of displacer is low, the polymer surface excess is positive. As we increase the proportion of displacer in the mixture, we observe a decrease in the adsorbed amount. At a certain composition the adsorbed amount of polymer becomes zero. The concentration at which the polymer surface excess just vanishes will be denoted as the *critical displacer concentration* ϕ_{cr}. Beyond ϕ_{cr}, the surface excess of the polymer is negative (and very small if the polymer concentration is low).

Recent polymer adsorption theories, such as those of Roe (3) and of Scheutjens and Fleer (4) allow the calculation of displacement isotherms, so that we could study the dependency of these isotherms on various parameters by numerical methods. However, all the essential features of displacement can also be demonstrated by means of a simple analytical expression for the critical point, which can be derived in a straightforward way.

The model underlying this equation is the lattice model for a regular solution, adjacent to an adsorbing wall. Layers of lattice sites parallel to the wall are numbered 1, 2, .., i, ... and each site may be occupied by either a polymer segment (p), a solvent molecule (o) or a displacer molecule (d). Each site has z nearest neighbours, fractions λ_0 and λ_1 of which are in the same, and in each of the two neighbouring layers, respectively. As we have three components, we have three adsorption energy parameters, one for each pair: χ_s^{po} (polymer from solvent), χ_s^{pd} (polymer from displacer) and χ_s^{do} (displacer from solvent). Because of their exchange character, these three parameters are not independent but are related in a cyclic way:

$$\chi_s^{po} = \chi_s^{pd} + \chi_s^{do} \tag{1}$$

This relation expresses the simple fact that a polymer/displacer exchange followed by a displacer/solvent exchange, has the same effect as a polymer/solvent exchange.

The energy of interaction between the components is conveniently described by means of three mutually independent Flory Huggins parameters: χ^{pd}, χ^{do} and χ^{po}. Indices refer to the respective component pairs.

The theory of polymer adsorption is complicated for most situations, because in general the free energy of adsorption is determined by contributions from each layer i where the segment density is different from that in the bulk solution. However, at the critical point the situation is much simpler since the segment density profile is essentially flat. Only the layer immediately adjacent to the adsorbing surface contributes to the free energy and we can describe the equilibrium entirely by considering only the changes occuring in that layer.

Let us calculate the change in free energy Δf associated with the exchange of adsorbed displacer molecules against segments in the bulk solution. Volume fractions ϕ will be assigned an upper index referring to the corresponding component (p, o or d), and a lower index referring to either the surface layer (s) or the bulk solution (*). We will assume that the solution is dilute in polymer: $\phi_*^p \ll 1$. For each displacer molecule exchanged we have the following free energy contributions (in units kT): (i) the displacer/polymer adsorption energy, χ_s^{pd}, (ii) the conformational entropy loss per polymer segment, $-\chi_{sc}$, (iii) the configurational entropy change of displacer, $\ln(\phi_s^d/\phi_*^d)$ and (iv) a mixing term to be worked out below, denoted as $-\Delta h^{pd}$. Furthermore, for each complete polymer molecule adsorbed there is an entropy change $-\ln(\phi_s^p/\phi_*^p)$. However, at the critical point the polymer surface excess is zero by definition, so that $\phi_s^p \approx \phi_*^p$ and this latter entropy change vanishes. We thus arrive at the following relation, corresponding to the equilibrium ($\Delta f = 0$) at the critical point (where $\phi_*^d \equiv \phi_{cr}$)

$$\chi_s^{pd} - \chi_{sc} + \ln(\phi_s^d/\phi_{cr}) - \Delta h^{pd} = 0 \qquad (2)$$

For the calculation of Δh^{pd} we must count contacts within the surface layer, and between the surface layer and the neighbouring layer (which has bulk composition). This calculation is simplified very much if we assume that at the critical point the surface is almost saturated with displacer (i.e. $\phi_s^d \approx 1$), since not only the polymer, but also the still more weakly adsorbing solvent will have been almost completely displaced. Before exchange, we have a displacer molecule at the surface, and a segment in the solution, giving contributions to the mixing energy $h_s^d = \lambda_1 \phi_*^o \chi^{do}$ and $h_*^p = \phi_{cr}\chi^{pd} + \phi_*^o\chi^{po}$, respectively. (Note that contributions to h_s^d due to contacts with polymer are neglected, since the polymer concentration is low everywhere.) After exchange, we have a displacer molecule in the bulk solution: $h_*^d = \phi_*^o\chi^{do}$ and a polymer segment at the surface: $h_s^p = \lambda_o\chi^{pd} + \lambda_1(\phi_{cr}\chi^{pd} + \phi_*^o\chi^{po})$. The result of the exchange process, Δh^{pd}, is obviously equal to $h_s^p + h_*^d - (h_s^d + h_*^p)$. Inserting the above contributions and making use of the relations $\lambda_o = 1 - 2\lambda_1$, and $\phi_*^o = 1 - \phi_{cr}$ we arrive at

$$-\Delta h^{pd} = \lambda_1\chi^{pd} + (1 - \phi_{cr})(1 - \lambda_1)\Delta\chi \qquad (3)$$

where $\Delta\chi$ is a combined solvency interaction parameter:

$$\Delta\chi = \chi^{po} - \chi^{pd} - \chi^{do} \qquad (4)$$

Substituting the result Equation 3 into Equation 2 and again using $\phi_s^d \approx 1$ we obtain the final result:

$$\ln \phi_{cr} = \chi_s^{pd} - \chi_{sc} + \lambda_1 \chi^{pd} + (1 - \phi_{cr})(1 - \lambda_1)\Delta\chi \qquad (5)$$

Equation 5 covers the essentials of the displacement process. We discuss a few consequences.

For strong displacers, χ_s^{pd} is strongly negative, and ϕ_{cr} is very small. With decreasing displacer strength, i.e. increasing χ_s^{pd}, ϕ_{cr} increases and eventually becomes unity. For still weaker displacers, $\ln \phi_{cr}$ may even become positive, so that ϕ_{cr} lies in the physically inaccessible region $\phi_{cr} > 1$. Figure 2 gives a set of displacement isotherms calculated numerically (from the Roe theory (5) for multicomponent systems) for athermal mixtures and various values of χ_s^{pd}. The position of ϕ_{cr}, read from these isotherms, is in excellent agreement with Equation 5. Even the 'inaccessible' point determined by extrapolation (dotted line) is accurately predicted.

Solvency effects are accounted for in the last two terms of Equation 5. If all the components mix without enthalpy effects (completely athermal system), $\chi^{pd} = 0$ and $\Delta\chi = 0$. For non-zero χ^{pd}-values, Equation 5 predicts a shift in $\ln \phi_{cr}$ with respect to the athermal situation. For non-zero $\Delta\chi$-values, an additional shift is predicted, unless $\phi_{cr} = 1$. Note that due to the last term, Equation 5 is implicit and may even have two solutions for ϕ_{cr} when $\Delta\chi < 0$. Indeed, for suitable values of $\Delta\chi$ and χ_s^{pd} we may observe *two* critical points. At both points the polymer surface excess reverses sign so that there is a descending and an ascending branch in the displacement isotherm. Numerical calculations (8) have shown that such isotherms occur in the case of strong repulsive interaction between displacer and solvent, i.e. χ^{do} large and positive (of the order of 1.5). Since the polymer surface excess must closely follow the surface concentration of the solvent, we conclude that the latter quantity must pass through a minimum at some composition of the solvent/displacer mixture, because the solution deviates strongly from ideal behaviour. Everett (9) has shown quite generally that such non-ideality effects indeed lead to maxima and minima in the composite isotherm of a binary mixture of low molecular weight substances.

Applications

The critical adsorption energy. A critical adsorption energy is predicted by many theories (2-6). Its value is dependent on conformational properties of the polymer and usually estimated as a few tenths of kT (7). Yet, a method to determine χ_{sc} experimentally has never been suggested. Displacement studies provide such a method. Inspection of Equation 5 bears out that χ_{sc} is obtained from a displacement isotherm, provided that χ_s^{pd} and the solvency terms vanish. This condition is met by taking as the displacer a molecule which is (nearly) identical to the repeating unit of the polymer, i.e. the polymer is displaced by its own monomer. Such

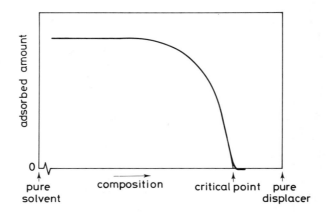

Figure 1. General shape of displacement isotherm and location of the critical point (schematically).

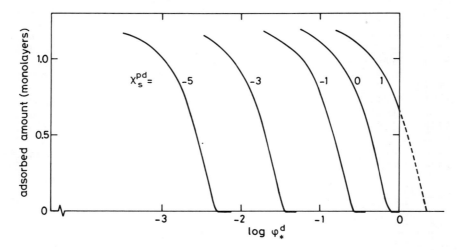

Figure 2. Theoretical displacement isotherms for various χ_s^{pd} values, calculated from the Roe theory; Athermal systems ($\Delta\chi = 0$, $\chi^{pd} = 0$). The dotted line is the extrapolation of the isotherm into the physically inaccessible region $\phi_*^d > 1$.

a monomeric displacer and a segment interact essentially equally strongly with the surface, so that the (exchange) adsorption energy parameter χ_s^{pd} is all but zero. Also, the displacer/segment interaction is likely to be athermal, or nearly so ($\chi^{pd} \simeq 0$) and the displacer/solvent and polymer/solvent interactions are not expected to differ very much ($\chi^{po} \approx \chi^{do}$) resulting, according to Equation 4 in $\Delta\chi \simeq 0$.

Figures 3 and 4 give displacement isotherms of PVP adsorbed on pyrogenic silica. The polymer surface excess is plotted versus the volume fraction of displacer ϕ_*^d. Results in Figure 3 are for water as the solvent and in Figure 4 for dioxane as the solvent. Various displacers were used, as indicated in the figures. One of the displacers was N-ethyl pyrrolidone (NEP), which can be considered as the 'monomer' of PVP. From the isotherm in dioxane, it was found that ln ϕ_{cr} = 0.14. The aqueous system shows strong non-ideality, the displacement isotherm having a second, ascending branch. It is obvious that at the point ϕ_*^d = 1 mixing effects do not play a role any longer so that an isotherm through that point and having the proper 'athermal' slope leads naturally to an 'athermal' critical point (see dotted curve in Figure 3). Hence, both for water and dioxane, ln ϕ_{cr} = 0.14. (The identity $\chi^{po} = \chi^{do}$ is apparently not satisfied for aqueous solutions of NEP and PVP. In the polymer where monomers are linked in a chain, hydrophobic parts are largely screened from interactions with the solvent. For free monomers such screening is not possible so that they experience more unfavourable interactions with the solvent. The adsorption energy parameter χ_s is not affected by the different chemical surrounding of free monomer and polymer segments, since the mechanism for interaction with the surface is hydrogen bonding in both cases (8).)

It follows from Equation 5 that for PVP on silica, χ_{sc} = -0.14 is a reasonable estimate. Here, we have the first reported experimental value of χ_{sc}. Surprisingly, it is a negative value, whereas a positive one was expected theoretically. However, we can rationalize our finding by taking into account that, where segments lose conformational entropy upon adsorption, small molecules may lose much more rotational entropy, thereby competing less effectively with segments (8). Such rotation is, as far as we know, not included in any existing polymer adsorption model.

Determination of the segmental adsorption energy. The determination of χ_s^{po} is also possible. Since χ_s^{pd} can be found from Equation 5 if χ_{sc} and the solvency terms are known, we can add χ_s^{do} and find χ_s^{po} by Equation 1. The determination of χ_s^{do} calls for a separate experiment, e.g., an adsorption isotherm of the displacer from solvent, in the absence of polymer. Following such a scheme we used the values of ϕ_{cr} obtained from the displacement isotherms of Figure 3 and 4 to determine segmental adsorption energy parameters χ_s^{po} for PVP on silica. The required additional information on χ_s^{do} was obtained from the initial slopes of dis-

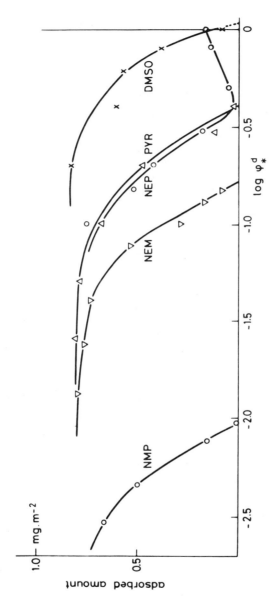

Figure 3. Experimental displacement isotherms of poly (vinyl pyrrolidone) from silica in water/displacer mixtures.
NMP: N-methyl pyrrolidine   PYR : Pyridine
NEM: N-ethyl morpholine   DMSO: dimethylsulfoxide
NEP: N-ethyl pyrrolidone

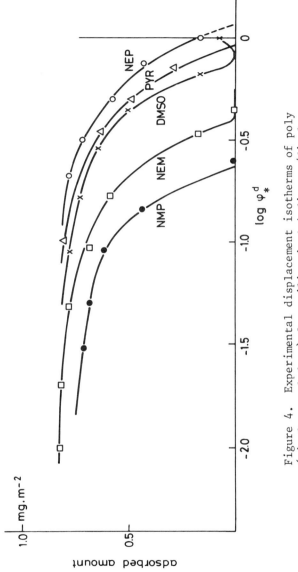

Figure 4. Experimental displacement isotherms of poly (vinyl pyrrolydone) from silica in 1.4–dioxane/displacer mixtures. For abbreviations see legends of Figure 3.

placer adsorption isotherms. Segmental adsorption energies were
calculated, using data for all four displacers. A full account of
the analysis is given in ref. 8. Here, we merely report that good
agreement was obtained and that segmental adsorption energies of
4 kT were found, both for adsorption from water and from dioxane.
The agreement with inferences from other experiments (e.g., calorimetry and spectroscopic studies (10, 11)) is quite satisfactory.
It is hoped that the method finds wider application.

Adsorption chromatography. A very interesting application of displacement is in adsorption chromatography. For effective separation to occur, it is necessary that the solute adsorbs weakly on
the stationary phase. Since polymers in a single solvent are
usually either not eluted (because they adsorb too strongly) or
move with the eluent front (because they do not adsorb at all)
solvent mixtures must be found which bring about the weak adsorption, i.e. close to the critical point. Experiments by Glöckner
et al. (12) and Belenky (13) have indeed shown that effective
separations occur only in a very narrow range of composition,
thereby clearly demonstrating the 'critical' character of displacement. It follows that ϕ_{cr} may be quite accurately determined by
chromatographic procedures. An example is shown in Figure 5, where
the retention factor R_F is plotted as a function of mixture composition. A sharp transition is observed.
     Snyder (14) has given adsorption chromatography its theore-
tical basis. He collected many adsorption energies for solvents
commonly used as eluents, and developed a method to predict the
'elution strength' ε_M (effective adsorption energy per unit of
surface area) of a solvent mixture on the basis of an ideal solution (Langmuir adsorption) model. A good correlation was found
when segmental adsorption energies, calculated by means of 'increment addition' according to Snyder, were compared with ε_M
values at a fixed retention factor (12). Although Snyder's expression does not include non ideality contributions, as does our
Equation 5, it seems to describe a large number of experimental
data reasonably well. A literature survey (15) reveals many
examples of succesful separations of polymer homologues. Snyder's
adsorption energies are absolute ones, instead of exchanged parameters. Thus, there should be a relation between χ_s^{op} and the difference in adsorption energy between a segment and a solvent
molecule, as tabulated by Snyder. A complication is that a correction is necessary for differences in molecular/segmental area,
and for solvency effects. Hence, although a more thorough analysis
is wanted, it is probable that the tables by Snyder constitute
a valuable source of information on χ_s, at least for silica and
alumina substrates.

Other applications. Displacement must also have its impact on
colloidal stability. The relation between the adsorption of polymers on colloidal particles and the resultant steric stability

against flocculation was, and still is, studied extensively.
Recently, a non-adsorptive flocculation mechanism has been studied
by various investigators (16-20). The conditions for non-adsorbing
polymer may be obtained by adding a suitable displacer. In other
cases, a sterically stabilized system may be destabilized by
merely removing the steric barrier by the action of a sufficiently
powerful displacer. Both possibilities, being also technologi-
cally interesting, deserve more attention.

So far, we dealt with the displacement of simple homopolymers. However, the phenomenon of displacement is by no means restricted to such simple macromolecules. Copolymers have been
succesfully eluted by means of adsorption chromatography (13).
Even complicated, charged macromolecules like proteins can be
succesfully displaced. As an example we give in Figure 6 the displacement isotherm for human plasma albumin from silica by morpholine (21). Of course, in this case where charge effects and a
variety of segment/surface interactions play a role, our simple
Equation 5 does not apply. Nevertheless, for practical work it is
important to realize that most macromolecules, often thought to
be irreversibly adsorbed, can be removed completely from the
adsorbent surface by the concerted action of a large number of
small molecules.

We conclude that binary mixtures of solvent and displacer
provide us with a valuable tool to obtain information on the
interaction between a polymeric adsorbate and the substrate.
Hopefully displacement studies will provide us with many new in-
sights in the near future.

Legend of symbols

Some symbols carry upper indices o, p, d. These indices refer to
the respective components solvent, polymer, displacer. Lower
indices s and * refer to surface phase and solution, respectively.

χ (χ^{pd}, χ^{do}, χ^{po})	Interaction parameter (for a component pair).
χ_s (χ_s^{po}, χ_s^{pd}, χ_s^{do})	(Segmental) adsorption energy (exchange of a specified component pair).

ϕ_{cr}	critical displacer concentration.
χ_{sc}	critical adsorption energy (per segment).
Δf	free energy of adsorption.
ϕ	volume fraction (upper index: component; lower index: phase).
Δh	enthalpy of mixing.
λ_1, λ_o	fraction of nearest neighbours in adjoining layer, in the same layer.
ε_M	effective adsorption energy of a binary solvent.

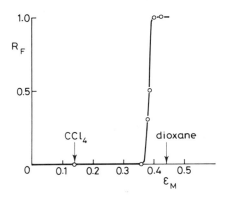

Figure 5. TLC retention factor R_F for poly(methyl methacrylate) on silicagel, as a function of the elution strength E_M of binary solvent (carbontetrachloride, CCl_4)/ displacer (1,4-dioxane) mixtures. Note the steep increase in R_F at $E_M \approx 0.38$, indicating a sharp adsorption/ desorption transition.

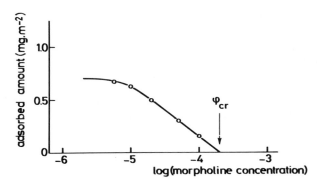

Figure 6. Displacement isotherm of Human Plasma Albumin from silica in aqueous morpholine solutions at pH = 8.5.

Literature Cited

1. Clark, A.T.; Robb, I.D.; Smith, R. J.C.S. Faraday I 1976, 72, 1489.
2. Silberberg, A. J. Chem. Phys. 1968, 48, 2835.
3. Hoeve, C.A.J. J. Chem. Phys. 1966, 44, 1505.
4. Hoeve, C.A.J. J. Polym. Sci. C 1970, 30, 361.
5. Roe, R.J. J. Chem. Phys. 1974, 60, 4192.
6. Scheutjens, J.M.H.M.; Fleer, G.J. J. Phys. Chem. 1979, 83, 1619.
7. Scheutjens, J.M.H.M.; Fleer, G.J. in "The Effect of Polymers on Dispersion Properties"; Tadros, Th.F., Ed.; Society of Chemical Industry: London, 1981; pp. 145-68.
8. Cohen Stuart, M.A.; Fleer, G.J.; Scheutjens, J.M.H.M. J. Colloid Interface Sci., submitted.
9. Everett, D.H. Trans. Faraday Soc. 1965, 61, 2478.
10. Cohen Stuart, M.A.; Fleer, G.J.; Bijsterbosch, B.H. J. Colloid Interface Sci. 1982, 90, 310.
11. Cohen Stuart, M.A.; Fleer, G.J.; Bijsterbosch, B.H. J. Colloid Interface Sci. 1982, 90, 321.
12. Glöckner, G. J. Polym.Sci. Polym. Symp. 1980, 68, 179.
13. Belenky, B.G.; Gankina, E.S.; Tennikov, M.B.; Vilenchik, L.Z. J. Chromatogr. 1978, 147, 99.
14. Snyder, L.R. "Principles of Adsorption Chromatography"; Marcel Dekker: New York, 1968.
15. Gankina, E.S.; Belenky, B.G. J. Liq. Chromatogr. 1982, 5, 1509.
16. Feigin, R.I.; Napper, D.H. J. Colloid Interface Sci. 1981, 75, 525.
17. Vincent, B.; Luckham, P.F.; Waite, F.A. J. Colloid Interface Sci. 1980, 73, 508.
18. Fleer, G.J.; Scheutjens, J.M.H.M.; Vincent, B. ACS SYMPOSIUM SERIES (this symposium).
19. Joanny, J.F.; Leibler, L.; De Gennes, P.G. J. Polym. Sci. Pol. Phys. Ed. 1979, 17, 1073.
20. Sperry, P.R. J. Colloid Interface Sci. 1981, 87, 375.
21. Meijer, D.N., unpublished data.

RECEIVED October 7, 1983

Flow-Enhanced Desorption of Adsorbed Flexible Polymer Chains

GERALD G. FULLER and JEN-JIANG LEE

Department of Chemical Engineering, Stanford University, Stanford, CA 94305

We have applied ellipsometry to the study of polymer chain desorption in flowing systems. Using this technique both the polymer film thickness and absorbance were measured under velocity gradients up to 7800 sec^{-1}. Three molecular weight samples of polystyrene ranging from 4 to 20 million were studied using cyclohexane at the theta condition as the solvent. Chrome was used as the adsorbent. The results indicate very substantial flow enhancement of the desorption rates. Complete removal of the polymer at the highest velocity gradient was possible over a period of 2-3 hours. At the highest velocity gradient and for the higher molecular weights, the film thickness was observed to decrease. Several possible mechanisms for this decrease are proposed.

The adsorption of macromolecules onto solids from solutions is not only of academic interest but is also of fundamental importance to numerous applications. The situation which has been most extensively studied is that of weakly adsorbing systems of high molecular weight, flexible chains. The resulting polymer layers are envisioned as being diffuse films where a relatively small fraction of the polymer segments are actually attached to the surface. The remaining segments are unattached and extend away from the surface with the resulting film thickness being roughly comparable to the radius of gyration of an isolated polymer chain in solution. Generally, the adsorption process has appeared to be an essentially irreversible phenomenon. Once a polymer film is established, only small decreases in absorbance are observed when the polymer solution residing above the polymer layer is displaced by pure solvent. This situation is largely insensitive to temperature and only slight increases in the level of desorption are found when the temperature of displacing solvent is increased (1,2). One possible explanation

0097-6156/84/0240-0067$06.00/0
© 1984 American Chemical Society

of the irreversibility is that each chain is multiply contacted
to the surface and the probability of the contact points detaching simultaneously is very small. In addition, the surface
concentration is often large enough that individual chains can
be highly entangled which would require a slow diffusion of
detached chains to the dilute bulk phase.

Grant et al. (3) used a radiotracer technique to study the
adsorption and desorption of two polystyrene samples
(M_w = 76×10^3, 1×10^6) in both good and poor solvents. The adsorbent was either a flat chrome surface or a liquid mercury
surface. Desorption into a θ-solvent from the chrome surface
showed that the higher molecular weight sample underwent slower
desorption. A recent work by Furusawa et al. (4) used gel
permeation chromatography to study the preferential adsorption
and displacement of high molecular weight polystyrenes in a
θ-solvent. The results gave a clear indication that the smaller
polymers were displaced extensively by the larger-sized
molecules. The degree of displacement was greatly dependent on
the difference between the molecular weights of the polymers
used. These results showing decreased desorption with increasing molecular weight are consistent with the desorption mechanism mentioned above. Higher molecular weight molecules would
have more train segments per molecule attached to the surface
and thus making it less probable to detach from the surface.
Furthermore, the diffusion coefficient is smaller for the higher
molecular weight molecule and the diffusion distance is larger
as the adsorbed layer may be thicker.

Other studies investigating polymer desorption have focused
on the effect of solvent quality (2,5). In the work of Schick
and Harvey, Jr. (5), the adsorption and desorption of
polystyrene (M_w = 292,000) from nonporous Graphon carbon black
into six solvents were studied. Two types of experiments
concerning the solvent power on the desorption were performed on
the adsorbed polystyrene. In the first type of experiment, only
the original solvent was used to dilute the system and,
irrespective of solvent power, no appreciable amount of desorption was detected. Another type of experiment consisted of
stepwise adsorption and desorption with changing solvents. In
one set of experiments, the same solution concentration was used
when switching from one solvent to another, while in the other
set of experiments, the concentration corresponding to the
supernatant concentration in the preceding step was used. The
results from both sets indicated substantial desorption if the
solvent was replaced by a better one.

There has been very little theoretical work on the problem
of desorption. Recently, Cohen Stuart et al. (6) have proposed
a theory by taking into account the polydispersity of the sample
in order to explain experimentally often observed "rounded" isotherms and the apparent irreversibility. For monodisperse
systems, the bulk solution concentration was estimated to be on
the order of 10^{-3} PPM for polymers in order to observe

substantial desorption. Silberberg, on the other hand, viewed
the apparent irreversibility as due to the lack of strong
driving forces (7).

In this paper we will demonstrate that substantial desorption can occur if very large hydrodynamic forces are applied to
weakly adsorbed, high molecular weight, flexible polymers residing on solid surfaces. Previous studies which have investigated
the problem of polymer desorption have exclusively considered
quiescent systems where the bulk fluid above the polymer film is
at rest. In contrast, however, most processes of practical
importance such as polymer flooding in enhanced oil recovery,
chromatography, and lubrication are flow processes where hydrodynamic forces may affect the polymer segments extending out
into the bulk fluid. Such forces could alter the conformation
of the polymer films and lead to increased rates of desorption. To this end, we have applied the technique of ellipsometry to the study of the response of polymer films in flowing
environments. Specifically, this method allows both the average
film thickness and adsorbance to be obtained simultaneously
during the flow. Our first studies (8) focused on the initial
response of polymer films to large velocity gradients. Here the
polymer (polystyrene) is allowed to be adsorbed from a θ-solvent
onto a solid surface (chrome) until equilibrium is established. Following that procedure, a velocity gradient is then
applied to the surface for a short period of time (1-2 minutes)
and the thickness and adsorbance are determined. The thickness
was observed to slightly decrease when the velocity gradient was
increased to large enough values but the adsorbance was left
unchanged. In this paper, the consequence of applying the flow
over long periods of time is analyzed in order to determine the
extent to which hydrodynamic forces can increase the rate of
desorption.

Experimental

Materials. Three high molecular weight polystyrenes (PS) of
narrow distribution were used and their properties are given in
Table I. The ultrahigh molecular weight PS-20 was purchased
from the Pressure Chemical Co. and PS-4 and PS-8 were supplied
by the Toyo Soda Co.. Reagent grade cyclohexane was used as the
θ-solvent. The adsorbent consisted of two mirrors of optically
flat hard chrome electroplated onto steel disks. Prior to each
adsorption the chrome mirrors were cleaned following standard
procedures (8).

Ellipsometry. The automated ellipsometer is essentially equivalent to that described by Hauge and Dill (9). Data acquisi-
tion and analysis was made through the use of a Digital
Equipment Corporation MINC 11/23 computing system. The detailed
description of the system was reported previously (8). The
measured ellipsometric angles ψ and Δ are converted into the

average thickness d and refractive index n_f of the polymer
film. The adsorbance A is calculated using the following
equation:

$$A = (n_f - n_o) \, d/(dn/dc) \qquad (1)$$

where n_o is the refractive index of cyclohexane and is taken
to be 1.415 at a light wavelength $\lambda = 6328$ A and temperature
of 34.8°C. (dn/dc) is the refractive index increment of the
solution and is 0.168 cm^3/g for polystyrene in cyclohexane.

Flow Cell. The flow cell is pictured in Figure 1 and in some
respects is similar to the one used by Stromberg et al. (10).
The cell consists of two chromium mirrors which are parallel and
facing each other. Each mirror rests within an aluminum base or
lid respectively and the base and the top lid are themselves
squeezed between two aluminum blocks which support circulating
water from a constant temperature bath. The top lid has two
fused quartz windows of low birefringence and an opening for
insertion of a thermistor directly in contact with the liquid.
The two blocks are pressed together tightly using a Viton o-ring
to seal the unit. Very high velocity gradients of up to 7800
sec^{-1} are accomplished by pumping liquids through the narrow
slit between the two chrome mirrors, which serves as flow
boundary as well as the adsorbent surface. Apparent velocity
gradients $\dot{\gamma}$ are calculated by the following equation assuming a
fully developed velocity profile:

$$\dot{\gamma} = 6Q/WB^2 \qquad (2)$$

where Q is the volume flow rate, W the width of the slit
(1.92 cm), and B the gap thickness between the mirrors
(0.06 cm). Due to the entrance effects, the actual velocity
gradient is generally greater than the apparent velocity
gradient calculated in this manner. However, the discrepancy is
estimated to be less than 15% for the worst case which
corresponds to the highest Reynolds number used in this work
(11). The current design of the cell allows us to study a wide
range of polymer/solvent pairs. Since the light only passes
through quartz windows at normal incidence, there is no problem
of mismatching of refractive indices.

Adsorption and Desorption. The adsorption of PS was carried
out by introducing the polymer solutions into the cell via a
hypodermic syringe. The solution concentrations used for
adsorption were 700 PPM for PS-20, 1000 PPM for PS-8, and
1200 PPM for PS-4. According to the previous work by Takahashi
et al. (12), those concentrations are large enough to obtain
saturated surface coverages. The solution was kept in the cell
over a period of one day to insure equilibrium. At the end of
one day the supernatant solution was displaced by the pure
solvent. For studies of flow-enhanced desorption the pump was

Table I.

Molecular Weight Characteristics and Quiescent Adsorption
at the θ-Condition of the Polystyrene Samples

Sample	M_w	M_w/M_n	A_θ (mg/m^2)	d_θ (A)
PS-4	3.84×10^6	1.05	4.15	1700
PS-8	8.42×10^6	1.17	4.66	2250
PS-20	20×10^6	<1.20	4.60	3100

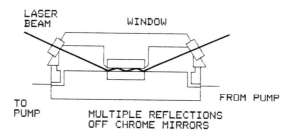

Figure 1.   The flow cell.

turned on for at least two hours. Three velocity gradients
($\dot{\gamma}$ = 2600, 5200, and 7800 sec^{-1}) were used for all three
molecular weight systems.

Results and Discussion

The quiescent adsorbance and thickness of each sample are listed
in Table I. The desorption under flowing solvent is shown in
Figures 2 to 4. Figure 2 shows the flow effects on PS-4 and
Figures 3 and 4 represent the results of PS-8 and PS-20
respectively. In each figure, the fraction of adsorbed amount
remaining A/A_o is plotted against time where A_o is the
adsorbance at zero time. As indicated by the error bars, the
experimental error becomes significantly larger when flow is
applied due to minor fluctuations in flow rates and temperature. Each plot in Figures 2 and 4 includes data for three
separate velocity gradients: (+) 2600 sec^{-1}, (Δ) 5200
sec^{-1}, and (∇) 7800 sec^{-1}. No detectable changes in
adsorbance under quiescent solvent dilution were observed and
the zero flow state is represented by the horizontal lines on
each plot. It is of interest to compare our results of no-flow
desorption with those reported by Grant et al. (3). They used
two PS samples to study the molecular weight dependence and
reported that in two hours only about 10% of adsorbed 1x10^6 PS
molecules desorbed from chrome into the θ-solvent. During the
same period of time the fraction of adsorbed 76×10^3 PS remained
at the level of 80%. We have used higher molecular weight PS
samples and the results of no desorption are consistent with the
overall trend that the adsorbed polymers of higher molecular
weights are more difficult to desorb into the solvent.

Examination of Figures 2 to 4 clearly indicates flow
enhancement of the desorption as seen by the substantial
decreases in adsorbance once flow is applied. The overall trend
of the desorption curves for the three molecular weight samples
is similar and is characterized by a fairly rapid initial
desorption followed by an approach to steady state. The desorption rate increases with the velocity gradient whereas the
steady state adsorbance decreases as the flow is increased.

When the molecular weight is increased, the flow
enhancement becomes more distinctive as seen by comparing
Figure 2 against Figures 3 and 4. The molecular weight effect
is most apparent at the highest velocity gradient as seen in
Figure 5 where the data for all three molecular weight samples
have been plotted. At this highest velocity gradient it is
apparent that complete removal of the polymer is possible over a
period of 2-3 hours. At lower velocity gradients, on the other
hand, the desorption curves level off to yield finite, steady
state adsorbances.

Figures 6 and 7 are the plots of the film thickness ratio
d/d_o versus time where d_o is the film thickness at zero time.
No changes in the film thickness were observed for PS-4 under
flowing conditions and, therefore, no plot of d/d_o versus time

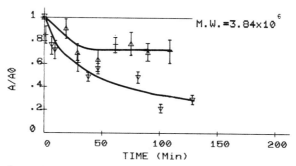

Figure 2.   Desorption curves of PS-4 at various velocity
gradients: (+) 2600 sec^{-1} ; (Δ) 5 200 sec^{-1} ;
(∇) 7800 sec^{-1} .

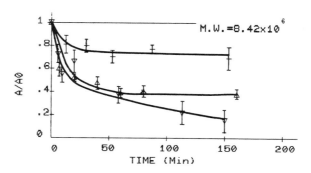

Figure 3.   Desorption curves of PS-8 at various velocity
gradients. See Figure 2 for symbols.

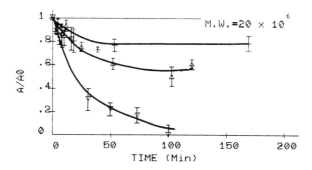

Figure 4.   Desorption curves of PS-20 at various velocity
gradients. See Figure 2 for symbols.

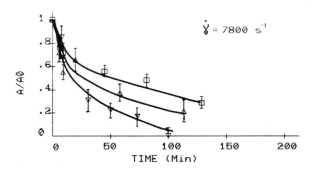

Figure 5.   Molecular weight dependence on the polymer desorption at $\dot\gamma$ = 7800 sec^{-1}: ($\square$) PS-4; (Δ) PS-8; (∇) PS-20.

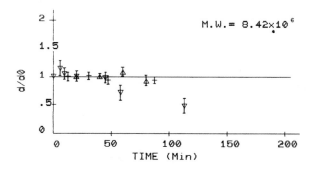

Figure 6.   Effect of shear on the average film thickness of PS-8. See Figure 2 for symbols.

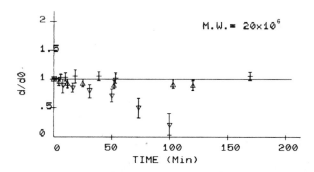

Figure 7.   Effect of shear on the average film thickness of PS-20. See Figure 2 for symbols.

was included for this sample. In addition, as seen from Figures 6 and 7, thickness changes were only seen at the highest velocity gradient for the PS-8 and PS-20 samples. At the highest velocity gradient both of the higher molecular weight samples showed significant reduction in thickness. Furthermore, the film thickness did not immediately recover after the flow was arrested. Combining the curve in Figure 6 for $\dot{\gamma}$ = 7800 sec^{-1} with the corresponding desorption curve in Figure 3, the data for PS-8 indicate that for the first 50 minutes, the flow enhanced removal of polymer reduced the polymer density within the layer while maintaining the average layer thickness. After 50 minutes, both the layer thickness and the adsorbance decreased. For PS-20 the decrease in thickness began at an even earlier time as shown in Figure 7.

Several mechanisms of flow-enhanced desorption can be proposed which would be compatible with the data reported here and current understanding of the conformation of adsorbed polymer layers in the quiescent state. At low velocity gradients the removal of polymer occurs in a manner which conserves the film thickness. Since the adsorbance achieves a steady state value at lower velocity gradients and lower molecular weights, it appears that chains which are more weakly attached are stripped off first leaving strongly attached molecules behind. At high velocity gradients the removal of polymer is accompanied by a decrease in thickness. However, a rectilinear flow with a velocity gradient of 7800 sec^{-1} most likely is not sufficiently large to induce breakage of chains of molecular weight 8-20 million based on the observations reported by Cutler et al. (13). One possible explanation for the thickness decrease is a compression of the film and subsequent rearrangement of the chains into a compressed profile which does not immediately relax after the flow is removed. Another possibility is that the flow first strips off higher molecular weight material leaving smaller chains behind. This explanation, however, would suggest that decreases in thickness should have accompanied the measurements at all of the velocity gradients and for the lower molecular weights. The precise mechanism is not well understood, however, and further studies are recommended.

Conclusions

We report here, for the first time, that hydrodynamic forces can dramatically increase the rate of desorption in polymer systems which are otherwise irreversibly adsorbed under no-flow conditions. Indeed, at high enough shear stresses, complete removal of the polymer is possible. The technique of ellipsometry is well suited for this problem as simultaneous measurements of both film thickness and adsorbance are possible during the flow process.

Such effective desorption under flow would be of importance to a number of industrial applications. For example, in the flow of polymer solutions through porous media in enhanced oil recovery, adsorption of polymer has a detrimental effect in that the solution viscosity is decreased as it becomes depleted of polymer and the hydrodynamic resistance of the media increases as the pore size is reduced. It may be, however, that flow enhancement of desorption may substantially reduce this problem if the velocity gradients become large enough. We are currently investigating polymer systems of interest to the polymer flooding process in order to determine the level of desorption under flowing conditions.

Literature Cited

1. Frisch, H.L.; Hellman, M.Y. J. Polymer Sci. 1959, 38, 441.
2. Ellerstein, S.; Ullman, R. J. Polymer Sci. 1961, 55, 123.
3. Grant, W.H.; Smith, L.E.; Stromberg, R.R. Chem. Soc. Faraday Discuss. 1975, 59, 209.
4. Furusawa, K.; Yamashita, K.; Konno, K. J. Colloid Interface Sci. 1982, 86, 35.
5. Schick, M.J.; Harvey, E.N., Jr. in "Interaction of Liquids at Solid Substrates"; Alexander, A.L., Symposium Chairman; ADVANCES IN CHEMISTRY SERIES, No. 87, American Chemical Society; Washington, D.C. 1968; p. 63.
6. Cohen Stuart, M.A.; Scheutjens, J.M.H.M.; Fleer, G.J. J. Polymer Sci. Polymer Phys. Ed. 1980, 18, 559.
7. Silberberg, A., in "The Effects of Polymers on Dispersion Properties"; Tadros, Th.F., Ed.; Academic Press: London, 1982, p. 417.
8. Lee, J.J.; Fuller, G.G. "Ellipsometry Studies of Adsorbed Polymer Chains Subjected to Flow", submitted to Macromolecules.
9. Hauge, P.S.; Dill, F.H. IBM J. Res. Develop. 1973, 17, 472.
10. Stromberg, R.R.; Tutas, D.J.; Passaglia, E. J. Physical Chemistry 1965, 69, 3955.
11. Sparrow, E.M.; Lin, S.H.; Lundgren, T.S. Phys. Fluids 1964, 7, 338.
12. Takahashi, A.; Kawaguchi, M.; Hirota, H.; Kato, T. Macromolecules 1980, 13, 884.
13. Cutler, J.D.; Zakin, J.L.; Patterson, G.K. J. Appl. Polymer Sci. 1975, 19, 3235.

RECEIVED October 7, 1983

Adsorption-Desorption Behavior of Polyvinyl Alcohol on Polystyrene Latex Particles

M. S. AHMED, M. S. EL-AASSER, and J. W. VANDERHOFF

Emulsion Polymers Institute and Departments of Chemical Engineering and Chemistry, Lehigh University, Bethlehem, PA 18015

The adsorption of fully and partially hydrolyzed (88%) polyvinyl alcohol (PVA) on 190–1100nm monodisperse polystyrene latex particles was investigated. The effect of molecular weight was investigated for 190 nm-size particles using the serum replacement adsorption and desorption methods. The adsorption density at the adsorption-isotherm plateau followed the relationships $\Gamma \alpha M^{0.5}$ for the fully hydrolyzed PVA and $\Gamma \alpha M^{0.72}$ for the 88%-hydrolyzed PVA. The same dependence was found for the adsorbed layer thickness measured by viscosity and photon correlation spectroscopy. Extension of the adsorption isotherms to higher concentrations gave a second rise in surface concentration, which was attributed to multilayer adsorption and incipient phase separation at the interface. The latex particle size had no effect on the adsorption density; however, the thickness of the adsorbed layer increased with increasing particle size, which was attributed to changes in the configuration of the adsorbed polymer molecules. The electrolyte stability of the bare and PVA–covered particles showed that the bare particles coagulated in the primary minimum and the PVA–covered particles flocculated in the secondary minimum and the larger particles were less stable than the smaller particles.

Polymer adsorption is important in the flocculation and stabilization of colloidal sols and has been reviewed by Vincent et al. (1) and Tadros (2). Polyvinyl alcohol (PVA) has been used in these studies because of its practical application in textiles, adhesives, and coatings. The adsorption of PVA has been studied on silver iodide by Fleer (3) and Koopal (4), and on polystyrene (PS) latex particles by Garvey (5). The adsorption isotherms reported by these workers extend up to 600 ppm PVA. The adsorption at

0097–6156/84/0240–0077$06.00/0

higher concentration is of particular importance, particularly in
the emulsion polymerization of vinyl acetate, where PVA emulsifier
is used in the concentration range 4-6% w/v based on water phase.
The determination of adsorption isotherms at liquid-solid
interfaces involves a mass balance on the amount of polymer added
to the dispersion, which requires the separation of the liquid
phase from the particle phase. Centrifugation is often used for
this separation, under the assumption that the adsorption-desorption equilibrium does not change during this process. Serum replacement (6) allows the separation of the liquid phase without
assumptions as to the configuration of the adsorbed polymer molecules. This method has been used to determine the adsorption
isotherms of anionic and nonionic emulsifiers on various types of
latex particles (7,8). This paper describes the adsorption of
fully and partially hydrolyzed PVA on different-size PS latex
particles. PS latex was chosen over polyvinyl acetate (PVAc) latex because of its well-characterized surface; PVAc latexes will
be studied later.
The investigations include the effect of (i) PVA molecular
weight, particularly at higher concentrations which give different
adsorption isotherms; (ii) latex particle size over the range 190-
1100nm using a low-molecular-weight fully-hydrolyzed PVA; (iii)
electrolyte on bare and PVA-covered particles of different sizes.

Experimental Details

Polystyrene Latexes. The polystyrene latexes used were the monodisperse LS-1102-A, LS-1103-A, and LS-1166-B (Dow Chemical Co.)
with average particle diameters of 190, 400, and 1100nm, respectively. The latexes were cleaned by ion exchange with mixed Dowex
50W-Dowex 1 resin (9). The double-distilled and deionized (DDI)
water used had a conductivity of 4×10^{-7} ohm^{-1} cm^{-1}. The surface
groups of the ion-exchanged latexes determined by conductometric
titration (10) were strong-acid sulfates; the surface charge densities were 1.35, 3.00 and 5.95 $\mu C/cm^2$, respectively.

Polyvinyl Alcohols. The commercial PVA's (Air Products and
Chemicals, Inc.) used are described in Table I.

Table I. Specifications of Polyvinyl Alcohol (Vinol) Samples

Grade	Hydrolysis %	Viscosity cps*	$\bar{M}n$	$\bar{M}w$
Vinol 107	98.0 - 98.8	5-7 (Low)	23,000	35,800
Vinol 325	98.0 - 98.8	28-32 (Medium)	80,000	118,100
Vinol 350	98.0 - 98.8	55-65 (High)	107,150	161,600
Vinol 205	87.0 - 89.0	4-6 (Low)	26,400	34,500
Vinol 523	87.0 - 89.0	21-25 (Medium)	79,100	120,400

*4% aqueous solutions at 20°C.

The PVA solutions were prepared by dispersing the powdered polymer in water using sufficient agitation to wet all particles and then increasing the temperature to 95°C (fully hydrolyzed PVA) or 80°C (88%-hydrolyzed PVA) until the PVA was competely dissolved, as recommended by the supplier. The clear solutions were filtered hot through Whatman filter paper and cooled. The PVA contents were determined gravimetrically. Freshly prepared solutions were used for all experiments; the solutions were discarded after 36 hours.

Adsorption Isotherms. The adsorption isotherms were determined using the serum-replacement adsorption or desorption methods (7). For the adsorption method, the latex samples (50 or 100 cm^3; 2% solids) containing varying amounts of PVA were equilibrated for 36 hours at 25°C, placed in the serum replacement cell equipped with a Nuclepore membrane of the appropriate pore size, and pressurized to separate a small sample of the serum from the latex. For the desorption method, the latex samples (250 cm^3; 2.5% solids) were equilibrated for 36 hours at 25°C and subjected to serum replacement with DDI water at a constant 9-10 cm^3/hour. The exit stream was monitored using a differential refractometer. The mean residence time of the feed stream was ca. 25 hours. It was assumed that equilibrium between the adsorbed and solute PVA was maintained throughout the serum replacement. For both methods, the PVA concentration was determined using a Δn-C calibration curve.

Thickness of the Adsorbed PVA Layer. The thickness of the adsorbed PVA layer (δ) was measured using two independent methods: capillary viscometry and photon correlation spectroscopy.

Viscosity Measurements. The latex viscosity measurements were made at 25±0.1°C using a Cannon-Ubbelohde capillary viscometer (capillary constant 0.01). For the bare particles, the latex samples were cleaned by serum replacement, and part of the serum was separated; the relative viscosity of the serum was virtually the same as that of the DDI water, so that either could be used indiscriminately for diluting the samples for viscosity measurement. For the PVA-covered particles, the samples from the plateau region of the adsorption isotherm were washed further with water until no PVA was detected in the serum by differential refractometry. The relative viscosity of the serum of these samples was also virtually the same as that of the DDI water. The most concentrated samples (ϕ = 0.025) were diluted with DDI water and measured. Dilution of these samples does not result in desorption of the PVA because of the near-irreversible nature of its adsorption. The PS latexes are negatively charged; therefore, 1mM aqueous reagent-grade sodium chloride was added to suppress the electroviscous effect. The electrolyte concentration was not adjusted to constant ionic strength for the reasons described by Fleer (3).

Photon Correlation Spectroscopy. The photon correlation spectroscopy (PCS) measurements were made using a Chromatix KMX-6DC low-
angle light-scattering photometer connected with a 64-channel digital
correlator interfaced with a PDP1103 data processing system (Digital Equipment). The light source of the Chromatix KMX-6DC is a
2mw He-Ne laser (λ_o = 632.8nm). This instrument gave accurate
measurements within 1-2 minutes. The latex samples used were the
same as those used for the viscosity measurements except that the
particle concentrations in 1mM sodium chloride were in the 0.005-
0.020% range. All measurements were made at ambient temperature
at an angle of 174° following the procedure of Derderian et al.
(11).

Electrolyte Stability. The electrolyte stability of the bare and
PVA-covered latexes was measured from the rate of flocculation
upon addition of sodium chloride solution. The measurements used
a Beckman 5270 spectrophotometer equipped with two 1cm-pathlength
4cm^3-capacity cells and an optical density-time recorder set at
the longest possible wavelength, 1370nm. Sodium chloride solutions were added to the sample cell using a 1 cm^3 syringe; the
quick injection was considered sufficient to mix the sample thoroughly. The latex particle concentration was 0.015%. The latex
concentration in the reference cell was such that the concentrations in both cells were the same after electrolyte injection.
The principle of this method is that the initial slope (time =
zero) of the optical density-time curve is proportional to the
rate of flocculation. This initial slope increases with increasing electrolyte concentration until it reaches a limiting value.
The stability ratio W is defined as reciprocal ratio of the limiting initial slope to the initial slope measured at lower electrolyte concentration. A log W-log electrolyte concentration plot
shows a sharp inflection at the critical coagulation concentration
(W = 1), which is a measure of the stability to added electrolyte.
Reerink and Overbeek (12) have shown that the value of W is determined mainly by the height of the primary repulsion maximum in
the potential energy-distance curve.

Electrophoretic Mobility. The electrophoretic mobilities of the
bare and PVA-covered latex particles were measured using the fully
automated Pen Kem 3000 system. The particles in a cylindrical
capillary cell are illuminated by a laser light source positioned
perpendicularly to the cell. The light beam can be focused at any
point in the cell, but the measurements are usually made at the
stationary flow level. The light scattered at 90° by the particles
is collected and focused on a rotating grated disc. The light
passed by the disc impinges in pulses on a photomultiplier tube,
the output of which is analyzed by a spectrum analyzer to give a
frequency difference spectrum. For the population of particles
undergoing electrophoresis, the system takes multiple averages
and gives a distribution of frequencies, which is proportional to
the mobility distribution of the sample.

Results and Discussion

Effect of PVA Molecular Weight on Adsorption.

Figures 1 and 2 show the adsorption isotherms of the fully (98%) hydrolyzed and partially (88%) hydrolyzed PVA's, respectively, determined by the adsorption and desorption methods. These isotherms may be analyzed in two ways: moving from left to right (adsorption) and moving from right to left (desorption). For the adsorption method, the PVA surface concentration increases rapidly, and then more gradually, with increasing bulk PVA concentration to a plateau. The gradual increase or rounding of the isotherm is more pronounced with the higher molecular weight PVA's. Cohen-Stuart et al. (13) proposed the terms "sharp" and "rounded" to describe isotherms obtained with polymer adsorbates of different molecular dispersity; a polymer of narrow molecular weight distribution gives a sharp isotherm, and one of broad molecular weight distribution gives a rounded isotherm. This nomenclature may be applied to the isotherms of Figure 1 and 2: the low-molecular-weight Vinol 205 (polydispersity 1.3) gave a sharp isotherm; all other PVA's (polydispersities ca. 1.5) gave rounded isotherms, with the degree of rounding being more pronounced with the high-molecular-weight PVA's.

Figure 1 shows scattered data points in the low bulk PVA concentration range for the high-molecular-weight fully-hydrolyzed Vinol 325 and Vinol 350. This scatter may be explained by the "bridging" flocculation which is postulated for partial coverage of the particles by the polymer adsorbates: a single polymer molecule may be adsorbed on two or more particles simultaneously. In this case, the surface polymer concentration should be lower than in the absence of bridging, which would affect the adsorption isotherm. The scatter observed for Vinol 325 and Vinol 350 is in the region of partial coverage. The method of mixing the polymer with the colloidal sol affects the flocculation by bridging; however, adding the PVA solution to the latex or vice-versa gave no difference in the adsorption isotherm.

Hydrodynamic chromatography and photon correlation spectroscopy were used to detect these flocs. Hydrodynamic chromatography showed no evidence for the presence of flocs; however, in this method, the particles are subjected to higher shear (about 600–1000 sec^{-1}), which may break down the flocs to primary particles. Photon correlation spectroscopy showed that the particle size increased to twice the bare particle size at partial coverage and then decreased to a smaller size (but still larger than the bare particle size) at the plateau region. Table II gives the particle size variations for Vinol 350 adsorbed on the 190nm-size particles. The larger particle sizes observed at partial coverage are consistent with flocculation by bridging. The smaller particle sizes

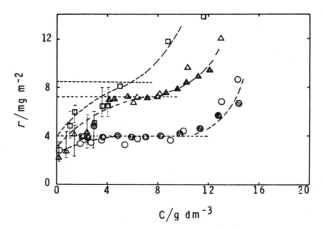

Figure 1. Adsorption isotherms of fully hydrolyzed PVA
samples on 190nm polystyrene particles: (o) Vinol 107; (Δ)
Vinol 325; (□) Vinol 350; open points by adsorption method
and shaded points by desorption method.

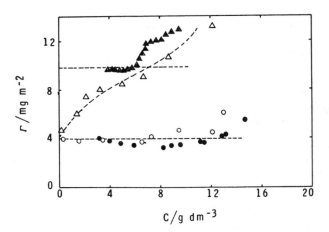

Figure 2. Adsorption isotherms of partially hydrolyzed
(88%) PVA samples on 190nm polystyrene particles: (o) Vinol
205; (Δ) Vinol 523; open points by adsorption method and
shaded points by desorption method.

observed at the plateau region are consistent with the absence of
flocculation at full surface coverage. The increase in size (48
nm) at the plateau region relative to that of the bare particles
is a measure of the thickness of the adsorbed PVA layer.

Table II. Particle size and δ as a function of surface coverage
for the 190nm-Vinol-350 samples by PCS

Description	Particle size (nm)	δ (nm)
Bare particle	180±4.5	---
Increasing surface	295±5.7	---
coverage but below	307±13.0	---
the apparent plateau	313±3.9	---
region of the isotherm	363±12.1	---
At or slightly above	276±4.0	48±4.3
the plateau adsorption		

Transmission electron microscopy also gave evidence for bridging flocculation at partial coverage. Figure 3 shows electron micrographs of the bare particles and the particles covered partially with adsorbed Vinol 350. The partially covered particles are interconnected with fibrillar links, which are not observed in the bare-particle sample.

These results confirm the existence of weak or labile flocs at partial PVA coverage, particularly with the high-molecular-weight fully-hydrolyzed Vinol 325 and Vinol 350. In contrast, the partially-hydrolyzed Vinol 523, which is comparable in molecular weight to the Vinol 325, gave an adsorption isotherm with little scatter, indicating the absence of flocculation. Partially hydrolyzed PVA shows specific interactions with polystyrene surfaces (mentioned below), and the absence of flocculation in this case is consistent with the theory proposed by Clark and Lal (14) for bridging flocculation.

Table III shows that the adsorption densities at the plateau region increase with increasing PVA molecular weight, despite the distribution of molecular weights for each sample. The adsorption density of Vinol 350 is given in parentheses because of the difficulty in establishing its exact value. For the fully hydrolyzed PVA's, which show no specific interactions with polystyrene surfaces, the increase in adsorption density is proportional to the 0.5 power of the molecular weight, in good agreement with theory, which predicts $\Gamma \alpha M^{0.5}$ for weak surface interactions under theta conditions. For the partially hydrolyzed PVA's, which show specific interactions with polystyrene surfaces, the increase in adsorption density is proportional to the 0.72 power of the molecular weight.

Table III. Adsorption density at the apparent plateau for the different PVA's

Sample	$\Gamma/(mg\ m^{-2})$	repeat units/100$\overset{\circ}{A}^2$
Vinol 107	4.00	55
Vinol 325	7.20	98
Vinol 350	(8.50)	(116)
Vinol 205	4.00	49
Vinol 523	9.86	121

For comparable molecular weights, Garvey (5) found adsorption densities of fractionated 88%-hydrolyzed PVA on polystyrene latex particles that were only one-half of those reported here; however, the adsorption densities increased with the 0.5 power of the molecular weight, in good agreement with theory. For the same system, Boomgaard et al. (15) found adsorption densities 50-100% greater than those found by Garvey and attributed the difference to the different polystyrene surfaces in the two works.

On adsorption, partially hydrolyzed PVA shows specific interactions with the substrate: the more hydrophobic acetyl groups adsorb preferentially on hydrophobic polystyrene surfaces. Partially hydrolyzed PVA is a better stabilizer than fully hydrolyzed PVA because of its increased degree of blockiness of acetyl units. The 88%-hydrolyzed PVA samples used in this study have mean acetyl run lengths of three units. Consequently, the adsorption density of partially hydrolyzed PVA's of comparable molecular weights should be higher than that of the fully hydrolyzed PVA's. This is the case for Vinol 523 which has a molecular weight comparable to that of Vinol 325. However, the adsorption densities of fully hydrolyzed Vinol 107 and partially hydrolyzed Vinol 205 are the same, even though the molecular weight of Vinol 205 is slightly lower than that of Vinol 107. The molecular weight of partially hydrolyzed PVA would be expected to be higher than that of the fully hydrolyzed analog if both were prepared by hydrolysis of the same polyvinyl acetate. Since Vinol 205 also has a narrower molecular weight distribution, it may have been made from a different polyvinyl acetate and therefore may not be suitable for comparison.

Extension of the adsorption isotherms gave a second rise in surface concentration because of multilayer adsorption. Silberberg (16) has explained multilayer adsorption in terms of an incipient phase separation at the surface. The phase separation process should be concentration-dependent; since the surface concentration is usually higher than the bulk concentration, and is higher, the higher the molecular weight, this process should occur at lower concentrations for the higher-molecular-wieght PVA's. Figures 1 and 2 show that this second rise occurs at a lower bulk concentration for the higher molecular weight PVA's. Extension of the isotherms to still higher concentrations was not possible because of the limited concentration range over which the differential refractometer can measure.

For the desorption method (moving from right to left), the isotherms can be divided into two regions: (i) a region where the surface concentration decreases upon moving to the left; (ii) a region in which the surface concentration remains unchanged. The fact that polymer adsorbed in the multilayer region can desorb indicates that the polymer coil had no attachment to the surface, as hypothesized by Silberberg (16). Gel permeation chromatography of the desorbed fractions showed the same molecular weight distribution as the original PVA, indicating that the absorption was not preferential; however, these desorbed fractions are from a region of saturation or near-saturation adsorption. Preferential adsorption is important in the rounded part of the isotherm (discussed earlier); however, the fact that the same distribution was restored upon saturation indicates the transitory nature of this phenomenon. Also, the gel permeation chromatograms showed no evidence of aggregation whereas the occurrence of phase separation suggests the formation of aggregates. It may be argued that gel permeation chromatography requires extreme dilution of the samples and that any aggregates that may exist would disperse upon dilution; however, it has been shown (17) that, for these PVA's, this method distinguishes aggregates which are not dispersed upon dilution.

The second region in which the surface concentration remains unchanged indicates that the adsorption is irreversible; however, the concentrations involved may be too low and the times too long for any desorption to be observed, as proposed by Scheutjens et al. (18). Comparison of the isotherms determined by adsorption and desorption shows good agreement for the low-molecular-weight PVA's. For Vinol 350, it was not possible to determine the isotherm by desorption because of an irregular decay in concentration upon desorption. With Vinol 523, the agreement in the multilayer adsorption region is poor. Nonetheless, the desorption isotherms give well-defined plateau values, which is not the case for the adsorption method.

Effect of PVA Molecular Weight on Adsorbed Layer Thickness. Figure 4 shows the variation of reduced viscosity with volume fraction for the bare and PVA-covered 190nm-size PS latex particles. For the bare particles, η_{red}/ϕ is independent of ϕ and the value of the Einstein coefficient is ca. 3.0. For the covered particles, η_{red}/ϕ increases linearly with ϕ. Table IV gives the adsorbed layer thicknesses calculated from the differences in the intercepts for the bare and covered particles and determined by photon correlation spectroscopy, as well as the root-mean-square radii of gyration of the free polymer coil in solution. The agreement of the adsorbed layer thicknesses determined by two independent methods is remarkable. The increase in adsorbed layer thickness follows the same dependence on molecular weight as the adsorption density, i.e., $\delta \alpha M^{0.5}$ for the fully hydrolyzed PVA's and $\delta \alpha M^{0.72}$ for the partially hydrolyzed PVA's. Viscometric measurements

0.2 μm

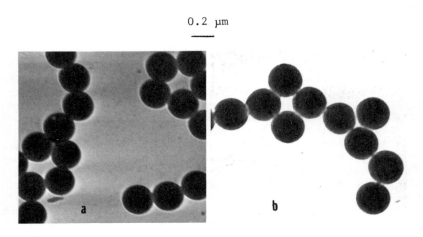

Figure 3.   TEM micrographs of 190nm polystyrene latex: (a) without PVA (b) with Vinol 350 at partial coverage.

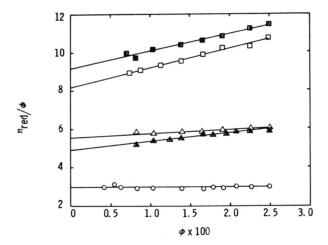

Figure 4.   Reduced viscosity ratio versus volume fraction of PS particles: (o) bare particles; (△) covered with Vinol 107; (□) covered with Vinol 325; (▲) covered with Vinol 205; (▨) covered with Vinol 523.

for Vinol 350 were not made because of the problems in generating the desorption isotherms described above; the value for the adsorbed layer thickness by photon correlation spectroscopy was taken from Table II at the point of saturation adsorption. The adsorbed layer thicknesses were 40-70% higher than the dimensions of the polymer coil in solution (assuming that the thickness of the coil adsorbed at the surface is twice the radius of gyration) except for Vinol 205, indicating that the polymer coil became distorted or elongated normal to the surface upon adsorption.

Table IV.   Adsorbed layer thickness δ and the rms radius of gyration $(\bar{s}^2)^{\frac{1}{2}}$

Sample	δ by viscosity,nm	δ by PCS,nm	$(\bar{s}^2)^{\frac{1}{2}}$,nm	$\delta/2(\bar{s}^2)^{\frac{1}{2}}$
190nm PS-107	22.0 ± 2.0	25.0 ± 2.0	7.4	1.48-1.69
190nm PS-325	37.9 ± 2.0	39.9 ± 2.5	13.2	1.44-1.51
190nm PS-350	---	48.2 ± 4.3	15.1	1.60
190nm PS-205	17.4 ± 2.0	16.0 ± 2.0	6.5	1.23-1.34
190nm PS-523	43.0 ± 2.0	45.5 ± 3.5	13.0	1.65-1.75

Effect of PS Latex Particle Size on PVA Adsorption. Figure 5 shows the adsorption isotherms of Vinol 107 on PS latex particles of 190, 400, and 1100nm diameter. The different-size latex particles give the same type of isotherm, and the adsorption densities at the plateau region are independent of particle size. It should be mentioned that, for these studies of different particle size, the concentration of polymer added must be adjusted so that the amount of polymer per unit surface area must be about the same for the different-size particles; the polymer concentration suitable for the smaller particles may be too great for the larger particles, which would give an isotherm with a higher plateau region. This aberration was observed in a desorption experiment with the 400nm-size particles, perhaps because of the adsorption of polymer aggregates, which are present in concentrated PVA solutions. Comparison of the desorption isotherms of Figure 5 show that the data points for the 400nm-size particles fall at a lower surface concentration in the higher bulk concentration region and do not match the isotherm determined by adsorption. The data points on 1100nm particles are limited because of the limited amount of sample that was available. To our knowledge, no results have been hitherto reported for the effect of particle size on polymer adsorption isotherms for particles of the same surface characteristics.

Effect of PS Latex Particle Size on Adsorbed Layer Thickness. Figure 6 shows the variation of reduced viscosity with volume fraction for 190, 400, and 1100nm-size bare and PVA-covered PS latex particles. The viscosity variation of the different-size bare particles was the same, with an Einstein coefficient of ca. 3.0. The

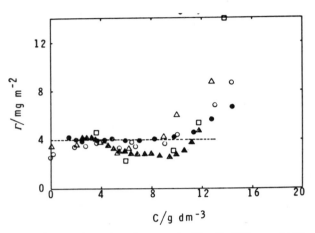

Figure 5. Adsorption isotherm of Vinol 107 on different size polystyrene particles: (o) 190nm particles; (Δ) 400nm particles; (□) 1100nm particles. Open points by adsorption method and shaded points by desorption method.

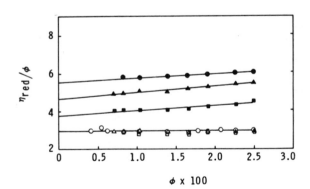

Figure 6. Reduced viscosity ratio versus volume fraction of PS particles of different sizes: (o) 190nm particles; (Δ) 400nm particles; (□) 1100nm particles; open points for bare particles and closed points for covered particles.

viscosity behavior of the different-size PVA-covered particles was
linear, with the same slopes but different intercepts. Table V
gives the adsorbed layer thicknesses calculated from the viscosity
measurements and determined by photon correlation spectroscopy.

Table V: Adsorbed layer thickness δ and the effective flat layer
          thickness δ_{eff}

Sample	δ by viscosity,nm	δ by PCS,nm	δ_{eff},nm
190nm PS-107	22.0 ± 2.0	25.0 ± 2.0	27.9-32.2
400nm PS-107	32.7 ± 2.0	33.6 ± 3.5	38.3-39.6
1100nm PS-107	54.4 ± 2.0	---	59.9

The adsorbed layer thickness for the 1100nm-size particles could
not be measured by photon correlation spectroscopy because of the
1000nm upper limit of this instrument. Again, the agreement between the two methods is excellent. It is interesting that the
adsorbed layer thickness increases with increasing latex particle
size and that these values vary with the 0.5 power of the particle
radius. i.e., $\delta \alpha R^{0.5}$, where R is the particle radius. This relationship holds for the 190-1100nm range studied, but there must
be some limits to its applicability in terms of thickness and particle size.

   Garvey (5) experienced difficulty in measuring the adsorbed
layer thickness of 165nm-size latex by ultracentrifugation and
therefore used the smaller 38nm-size latex for these measurements;
however, he also experienced difficulty in measuring the adsorption isotherm of the latter latex and therefore assumed that the
adsorption per unit area was the same for both latexes, and compared the thickness values obtained for the 165nm-size latex by
photon correlation spectroscopy with the thickness values obtained for the 38nm-size latex by ultracentrifugation. The thickness
values for the 38nm-size latex with various PVA fractions measured
by ultracentrifugation were smaller than those for the 165nm-size
latex by photon correlation spectroscopy. Garvey attributed this
difference in thicknesses to the different particle sizes of the
latexes. In order to account for this difference he made the
following assumptions: (i) on different-size particles, the adsorbed layer is homogeneous with respect to segment density; (ii) on
different-size particles, the adsorbed layers occupy a constant
volume per unit surface area. He then defined the effective flat
surface thickness δ_{eff} as the ratio of the total volume of the
adsorbed layer to the surface area of the particle. The implication of this work is that the increase in thickness observed with
the larger particles is due only to the geometry of the system.

   It will be shown below that, for different-size particles,
the term δ_{eff} has no significance and that the assumption of constant volume of the adsorbed layer is inappropriate. Table V
shows that the value of δ_{eff} calculated according to Garvey's pro-

cedure increases with increasing particle size. Instead, we offer
the following explanation for the increase in adsorbed layer thickness with increasing particle size: (i) the same adsorption per
unit area for different-size particles could result from a decrease in the number of loops, so that, on the average, the loops
on the larger particles are longer and broader; (ii) the same adsorption per unit area for different-size particles could result
from chain segments being thrown into loops, so that again, on the
average, the loops of the larger particles are longer and broader;
(iii) both of the foregoing explanations giving longer and broader
loops on the larger particles. The implication of these explanations is that the adsorption on the larger particles is relatively
weak, which could readily be established. Microflow calorimetric
measurements of the heat of adsorption and NMR measurements of the
bound fractions are underway. Therefore, we shall defer present-
ing a detailed model until these data are available. Nevertheless,
the effect of particle size on the adsorption layer thickness is
not due merely to the geometry of the system but is more complex.

Approximate limits to the adsorbed layer thickness can be defined. The lower limit is about twice the radius of gyration for
particles of the appropriate size. This particle size can be calculated from the radius of gyration and the relationship $\delta \alpha R^{0.5}$.
The adsorbed layer thickness increases with increasing particle
size, and the measured thicknesses are always greater than twice
the radius of gyration, the difference increasing with increasing
particle size. The upper limit cannot be defined at present.
Moreover, these limits are conjectural and require more experimental evidence for their verification.

Electrolyte Stability of Bare and PVA-Covered PS Latex Particles.
Figure 7 shows the variation of log W with log of sodium chloride
concentration for the bare and Vinol 107-covered 190 and 400nm-
size PS latex particles. The differences between the different
sizes, and the bare and PVA-covered particles, are evident. In
all cases, the value of W decreases with increasing salt concentration to an inflection point with the horizontal line W=1. For
the bare particles the decrease in W with time is steep compared
with those of the PVA-covered particles; the descending line
corresponds to the region of slow coagulation and the horizontal
line, to the region of fast coagulation. The concentration of the
electrolyte at which these two lines intersect is defined as the
critical coagulation concentration (CCC). Table VI gives the CCC
values along with the slopes of the descending lines of the log
W-log concentration plots. It can be seen that the CCC value of
the 400nm particles is about 2.4 times smaller than that of the
190nm particles, which is expected. The slope of the descending
line is also about 2.5 times smaller for 400nm-size particles
than for the 190nm-size particles. According to Reerink and
Overbeek (12), steeper slopes are expected for particles of larger
size; however, this is not always observed experimentally. For

the PVA-covered particles, the descending line corresponds to the region of slow flocculation and the horizontal line to that of fast flocculation, because of the presence of a strong nonionic steric barrier, which restricts the flocculation to the shallow secondary minimum. (This terminology is based on the nature of association; the term "flocculation" or "coagulation" is used depending on the reversibility or irreversibility of this association, respectively). The electrolyte concentration at which these two lines intersect is defined as the critical flocculation concentration (CFC). Table VI also gives the CFC values, along with the slopes of the descending lines. It can be seen that the CFC value of 400nm-size particles is about half that of the 190nm-size particles; however the slopes of the descending lines are identical.

These measurements are valid for coagulation of electrostatically stabilized particles in the primary minimum (e.g., the bare PS particles). For coagulation of particles sterically stabilized with a polymeric nonionic stabilizer, where the steric barrier to coagulation may be great and insensitive to electrolyte, these measurements may be less revealing. Nonetheless, such measurements have been used by other workers (19,20) to determine the effect of nonionic stabilizers on sol stability. They found that the electrolyte concentration required for coagulation/flocculation increased with increasing concentration of nonionic emulsifier on the particle, which was attributed to a reduction in the attractive forces and the strong steric barrier arising from the adsorbed layer. It is not known precisely what role the electrolyte plays in flocculation in the secondary minimum. The depth of the secondary minimum for these PVA-covered particles, calculated from the thickness of the adsorbed layer, neglecting the effect of the adsorbed layer and the retardation forces, is of the order of 0.25-0.50kT. Since the average kinetic energy of a particle is of the order of 1 kT, these particles should be stable indefinitely, and indeed this is the case for PVA-covered particles in the absence of electrolyte. The addition of electrolyte seems to have affected the depth of the secondary minimum, and since this minimum is less shallow for the 400nm-size particles than for the 190 nm-size particles, it is conceivable that the flocculation of the 400nm-size particles occurred at lower electrolyte levels than for the 190nm-size particles.

Table VI: Critical Coagulation/Flocculation Concentration and the slope of log W vs log C plot

Latex Sample	CCC/CFC,mM	$-\dfrac{d\log W}{d\log(c)}$
190nm Bare Particles	225	1.69
190nm Covered Particles	98	0.23
400nm Bare Particles	95	0.66
400nm Covered Particles	40	0.22

It is interesting to compare these results with the electrophoretic measurements made under identical electrolyte concentrations. Figure 8 shows that the variation of electrophoretic mobility with sodium chloride concentration is different for the
bare and the PVA-covered particles. For the bare particles, the
mobility remains constant up to a certain salt concentration, then
increases to a maximum and decreases sharply, finally approaching
zero. The maximum in electrophoretic mobility-electrolyte concentration curve with bare particles has been explained earlier
(21) by postulating the adsorption of chloride ions on hydrophobic polystyrene particles. In contrast, for the PVA-covered particles, the mobility decreases with increasing electrolyte concentration until it approaches zero at high salt concentration.
It is interesting to note that the electrolyte concentration at
which the mobility reaches zero are close to the CCC/CFC values
reported above.

Conclusions

The use of high PVA concentrations in adsorption experiments gives
a rapid rise, followed by an apparent plateau in surface concentration, and then a second rise in surface concentration. In contrast, adding excess PVA to a dispersion is often thought to give
monolayer adsorption. The effect of increasing the PVA molecular
weight or decreasing its degree of hydrolysis is to increase the
adsorption density and the adsorbed layer thickness. Good agreement between adsorption and desorption experiments is observed
with lower molecular weight PVA's. Desorption experiments provide well-defined plateau values, irrespective of the PVA molecular weight, which may be difficult by adsorption experiments. The
adsorption density is independent of the particle size of the substrate; however, the effect of particle size is manifested by an
increase in the thickness of the adsorbed layer with increasing
particle size. The increase in thickness results from changes in
the configuration of the adsorbed molecules on surfaces of different curvature. Addition of an electrolyte is shown to have a
different effect on bare and PVA-covered particles. The bare particles coagulate in the primary minimum at relatively high electrolyte concentrations and the PVA-covered particles flocculate in
the secondary minimum at relatively low electrolyte concentrations.

Acknowledgments

The authors would like to thank Dr. Dennis Nagy (Air Products and
Chemicals, Inc.) for his assistance with PCS measurements, Dr. F.
M. Fowkes for his helpful discussions, and Air Products &
Chemicals, Inc., for providing the PVA samples and the Beckman
spectrophotometer facilities.

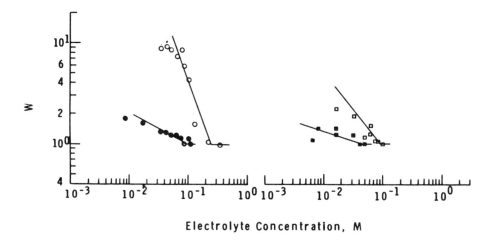

Electrolyte Concentration, M

Figure 7. W versus electrolyte concentration (NaCl) for different-size particles: (o) 190nm particles; (□) 400nm particles; open points for bare particles and closed points for particles covered with Vinol 107 at saturation.

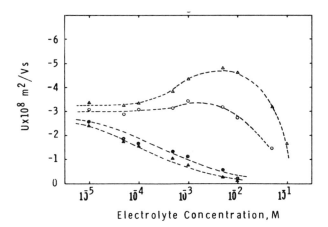

Electrolyte Concentration, M

Figure 8. Electrophoretic mobility versus electrolyte concentration (NaCl) for different-size particles: (o) 190nm particles; (Δ) 400nm particles; open points for bare particles and closed points for particles covered with Vinol-107 at saturation.

Literature Cited

1. Vincent, B., and Whittington, S., "Polymers at Interface and in Disperse Systems, in "Colloid and Surface Science", Ed. E. Matijevic, 1982, p.1.
2. Tadros, Th.F., "Polymer Adsorption and Dispersion Stability", in "The Effect of Polymers on Dispersion Properties", Ed. Th. F. Tadros, 1982, p.1.
3. Fleer, G.J., Ph.D. Thesis, Meded. Landbouwhogeschool, Wageningen, 1971, 71-20.
4. Koopal, L.K., Ph.D. Thesis, Meded. Landbouwhogeschool, Wageningen, 1978, 78-12.
5. Garvey, M.J., Ph.D. Thesis, University of Bristol, 1974.
6. Ahmed, S.M., El-Aasser, M.S., Pauli, G.H., Poehlein, G.W., and Vanderhoff, J.W., J. Colloid Interface Sci., 1980, 73, 388.
7. Ahmed, S.M., El-Aasser, M.S., Micale, F.J., Poehlein, G.W., and Vanderhoff, J.W., in "Polymer Colloids II", Ed. R.M. Fitch, 1980, p. 265.
8. Ahmed, M.S., M.S. Thesis, Lehigh University, 1981.
9. Vanderhoff, J.W., and Van den Hul, H.J., J. Colloid Interface Sci., 1968, 28, 336.
10. Van den Hul, H.J., and Vanderhoff, J.W., Brit. Polymer J., 1970, 2, 121.
11. Derderian, E.J., and MacRury, T.B., J. Dispersion Sci. Tech., 1981, 2, 345.
12. Reerink, H., and Overbeek, J. Th. G., Faraday Society Disc., 1954, 18, 74.
13. Cohen-Stuart, M.A., Scheutjen, J.M.H.M., and Fleer, G.J., J. Poly. Sci.: Polymer Physics Ed., 1980, 18, 559.
14. Clark, A.T., and Lal, M., in "The Effect of Polymers on Dispersion Properties" Ed. Th. F. Tadros, 1982, p. 169.
15. Boomgaard, Th.V., King, T.A., Tadros, Th.F., Tang, H., and Vincent, B., J. Colloid Interface Sci., 1978, 66, 68.
16. Silberberg, A., J. Colloid Interface Sci., 1972, 38, 217.
17. Ahmed, M.S., El-Aasser, M.S., and Vanderhoff, J.W., Paper presented at 56th Colloid and Surface Sci. Symp., Blacksburg, Va., 1982.
18. Scheutjens, J.M.H.M., and Fleer, G.J., J. Phys. Chem., 1979, 83, 1619.
19. Mathai, K.G., and Ottewill, R.H., Trans. Faraday Soc., 1966, 62, 759.
20. Ottewill, R.H., and Walker, T., Kolloid-Z.u.Z. fur Polymere, 1968, 227, 108.
21. Ma, C.M., Micale, F.J., El-Aasser, M.S., and Vanderhoff, J.W., in "Emulsion Polymers and Emulsion Polymerization" Ed. D.R. Bassett and A.E. Hamielec, ACS Symp. Ser. 165, 1981, 251.

RECEIVED October 7, 1983

Adsorption of Cellulose Ethers from Moderately Saline Aqueous Solutions

J. E. GLASS, S. SHAH, D–L. LU, and S. D. SENEKER

Polymers and Coatings Department, North Dakota State University, Fargo, ND 58105

Nonionic cellulose ethers, hydroxyethyl(HE) and
hydroxypropyl (HP) cellulose, of variable molar
substitution (M.S.) levels, were adsorbed on peptized
sodium montmorillonite surfaces from fresh and
saline (NaCl) aqueous solutions. The amounts
adsorbed for 2 M.S. HEC and HPC and 4 M.S. HEC were
insensitive to electrolyte concentration; the 4 M.S.
HPC exhibited a notable increase in adsorption with
increasing NaCl concentration. Entrapment in the
interlayer of recovered sodium montmorillonite did
not vary with salinity; the extent of entrapment was
greater with the 4 M.S. HE and HP celluloses than
either of the 2.0 M.S. polymers. Mixed ethers of
HEC (2 M.S.) containing an anionic (carboxymethyl)
or cationic (3-O-2-hydroxypropyltrimethylammonium
chloride) group at 0.4 M.S. levels did not adsorb
from fresh water. Adsorption of these polar mixed
ethers increased with increasing electrolyte until
electrostatic and solvation effects were negated in
0.54N NaCl solutions and the adsorbed amounts
typical of a 2 M.S. HEC were observed. Interlayer
entrapments comparable to the equivalent M.S. HEC
were observed at lower (0.18N) electrolyte
concentrations.

It has been shown(1) that carbohydrate polymers containing
pendant ether linkages adsorb on peptized montmorillonite
surfaces from fresh water solutions in amounts greater than
underivatized carbohydrate polymers having the same solution
conformational characteristics. In this study it was also
demonstrated that ether linkages promote interlayer entrapment
of the segmentally rigid macromolecules in smectite clays. This
does not occur with underivatized carbohydrate polymers.
    Several anionic carbohydrate polymers (e.g., carboxy-
methyl cellulose, xanthomonas campestris polysaccharide,
cellulose sulfate ester, etc.) do not adsorb from fresh water
solutions, but their adsorption in saline solutions plays an

0097–6156/84/0240–0095$06.00/0
© 1984 American Chemical Society

important role in many petroleum recovery processes. Adsorption studies from highly saline environments require a formidable experimental effort. As a forerunner to these studies the adsorption of nonionic cellulose ethers and the most hydrophilic of these, hydroxyethyl cellulose (HEC), containing both anionic and cationic groups at equivalent degrees of substitution (D.S.), were examined.

The long-term goal of this investigation is an understanding of the effect of a particular mode of adsorption on montmorillonite which ensures that under pressure the clay platelets align parallel to a solid surface even under saline conditions. This is an important phenomenon in petroleum recovery processes.

EXPERIMENTAL

The general experimental methods of analysis and materials used in this study have been previously described(1,2) with the exception of the ionic hydroxyethyl cellulose polymers. Carboxymethyl hydroxyethyl cellulose (CMHEC) was supplied by Hercules Inc.; it is used in fracturing (petroleum) applications. The cationic HEC was supplied by Union Carbide Corp.; the cationic group is 3-O-2-hydroxypropyltrimethyl-ammonium chloride. The polymer is used primarily in cosmetic applications. Both cellulose polymers contain a molar substitution (M.S.)(3) of hydroxyethyl groups of approximately 2.0; the polar group is present at an approximate M.S. (or D.S.) of 0.4. A more quantitative description of the polymers is provided in Table II. The unmodified HEC polymers, 2.0 and 4.3 M.S., were supplied by Union Carbide; the 2.5 M.S. by Hercules. Hydroxypropyl celluloses (HPC) of 2.0 and 4.0 M.S. were supplied by Hercules. These products have been quantitatively characterized(1,4) by M.S., percent unsubstituted vicinal diol (%uVD) and glucopyranosyl (%uGP) analyses and stochastic modeling.

Differential refraction(5) and colorimetric measurements(2) were used to determine the amount of carbohydrate polymer adsorbed from solution. A Phillips X-ray diffractometer was used to quantify the degree of interlayer expansion(6). The cation exchange capacity of the peptized sodium and potassium montmorillonite was 105±5 meq./100g.

In adsorption studies from saline environments it is necessary to prepare the water-soluble polymer and peptized montmorillonite in fresh water at high concentrations and to add each to a saline solution. Polyelectrolytes will frequently not "yield" the same viscosity as when they are dissolved in fresh water. Montmorillonite will flocculate in saline solutions. With fresh water mixing of components, reproducible results are obtained in the saline studies. After component mixing, agitation of the slurry is maintained with gentle stirring via micromagnetic Teflon bars. Analyses of the continuous phase before and after centrifugation of the polymer solutions were conducted to ascertain that precipitation of the polymer was not occurring. Variation in the montmorillonite concentration (.007g/cc to 0.014g/cc) did not influence the adsorption of hydroxyethyl cellulose (HEC) of variable molar substitutions from fresh water or from 0.54N sodium chloride solutions, nor the adsorption of the cationic HEC from the saline solution. The data indicate that the adsorptions noted in this study were not associated with a substrate induced precipitation of the water-soluble polymer. Adsorption on sodium montmorillonite as a function of water-soluble polymer concentration is illustrated in Figure 1 for HEC and the cationic HEC from fresh and saline solutions. The cationic HEC does not adsorb on the solid substrate from fresh water solutions.

RESULTS AND DISCUSSION

Fresh Water Solutions

The difference between hydrophobicities of the hydroxyethyl (HE) grouping and the hydroxypropyl (HP) unit is evident in the relative aqueous solution surface tensions(7,8) of the two cellulosic polymers; in these comparative references the M.S. of the products is not equal. The dramatic influence of the more hydrophobic HP groupings on surface pressures is illustrated in Figure 2.

The amounts adsorbed on montmorillonite (2500 ppm polymer, 0.8 to 1.0 wt.% peptized montmorillonite) and interlayer expansion (d_{001}) in the clays (Table I) recovered from fresh water solutions do not reflect the differences in hydrophobicities noted in Figure 2. Equivalent adsorption and d_{001} values are observed among polymers of equal M.S.. There is an insensitivity to the monovalent cation (i.e., potassium or sodium vs. ammonium used in previous studies(1)). Hydrophobicity is not important in adsorption on montmorillonite surfaces; the cation-ether ion-dipole interaction(1) is the critical factor. This is true in a different sense in the hydroxyethyl cellulose polymers containing ionic groups (CMHEC and HECN$^+$Me$_3$Cl$^-$; these shorthand chemical formulas will be used for the polymers in the remainder of this article). Neither ionic group affects the surface tension of water compared to the equivalent M.S. HEC (Figure 3), but both inhibit significant adsorption on montmorillonite from fresh water, despite the presence of hydroxyethyl (HE) units (at a 2.0 M.S. level) that through a cation-ether ion-dipole interaction promote adsorption and interlayer entrapment.

Montmorillonite is electronegatively charged (105 ± 5 meq./ 100g) in water and the carboxylate anions in CMHEC are repelled

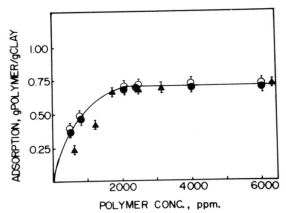

Figure 1:   Adsorption (g/g) dependence on water-soluble
            polymer (W-SP) concentration (ppm). Substrate:
            peptized sodium montmorillonite. Open symbols
            adsorbed from fresh water solutions, closed symbols
            from 0.54N NaCl solutions. W-SP:○,●, hydroxyethyl
            cellulose (HEC) M.S.= 2.0; ▲,HEC (M.S.=2.0)
            containing 3-0-2 hydroxypropyltrimethylammonium
            chloride (M.S.=0.4) (HECN$^+$Me$_3$Cl$^-$), polymer was
            extracted and gave pH=6.7 in clay slurry.

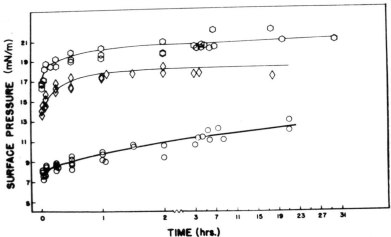

Figure 2:   Surface pressure (mN/m) dependence (air-water
            interface) on time (hrs.) for hydroxyethyl (HE)
            hydroxypropyl (HP) cellulose (1000 ppm).
            Molar substitutions of adduct:
            ○ ,M.S. = 2.40 (HE), 0.13 (HP)
            ◇ ,M.S. = 1.52 (HE), 0.62 (HP)
            ⬡ ,M.S. = 1.19 (HE), 1.03 (HP)

TABLE I

ADSORPTION AND INTERLAYER EXPANSION OF CELLULOSE
ETHERS FROM FRESH WATER ON PEPTIZED SODIUM
MONTMORILLONITE

CELLULOSE DERIVATIVE	M.S.^{3}	ADS(g/g)^a	d_{001}
Hydroxyethyl(HEC)	2.0	.68(.68)	2.1
	2.5	.70(.70)	2.2
	4.3	.98(.92)	2.4
Hydroxypropyl(HPC)	2.0	.66(.67)	2.1
	4.0	.97(.96)	2.6
Hydroxyethyl carboxymethyl (CMHEC)	2.0 0.4	.14(.12)	1.2^b
Hydroxyethyl -3-0-2-hydroxy- propyltrimethyl ammonium chloride (HECN$^+$Me$_3$Cl)	2.0 0.4	.16(.07)	1.2^b

a. Values in parentheses were determined colorimetrically, similar data were obtained with potassium
peptized clay. b. d_{001} of Na montmorillonite =1.2nm
at 0% relative humidity.

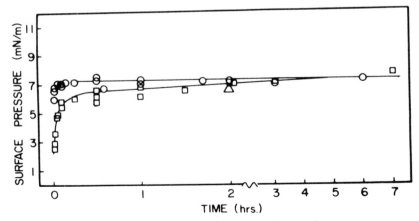

Figure 3:   Surface pressure (mN/m) dependence (air-water
interface) on time (hrs.) for HEC (O), M.S.= 2.0
and ionic HEC (M.S. = 2.0) mixed ethers.
Ionic groups : □ , carboxymethyl , M.S. = 0.4;
                △ , N$^+$Me$_3$Cl , note Figure 1.
Polymer concentrations: 1000 ppm.

despite the presence of HE groupings in a five fold excess on a
M.S. comparison (a two fold excess on a degree of
substitution, D.S.(4), basis). With the frequency and chain
extension(1) of HE groups it is surprising that a significant
adsorption is not observed from fresh water, for the substituent
distribution data in Table II indicate that the CM groups are
attached to the glucopyranosyl ring rather than to the hydroxyls
of the pendant HE groupings.

An equivalent M.S. HEC containing a 3-0-2-hydroxypropyl-
trimethylammonium chloride group (at an equivalent M.S. to the
CM grouping) also does not exhibit significant adsorption from
fresh water solutions. The lack of adsorption and the inability
of the HE groupings to promote interlayer entrapment in the
mixed ether polymers is reflected in d_{001} spacings equal to
those observed in untreated montmorillonite. It is well known
that amine containing compounds adsorb strongly on the surface,
particularly in the interlayer where the driving force is
protonation by the highly acidic surface. The quaternary amine
of $HECN^+Me_3Cl^-$ is charged and sterically restricted, and its
ability to inhibit the more prevalent HE groupings from
promoting adsorption and interlayer entrapment is surprising.
Based on the relative transport of water in thin films(9)
containing both quaternary amine and carboxylate groups the lack
of adsorption of $HECN^+Me_3Cl^-$ can be related to the high
solvation of the quaternary ammonium group.

Saline Solutions

With increasing electrolyte (sodium chloride) concentration
there appears to be a slight increase (within experimental
error) in adsorption among the lower M.S. nonionic cellulose
ethers (Figure 4). With increasing M.S. the amount adsorbed is
greater and the amount adsorbed with increasing salinity
increases for HPC, outside the limits of experimental error.
This can be understood in terms of solvation effects. Cellulose
is substituted in order to disrupt hydrogen bonding among the
glucopyranosyl hydroxyl groups; adducts such as ethylene or
propylene oxide do not increase the hydrophilicity of the
cellulose chain. The solubility of the high M.S. HEC is
dependent on the ether-water interaction; the 2 M.S. HEC and HPC
are less dependent. The dependence is greatest in the 4 M.S.
HPC, where essentially all of the glucopyranosyl hydroxyls have
been substituted by propylene oxide which imparts a significant
hydrophobicity to the macromolecule. These conclusions are
supported by the observation that the 4 M.S. HPC precipitates in
fresh water at 45°C and by its greater intrinsic viscosity
sensitivity to salinity (Figure 5). Precipitation of the 4 M.S.
HPC occurs at sodium chloride concentrations in excess of 1N,
which is greater than the salinities used in this study.

TABLE II

ADDUCT DISTRIBUTIONS IN SELECTED[a]CELLULOSE ETHERS

CELLULOSE DERIV.	M.S.	%uGP[b]	%uV.D.[b]	Int.Visc. dl/g
HEC	2.0	24	68	12.6
CMHEC	2.0 0.4	13	29	10.1[c]
HECN$^+$Me$_3$Cl	2.0 0.4	13	44	11.7[c]

a. Detailed characterization of nonionic cellulose
   ethers are given in reference 1.
b. See reference 4 for description of analysis of
   unsubstituted vicinal diol (%uVD) and glucopyranosyl
   (%uGP) and for other pertinent references.
c. Determined in 1N NaCl.

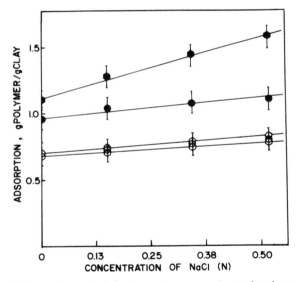

Figure 4:   Adsorption (g/g) dependence of nonionic cellulose
             ethers (2500 ppm) on salinity (N, NaCl) of aqueous
             solution.
             Substrate: peptized sodium montmorillonite.
             Open symbols, HEC: ○ , M.S. = 2.0; ◑,2.5;◔,4.3
             Closed symbols, Hydroxypropyl cellulose (HPC):
                        ● , M.S. =2.0; ⬢ ,4.0.

The hydration of polyoxyethylene (POE) is dramatically affected by the anion present(10) in the aqueous phase. The adsorption of HEC (both 2.0 and 4.3 M.S.) was therefore studied in Na_2SO_4 and Na_3PO_4 at equivalent normalities. The multivalent anions are more effective in precipitating POE than is the chloride ion. The amounts adsorbed and the interlayer expansions at normalities below precipitation conditions are given in Table III. The influence of multivalent anions on the intrinsic viscosity of variable M.S. HECs is illustrated in Figure 6. The increased amounts adsorbed are within experimental error, but the decrease in d_{001} with the 4.3 M.S. HEC is notable. The d_{001} changes in the absence of increased adsorption are not explainable in terms of solvation effects.

The observed changes in interlayer expansion (Table IV) in the montmorillonite clays also do not parallel the adsorption and intrinsic viscosity changes with salinity for the 4.0 M.S. HPC recovered from NaCl solutions. The latter polymer as noted above precipitates in NaCl solutions above 1N and notable, gradual increases in adsorption occur with increasing NaCl concentration. This trend is not observed in d_{001}. The greater interlayer entrapment of higher M.S. cellulose ethers has been related(4) to a combination of fewer unsubstituted glucopyranosyl units and to a higher frequency of extended ether chains from the cellulose backbone, which results in a higher density of cation-ether interactions. Additional studies are required to clarify the apparent conflict between adsorption and d_{001} changes with salinity in all of the salt solutions.

With increasing electrolyte concentration the cellulose mixed ethers exhibit a marked increase in adsorption (Figure 7). This is expected as a result of decreased electrostatic repulsion and hydration of the polar groups. The adsorption of CMHEC and $HECN^+Me_3Cl^-$ increases until at 0.54N NaCl solutions both approach that of an equivalent M.S. HEC. The decrease in electrostatic repulsions is accompanied by the decrease in intrinsic viscosities with salinity (Figure 8). The CMHEC contains approximately 20wt.% salt which did not affect adsorption from fresh water solutions. The cationic HEC contained only 3.2wt.% salt, which is minimal in 2500ppm W-SP solution concentrations. The salt in part arises from the neutralization acid (i.e., acetic, nitric, phosphoric, etc.,) used in the final step of cellulose ether syntheses. The pH of the cationic polymer (2500 ppm) solution was 5.0, with the peptized montmorillonite, 5.7. Extraction with a tertiary butanol(75%)-water(25%) solution lowered the ash content from 3.2 to 2.3 wt.% and raised the solution pH to 9.4 (at 2500 ppm). With peptized montmorillonite slurries the pH was 6.7, approximate with the 6.9 - 7.0 values observed with the other cellulose ethers. Extraction did not change the adsorption behavior of the cationic HEC. Adsorption on peptized montmorillonite from 0.54N NaCl solutions paralleled that observed with HEC (Figure 1 and

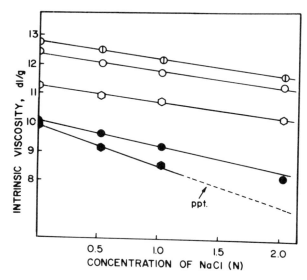

Figure 5: Intrinsic viscosity (dl/g) dependence on salinity
(N, NaCl) of aqueous solutions. W-SP: symbols given
in Figure 4.

TABLE III

HYDROXYETHYL CELLULOSE ADSORPTION BEHAVIOR
IN MULTIVALENT ANION SOLUTIONS

SALINITY		0.18N		0.36N		0.54N	
		g/g	d_{001}	g/g	d_{001}	g/g	d_{001}
HEC M.S.	SALT	---	----	---	----	---	----
2.0	Na_2SO_4	.74	2.1	.76	2.0	.78	2.1
	Na_3PO_4	.73	2.1	.76	2.1	.78	2.1
4.3	Na_2SO_4	1.04	1.9	1.06	1.9	1.08	1.8
	Na_3PO_4	1.04	2.2	1.06	2.2	1.08	2.1

d_{001} values in nm.; for experimental error in
adsorption note error bars in graphs.

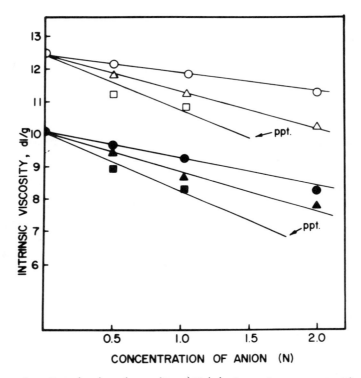

Figure 6:   Intrinsic viscosity (dl/g) dependence on salinity
             (N, NaCl) of aqueous solutions. Open symbols, HEC
             M.S. = 2.0; closed symbols, HEC M.S. = 4.3.
             Salts: O ,$\bullet$, NaCl; $\triangle$,$\blacktriangle$, Na_3PO_4; $\square$,$\blacksquare$, Na_2SO_4

TABLE IV

EXPANSION OF Na MONTMORILLONITE AFTER EXPOSURE
TO CELLULOSE ETHERS IN SALINE SOLUTIONS

CELLULOSE DERIVATIVE	M.S.^{3}	INTERLATER SPACINGS^a d_{001} at SOLUTION SALINITY (N NaCl)			
		0	.18N	.36N	.54N
HEC	2.0	2.1	2.1	2.1	2.1
	2.5	2.1	2.1	2.1	2.1
	4.3	2.4	2.5	2.5	2.5
HPC	2.0	1.8	1.8	1.8	1.8
	4.0	2.6	2.4	2.3	2.4
CMHEC	2.0				
	0.4	1.2	1.8	1.8	1.8
HECN$^+$Me$_3$Cl	2.0				
	0.4	1.2	2.1	2.1	2.1

a. Although the maximum, d_{001}, remains at the same
   angle there is peak broadening in the X-ray diffrac-
   tion pattern with increasing salinity.

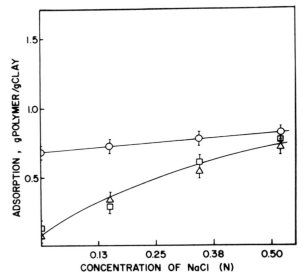

Figure 7: Adsorption (g/g) dependence of nonionic and ionic
           cellulose ethers (2500 ppm) on salinity (N, NaCl)
           of aqueous solution.Substrate:peptized sodium
           montmorillonite. W—SP symbols given in Figure 3.

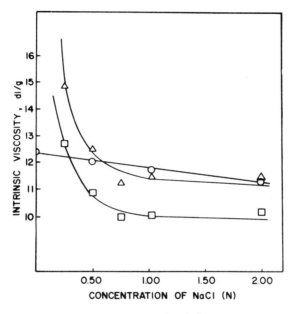

Figure 8:   Intrinsic viscosity (dl/g) dependence on salinity
(N, NaCl) of aqueous solutions. W-SP: symbols given
in Figure 3.

7). These observations were noted over a two-fold concentration (.7 to 1.4 wt.%) change in montmorillonite.

Interlayer Entrapment of Ionic HEC Mixed Ethers

The interlayer spacing of montmorillonite recovered from fresh water solutions containing either ionic HEC polymer is not expanded. With increasing electrolyte concentration entrapment is observed and the interlayer is expanded (Table IV). Reduction in the electrostatic repulsions permits the cation-ether ion-dipole interaction to assume greater importance. The cellulose ethers examined in this study vary in their hydrophobicity. This could affect the d_{001} distances through variable water uptake . This possible change in d_{001} was examined through variation in the relative humidity of the exposed montmorillonite (Table V). An increase in the interlayer spacings occurs with an increase in the percent relative humidity but the incremental change is constant, within experimental error, for all of the polymers studied.

TABLE V

INFLUENCE OF RELATIVE HUMIDITY ON INTERLAYER EXPANSION

W-SP	M.S.	d_{001}, nm 0%R.H.	40%R.H.
HEC	2.0	2.1	2.5
	2.5	2.2	2.7
	4.3	2.5	2.7(2.8)
HPC	2.0	2.1	2.5
	4.0	2.7(2.4)	3.3(2.9)
CMHEC	0.4/2.0	1.2(1.8)	1.3(2.2)
HECN$^+$Me$_3$Cl$^-$			
	0.4/2.0	1.2(2.1)	1.3(2.4)

The values in parenthesis are associated with adsorptions from 0.54N NaCl solutions. The values are listed only when different from the fresh water adsorption results.

- -

In the presence of electrolyte, montmorillonite will flocculate. If flocculation occurs macromolecules of lower molecular weight will exhibit greater adsorption due to the greater surface available to smaller hydrodynamic volumes.

Higher molecular weight polymers will adsorb less (an example of this is given in Figure 9). In the moderate salinities employed in this investigation, the lack of an adsorption dependence on molecular weight (Figure 10) indicates that flocculation did not occur. This will not be true in future studies at higher salinities and temperatures.

CONCLUSIONS

Cellulose ethers, both nonionic and ionic mixed ethers, adsorb at the aqueous/air interface in relationship to the amount and hydrophobicity of the nonionic groups; their adsorption from aqueous solutions on montmorillonite is governed in part by a cation-ether ion-dipole interaction. The adsorption of cellulose ethers on the latter is in proportion to the molar substitution (M.S.) of the ether linkages appendaged to the cellulose chain, not to their hydrophobicities. Increasing the salinity (NaCl) of the aqueous medium appears to effect only a slight increase, within experimental error, in adsorption. The high M.S. hydroxypropyl cellulose(HPC) is a notable exception; a significant increase in adsorption is observed with increasing salinity (up to 0.54N). This is related to decreasing solvation of the hydrophobic, high M.S. HPC. In all of the nonionic cellulose ethers studied, expansion of the interlayer due to polymer entrapment occurred in proportion to the M.S. of the polymer, but the d_{001} value did not change significantly with increasing salinity.

The presence of anionic or cationic groups at a 0.4 M.S. level inhibited adsorption and interlayer entrapment of 2.0 M.S. hydroxyethyl cellulose(HEC) from fresh water solutions. The lack of adsorption of the cationic HEC is surprising; it is related to hydration of the quaternary amine group. Increasing adsorption and interlayer entrapment is observed with both the cationic and anionic HECs with increasing sodium chloride concentration.

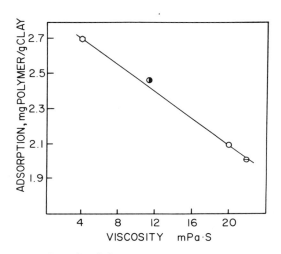

Figure 9:   Adsorption (mg/g) dependence of nonionic cellulose
            ethers (2500 ppm) on salinity (N, NaCl) of aqueous
            solution. Substrate: Berea sand (85 wt.%) blended
            with montmorillonite (15 wt.%). W–SP symbols:
            ◯ ,methyl cellulose, M.S. = 1.7;
            HEC – ◑ ,◯, M.S. = 2.0; ⊖, M.S. = 2.5.
            W–SP concentrations are 2500 ppm; the viscosity
            reflects the relative molecular weight of the W–SP.

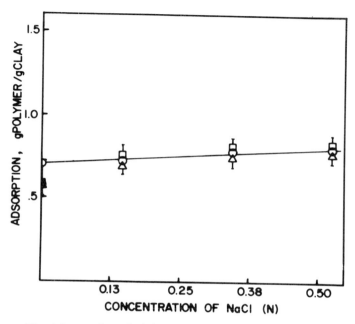

Figure 10: Adsorption (g/g) dependence of HEC (2.0 M.S.) of variable molecular weights (M_v: ○, 10^4, △ , 10^5, □ , 10^6) at 2500 ppm on salinity (N, NaCl) of aqueous solution.
Substrate: peptized sodium montmorillonite.

Literature Cited

1. Glass, J. E.; Ahmed, H.; Lu, D-L; Seneker, S. D.;
   McCarthy, G. J. J.Colloid Interf. Sci., in press.
2. Malone, T. R.; Raines, R. H.; Weintritt, D. J., Society of
   Petroleum Engineers Publication No.8741, 6200 N. Central
   Expressway, 64706, Dallas, Texas 75206.
3. Savage, A. B., in "Encyclopedia of Polymer Science and
   Technology"; Mark, H. F.; Gaylord, N. G.; Bikales, N. M.
   Eds.; Interscience, New York, 1965; Vol. 3, p. 512.
4. Glass, J. E.; Buettner, A. M.; Lowther, R. G.; Young, C. S.;
   Cosby, C. A. Carbohydr. Res, 1980,84,245.
5. Brice, B. A.; Halzer, H. J. Opt. Soc. Amer., 1951,41,1033.
6. "Crystal Structures of Clay Minerals and Their X-Ray Identification," Brindley, G. W.; Brown, G., Eds., Mineralogical
   Society Monograph No. 5, London,1980; Chapter 5.
7. Glass, J. E.J. Polym. Sci.,Part C,1971,34,141.
8. Chang, S.A.; Gray, D. G. J.Colloid Interf. Sci.,1978,67,255.
9. Hill, L. W.; Lu,D-L J. Water Borne Coatings, 1981,3,3.
10. Bailey, F. E.; Callard, R. W. J. Appl. Polym.Sci.,1959,1,56.

RECEIVED October 7, 1983

Adsorption of Nonionic Water-Soluble Polymers (W-SPs) at Aqueous–Air Interfaces

J. E. GLASS, H. AHMED, and M. E. GLASS

Polymers and Coatings Department, North Dakota State University, Fargo, ND 58105

The phenomenon of reorientation of hydrophobic units of segmentally flexible W-SPs at aqueous-air interfaces is examined and compared to adsorptive behavior at aqueous-latex surfaces in pigmented coatings. Structurally similar W-SPs, polymethyl vinyl ether, polyoxyethylene(POE), vinyl alcohol/vinyl acetate copolymers of variable hydrolysis and POE copolymers containing oxypropylene and oxybutylene units are examined. Equilibrium surface pressures are achieved rapidly if there is uniformity of the hydrophobic segments among the repeating units. The absolute surface pressures observed at 1000 ppm W-SP parallel nonpolar solubility parameters. The surface pressure of POE solutions in the absence of organic vapors deviates from this generalization, suggesting that POE retains its unique interaction with water molecules at the aqueous-air interface. The behavior of these polymers is compared with that of surfactant hydrophobe modified W-SPs of styrene/maleic acid, Na salt and urethane oxide types at both the aqueous-air interface and in latex pigmented coatings. Whereas the latter type polymers do not affect high surface pressures, rheological evidence indicates that the hydrophobes interact with the latex surfaces in the presence of surfactants, but this behavior is not observed in the unmodified but highly surface active W-SPs. An unusual temperature adsorption behavior for the 99% hydrolyzed PVAl copolymer is observed at the aqueous-air interface which is similar to the behavior of globular proteins.

In the early 1960s water-borne coating formulations became commercially significant and cellulose ethers, hydroxyethyl cellulose (HEC) and hydroxypropyl methyl cellulose (HPMC) became important commercial thickeners for such formulations. The use of these thickeners with small particle size latices did not impart the "good" rheological properties(1) of alkyd formulations. This led to a multitude of publications(2-6) that discussed their poor rheological properties; most concluded that the phenomenon arose from interparticle bridging between the cellulose ether thickener and the small particle latices. The latter were gradually

0097–6156/84/0240–0113$06.00/0

replaced by larger, heterodispersed particle size latices with improved rheological properties. A recent alternative explanation(1) for the poor rheological performance of small particle size latices thickened with cellulose ethers can be found in the integration of several individual research studies. For example theoretical(7,8) arguments based on entropy concepts have predicted the phase separation of high molecular weight polymers and latices, and experiments in simple, unpigmented systems(9-12) have supported the theory of latex flocculation in the presence of cellulose ethers. Higher low shear viscosities have been reported to result from latex particle agglomerates(13) and poor rheological performance of coatings(14).

Small particle latices impart better film properties than larger sized latices, as would be anticipated from the Young-Laplace equation(15), and there is still a desire within the coatings industry for alkyd coatings rheology in a water-borne, small particle size latex formulation. Water-soluble polymers that contain surfactant units as part of the macromolecular structure are commercially available for lubricant applications, and these "surfactant hydrophobe modified"(SHM) W-SPs appear to impart alkyd rheology to small particle size latices in water-borne paints(1). A possible mechanism for improved rheology is the adsorption of the hydrophobe segments on the latex particle with osmotic stabilization of the small latex particles against flocculation, to ensure good rheological behavior, by the hydrated loops of the unadsorbed units of the SHM W-SP. The current study is part of an effort to evaluate such a mechanism and produce better polymeric surfactants.

EXPERIMENTAL

The water-soluble polymers described in this investigation are similar to those previuosly studied(16) at aqueous-air and organic interfaces, with the exception that the 89 and 99% hydrolyzed vinyl alcohol/vinyl acetate copolymers were obtained from Air Products and the poly(methyl vinyl ether)(PMVE) from Union Carbide. The surfactant hydrophobe-modified W-SPs also have been described(1); the generic structures are illustrated in Figure 1. Molecular weights (determined by gel permeation chromatography) and surface pressure behavior of some of the commercial W-SPs are given in Table I. The surface tensions were measured by pendant drop (the long-term studies were conducted in a closed cell containing distilled water) or by Wilhelmy plate techniques(15). In the latter studies (Table I) equilibrium was reached within 15 minutes and the fluid appeared to completely wet the plate. The measurements were recorded on a Hewlett Packard 7074A recorder. The limited rheological data reported were determined with cone and plate viscometers(Brookfield and Ferranti-Shirley).

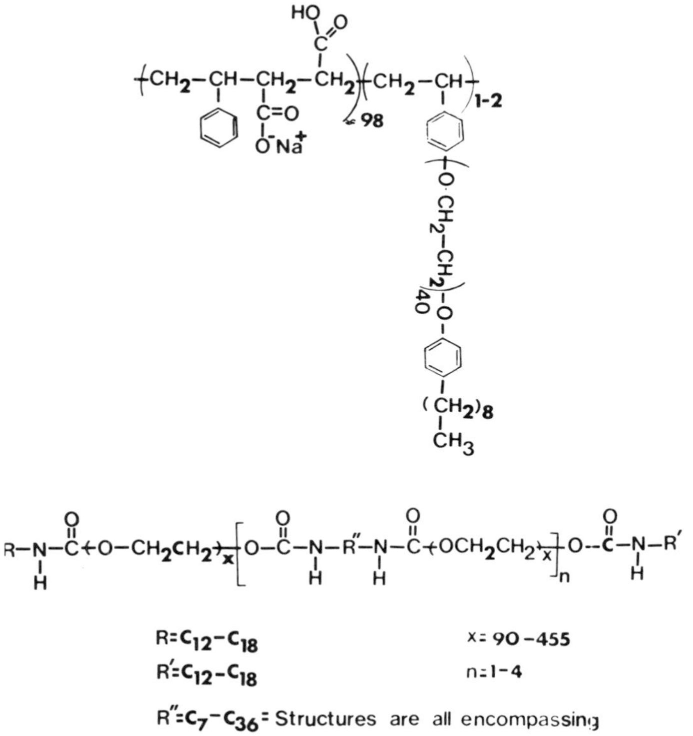

Figure 1 : Chemical structure of hydophobe-modified
            styrene/maleic acid terpolymer(SMAT) and generic
            structural formula for hydrophobically
            modified ethoxylate urethane polymers(HEUR).

TABLE I

SURFACTANT HYDROPHOBE MODIFIED W-SP[a] PROPERTIES

COMPOSITION TYPE	$\underline{M}_w$	SURFACE PRESSURE(mN/m)
Styrene/Maleic Acid, Na salt/Terpolymer	32,331	12
Urethane Oxide, Hydrophobe Modified	37,051	17
	93,992	15
Typical Surfactant used in Coatings Formulation	300	40

a. 1000ppm

- -

RESULTS AND DISCUSSION

The classic studies of Saunders([17]) demonstrated that in the presence of excess surfactant methyl cellulose (MC) would desorb from monodispersed polystyrene latices. MC is one of the most surface active water-soluble polymers (W-SPs) and it will readily dominate the surface pressure π ($\pi = \sigma_0 - \sigma$, where σ_0 is the surface tension of water and σ is the surface tension of the aqueous polymer solution) of the aqueous solution. For example, hydroxyethyl cellulose (HEC) lowers the surface tension of water much less than MC or HPMC, and when the combination of HEC and MC or HPMC in water is studied, there is no notable influence of HEC on the surface pressure (Figure 2).

The influence of the surfactant in the modified polymers of Figure 1 on π (aqueous solutions, Table I) is not overpowering. The surfactant's influence is diminished by the amphiphilic oxyethylene units which lie interfacially flat at the aqueous-air interface. The hydrophobes are structurally similar to the surfactants providing stability to commercial latices and should be capable of competing with the classical surfactants at the latex surface, but this ability is not reflected in π values. The oxyethylene units have been demonstrated([18]) to provide osmotic stabilization to latex particles.

It is known([1]) that when hydrophobe-modified W-SPs such as those in Figure 1 are formulated in water-borne latex coatings a significant time period (>48 hours) is required to reach steady state viscosities; this does not happen when either MC, HPMC, HEC or the polymers discussed below are used as thickeners. The overall phenomenon of competitive adsorption and the time dependence of segmentally flexible W-SPs with variable hydrophobicity is of interest in our laboratories and is in part examined in this article.

In previous studies(16) methyl cellulose (MC) and poly(oxyethylene) (POE) were adsorbed at aqueous–air and aqueous–organic liquid interfaces. Organic–liquid interfaces accelerate the attainment of equilibrium surface pressures. At the aqueous–air interface the attainment of equilibrium values with segmentally rigid MC was slower than with segmentally flexible PEO. With both polymers the presence of trace amounts of an organic vapor markedly increases the rate and the final value attained. The segmentally flexible polymers of similar structural features selected for study in this investigation are illustrated in Figure 3.

Rate of Equilibrium Surface Pressure Attainment

Propylene oxide is a surface active monomer structurally similar to ethylene oxide and therefore of interest as a SHM W-SP, but with more than ten repeating units this polymer is not water soluble. A compositional isomer methyl vinyl ether is water soluble; the adsorption behavior of this polymer (PMVE) is illustrated in Figure 4. At 1 ppm the rate of π increase is linear over three hours. The diffusion rate could be calculated if the W-SP's molecular weight were monodispersed. The polymer studied had a Gaussian molecular weight distribution, which is true of essentially all W-SPs even after attempts have been made to fractionally achieve monodispersibility. A detailed kinetic analysis of molecular diffusion and reorientation effects will not be undertaken until a monodispersed molecular weight W-SP has been prepared.

At 10ppm the rate of increase in π is rapid and an equilibrium value is approached, within experimental error, in approximately one hour. At 1000 and 5000 ppm equilibrium is approached almost instantaneously. The inclusion of the hydrophobic monomers, propylene oxide and butylene oxide in oxyethylene(POE) copolymers to achieve surface active macromolecules provides adsorption behavior (Figure 5) different from PMVE. At 5ppm POE/POP(7.7 mole percent) does not reach an equilibrium value in nine hours. In PMVE the structural composition is uniform; in the POE/POP copolymer it is not. The displacement of the oxyethylene segments by the more hydrophobic oxypropylene segments facilitates the time dependent process. Adsorption in highly coiled configurations at higher concentrations 100 ppm (Figure 5) and 1000 ppm (Figure 6) also facilitates a time dependence not exhibited in PMVE. Some of the

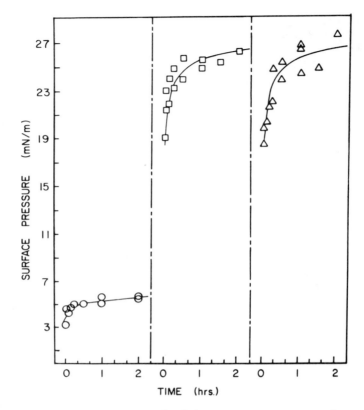

Figure 2 : Surface pressure(mN/m) dependence on time(hrs.)
of aqueous cellulose ether (both $M_y = 5 \cdot 10^5$)
solutions. ◯ ,1000 ppm hydroxyethyl cellulose
(HEC); ☐ ,250ppm hydroxypropyl methyl cell-
ulose(HPMC); △ ,250ppm HPMC, 1000ppm HEC.

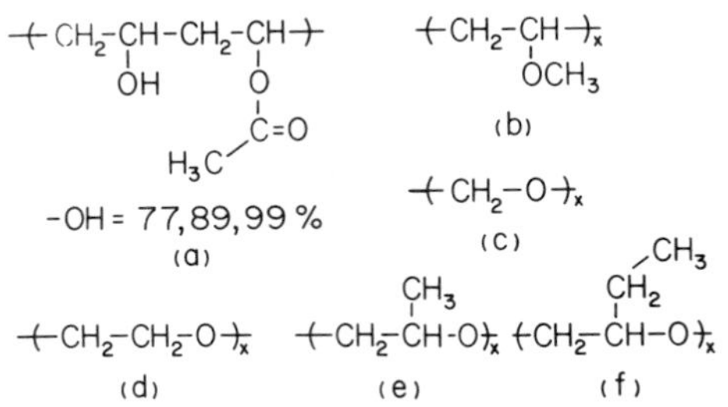

Figure 3 : Chemical structures of the synthetic polymers
considered in this study. Polymers c, e and f
are not water soluble.

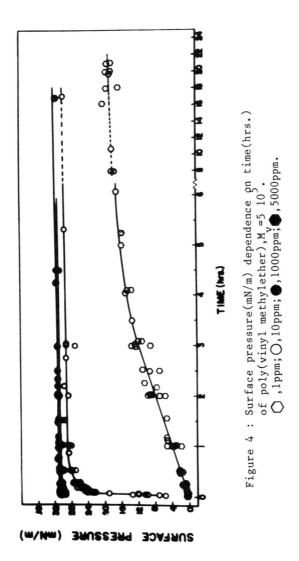

Figure 4 : Surface pressure(mN/m) dependence on time(hrs.)
of poly(vinyl methylether),M_V=5 10^5.
◯,1ppm;○,10ppm;●,1000ppm;⬡,5000ppm.

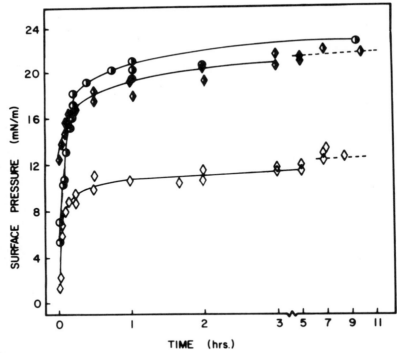

Figure 5 : Surface pressure(mN/m) dependence on time(hrs.)
of aqueous poly(oxyethylene) copolymers $M_v = 10^5$
with propylene oxide (POEOP-7.7 mole %) ◊,5ppm;
◖ ,100ppm;and butylene oxide (POEOB-3.4 mole %).
◑ ,100ppm.

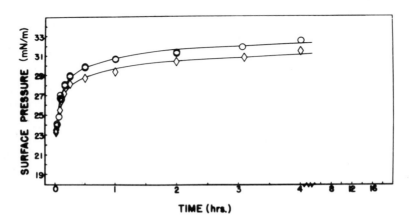

Figure 6 : Surface pressure(mN/m) dependence on time(hrs.) of
◊ ,POEOP and ○,POEOB aqueous solutions, both
1000ppm.

latter   studies   also   included   butylene   oxide   (3.4   mole
percent)/POE copolymers.

Water-soluble   vinyl   acetate/vinyl   alcohol   copolymers   also
are not uniformly distributed along the macromolecular chain and
exhibit   a   time   dependent   adsorption   behavior   (Figure   7).
Comparison of the 10 ppm 77% hydrolyzed PVAl copolymer data with
the POE/POP (7.7 mole %), 5 ppm data reveals a slower process for
the   PVAl   copolymer.   This   is   due   to   the   intermolecular
associations between the hydroxyl functions and their influence
on the unfolding and interfacial displacement process. This is a
dramatic influence in the adsorption of the 99% hydrolyzed PVAl,
which has been reported(19–21) to form supermolecular aggregates
in solution. The phenomenon is not evident in the 25°C adsorption
time dependence (Figure 8) due to the presence of only one mole
percent acetate functions. The influence of the interassociations
is evident in the variation in adsorption behavior between the
25° and 50°C data. Most synthetic W-SPs follow the behavior of
the   89%   hydrolyzed   PVAl   copolymer   (Figure   8).   The   unusual
temperature behavior of the 99% PVAl has been noted in several
globular protein studies(22–24).

Magnitude of Surface Pressure Attainment

At 1000 ppm the equilibrium surface pressure approached by
PMVE   aqueous   solutions   (Figure   4)   is   almost   32   mN/m.   This   is
significantly in excess of the equilibrium value of POE solutions
(9mN/m,(16). Incorporation of more hydrophobic oxypropylene and
oxybutylene units in POE copolymers results in equilibrium values
of approximately 32 mN/m (1000 ppm, Figure 6). The latter values
equal   those   of   commercial   POE/POP   copolymers   at   high
concentrations   (up   to   10   weight   %)   and   containing   high
percentages of POP(25). In the lower (approaching the limit of
solubility   in   water,   77%)   percent   hydrolysis,   the   vinyl
acetate/vinyl alcohol copolymer approaches an equilibrium value
of 30 mN/m (Figure 7). The solubility parameters(26) of both the
total and the polar, nonpolar and hydrogen bonding components
listed in Table II provide insight into the equilibrium surface
pressures obtained.

The solubility parameter of water is 17 or 23, depending on
the association structure of water used in the calculation. None
of the values listed in Table II are within two units of either
value and by the general rules of the solubility concept, none of
the polymers in Table II should be water soluble. Homopolymers
of monomers c, e, or f in Figure 3 are not water soluble. The
solubility values listed for the W-SPs studied do not correlate
with the equilibrium pressures observed. A general correlation is
noted if the values of the most hydrophobic segments (i.e., the
oxypropyl, oxybutyl and acetate) are compared with PMVE. The

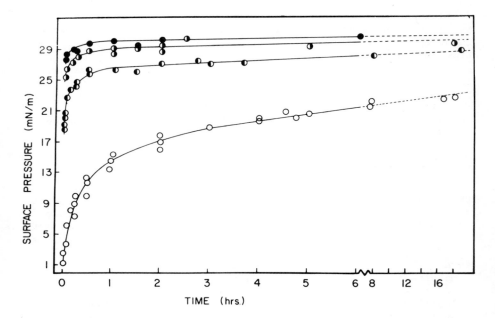

Figure 7 : Surface pressure(mN/m) dependence on time(hrs.) of
vinyl acetate/vinyl alcohol copolymers($M_v=10^5$),
77 % hydrolyzed (PVA1). ◯, 10ppm; ◑,100ppm;
◐ ,1000ppm; ●,5000ppm.

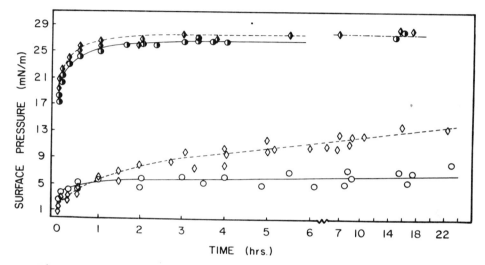

Figure 8 : Surface pressure(mN/m) dependence on time(hrs.) of
PVAl: open symbols 99% hydrolyzed; half-filled 89%
hydrolyzed. ◯ ,◑,25°C; ◇,◈,50°C; both 1000ppm.

POLYMER ADSORPTION AND DISPERSION STABILITY

TABLE II

=====SOLUBILITY PARAMETER (S.P.)[a] OF WATER-SOLUBLE POLYMER=========

WATER-SOLUBLE POLYMER	TOTAL S.P.	HYDROGEN BONDED S.P	POLAR S.P.	NONPOLAR S.P.
POLY(OXYMETHYLENE)[b]	11.7	5.8	6.6	7.7
POLY(METHYL VINYL ETHER)	9.4	2.3	1.9	8.9
POLY(OXYETHYLENE)	10.5	4.6	5.0	8.0
POE COPOLYMERS:				
OXYETHYLENE/OXYPROPYLENE (7.7 MOLE %)	10.4	4.4	4.7	8.1
OXYETHYLENE/OXYBUTYLENE (3.4 MOLE %)	10.5	4.5	4.9	8.0
POLY(OXYPROPYLENE)[b]	9.4	2.3	1.9	8.9
POLY(OXYBUTYLENE)[b]	9.3	2.1	1.5	8.9
VINYL ALCOHOL/VINYL ACETATE COPOLYMERS				
99% HYDROLYZED	14.0	8.6	5.0	9.9
89% HYDROLYZED	13.5	7.9	5.1	9.7
77% HYDROLYZED	13.0	7.3	5.1	9.4
POLY(VINYL ACETATE)[b]	10.2	3.8	5.6	7.7

(a) The molar additivity constant technique (Small, P. A., J. Appl. Chem., 1953, 3, 75.) using the multiple regression values obtained by Hoy (J. Paint Technol., 1970, 42, 76.) were used in calculating the SP. (b)Polymers are not water soluble.

general correlations suggest that the hydrophobic units in the high concentration studies adsorb to the exclusion of the more hydrophilic segments. The relatively low equilibrium values observed(16) with POE, which adsorbs relatively flat at most interfaces, is the result of the proximity of the oxygen in the interface and the retention of its unique interaction(27) with water. It is this interaction that effects water solubility not achieved with the other oxyalkylene polymers, especially POM.

Thickener-Latex Associations in Coatings Formulations

Hydroxypropylmethyl cellulose(HPMC) is one of the more surface active W-SPs; equilibrium surface pressures of 27 mN/m are observed at 250 ppm. The viscosity of an HPMC thickened small particle latex coating is considered too high at low shear rates to effect good flow and leveling of the applied coating before the film dries. Differences in the flow-out behavior of formulations containing the W-SPs discussed above occur with larger median particle size latices stabilized with a surface attached hydrocolloid. The variations (selectively listed in Table III) can be related to thickener-thickener associations(28). With small particle latices (100nm) the surface active W-SPs discussed in this article do not effect good coating flowouts.

TABLE III

Thickener[a]	Sag rating	Average flow-out heights (nm)
99% PVAl	40	520
POE	25	280
POEOP (8%)	30	280
HPMC	20	230
89% PVAl	18	180
77% PVAl	9	150

a. An interior coatings formulation, 57 PVC,32%NNV at 90 KU viscosity(14) was used in this study.

- -

A poor flowout is generally related to yield stress behavior. A method of assessing(1) this behavior of a coating is through Casson plots based on the following equation:

$$\eta^{0.5} = \eta_\infty^{0.5} + \tau^{0.5} \cdot \frac{1}{\dot{\gamma}^{0.5}} \tag{1}$$

where, η and η_∞ are the viscosities at a given and infinite shear rate, $\dot{\gamma}$, respectively, and τ is the shear stress. A linear relationship is observed (Figure 9) with most pigmented coatings; the yield stress is defined by the slope of the line. The data in Figure 9 indicate that the SHM W-SPs thickened coatings

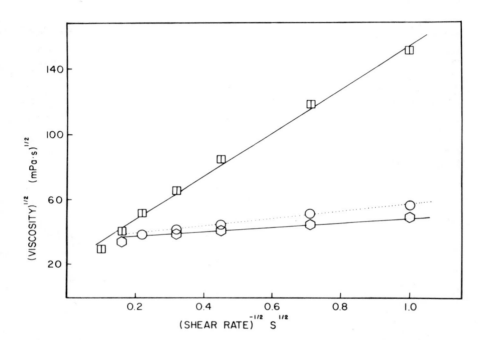

Figure 9 : Casson plot, slope of line reflects yield stress
value. Interior coating formulation including:
⊡,HPMC; ◯ ,SMAT;⬡,HEUR.

significantly decrease yield stress values in small particle latex formulations. This behavior in addition to the uniquely higher viscosities at high shear rates can not be matched by the highly surface active W-SPs discussed above. A preliminary conclusion is that the structures in Figure 1 may indeed associate with the small particle latices, their interaction and osmotic stabilization of the particles negating the formation of yield stresses.

CONCLUSIONS

The differences in time-dependent adsorption behavior between 99% PVAC at 25° and 50°C demonstrate the influence of intra- and intermolecular hydrogen bonding in the adsorption process. The limiting surface pressure of the hydrophobic water-soluble polymer appears to be 33 mN/m, approximately 7 mN/m below that of commonly used surfactants. The rate of attainment of equilibrium surface pressure values is faster if there is uniformity of the hydrophobic segments among the repeating units of the macromolecule.

The results observed above support the observations noted by Saunders(17) with methyl cellulose, i.e., water-soluble polymers that significantly lower the surface tension of water do not interact with the dispersed components of a coatings formulation containing excess surfactants, which are slightly more surface active than the water-soluble polymer. In contrast, rheological data (First Normal Stress Differences and storage moduli as a function of deformation rate (1)) suggest that hydrophobically-modified water-soluble polymers (H-M,W-SPs) interact with the dispersed components of a coatings formulation to provide osmotic stabilization and lower the yield stress (reflected in Figure 14) value. The inability of H-M,W-SPs to lower the surface tension of aqueous solutions suggests the association arises from cohesive interactions between the hydrophobe of the W-SP and the surfactants stabilizing the dispersed components. Although the W-SPs reported in this study are conformationally and segmentally flexible, the nature of the hydrophobe segments is not such as to induce a cohesive interaction and their position as part of the chain must place steric restrictions on the interfacial involvement of the hydrophobic segments.

The specific nature of the interactions among hydrophobes would suggest that the associative thickeners will vary in performance with the different latices and components used in coatings formulations. This has been observed(29) in formulations containing commercial products but it has not been quantified in well-defined formulations.

The studies in this article describe only the beginning of an investigation into an area of surface chemistry that will impact on several technological areas.

Literature Cited

1. Glass, J.E., ed. "The Influence of Associative Thickeners and Rheology on Coatings Performance," 1983, Fargo, N.D.: North Dakota State University Press.
2. Saunders, F. L.; Sanders, J. W. Colloid Sci.,1956, 11, 260.
3. Kreider, R. W. Off. Dig., 1964, 36, 1244.
4. Saunders, F. L. J. Colloid and Interf. Sci., 1967,23, 230.
5. Kreider, R. W. J. Polym. Sci., 1969, C-27, 275.
6. Wildt, H. A. J. Paint Techn., 1969, 41, 654.
7. Asakura, S.; Oosawa, F. J. Polymer Sci.,1958,33,183.
8. Sieglaff, C. L. J. Polymer Sci.,1959,41, 319.
9. De Hek, H.; and Vrij, A. J.Colloid Inter. Sci.,1979, 70,3.
10. De Hek, H.; Vrij, A. J. Colloid Interf. Sci., 1982, 88, 1.
11. Sperry, P. R.; Hopfenberg, H. B.; Thomas, N. L. J. Colloid Interf. Sci., 1981, 82, 1.
12. Sperry, P. R. J. Colloid Interf. Sci., 1982, 87, 2.
13. Zosel, A. Rheol. Acta, 1982, 21, 72.
14. Glass, J. E. J. Coatings Technol., 1978, 50, 72.
15. Adamson, A. W. "Physical Chemistry of Surfaces",1982, New York: John Wiley and Sons, Inc.
16. Glass, J. E. J. Polym. Sci., 1971, C-34, 141.
17. Saunders, F. L. J. Colloid and Interf. Sci., 1968,28, 475.
18. Napper, D. H. J. Colloid Interf. Sci.,1971,37,528.
19. Pritchard, J. G. "Poly(vinyl alcohol),basic droperties and uses," 1970, New York: Gordon and Breach, and references therein.
20. Gruber, E.; Soehendra, B.; Schurz, J. J. Polym. Sci., Polymer Sympos., 1974, N-44,195.
21. Klenin, V. J.; Klenina, O. V.; Kolnibolotchuk, N. K.; Frenkel, S. Y. J. Polym. Sci., Polymer Sympos.No. 42, 1973, 931, and references therein.
22. Katona, E.; Neumann, A. W.; Moscarello, M. A. Biochim. Biophys. Acta, 1978, 534, 275.
23. Lobos, Z. J.; St.-Pierre, L. E. J. Colloid and Interf. Sci., 1975, 51, 196.
24. Norde, W.; Lyklema, J. J. Colloid and Interf. Sci., 1978, 66,257.
25. Prasad, K. N.; Luong, T. T.; Florence, A. T.; Paris,C. J.; Vaution, C.; Seiller, M.; Puisieux, F. J. Colloid and Interf. Sci., 1979, 69, 225.
26. Hildebrand, J. H. and Scott, R. L. "The Solubility of Non-Electrolytes," 1950, New York:Reinhold Publishing Corp.
27. Assarsson, P. G.; Leung, P. S.; Safford, G. J. Polym. Preprints, 1969, 10, 1241.
28. Glass, J. E. JOCCA, 1976, 59, 86.
29. Glass, J. E.; Fernando, R. H.; Egland-Jongewaard, S. K.; Brown, R. G. manuscripts in preparation.

RECEIVED October 24, 1983

POLYMERS AT INTERFACES

Polymer Adsorption at the Lower Critical Solution Temperature and Its Effect on Colloid Stability

KUNIO FURUSAWA and YOSHIHIRO KIMURA—Department of Chemistry, The University of Tsukuba, Sakura-mura Niihari-gun, Ibaraki 305, Japan

TORU TAGAWA—Mitsubishi Chemical Industries Ltd., Kamoshida-cho, Yokohama, Kanagawa 227, Japan

Adsorption behavior and the effect on colloid stability of water soluble polymers with a lower critical solution temperature(LCST) have been studied using polystyrene latices plus hydroxy propyl cellulose(HPC). Saturated adsorption(As) of HPC depended significantly on the adsorption temperature and the As obtained at the LCST was 1.5 times as large as the value at room temperature. The high As value obtained at the LCST remained for a long time at room temperature, and the dense adsorption layer formed on the latex particles showed strong protective action against salt and temperature. Furthermore, the dense adsorption layer of HPC on silica particles was very effective in the encapsulation process with polystyrene via emulsion polymerization in which the HPC-coated silica particles were used as seed.

Among the various branches in colloid and interface science, polymer adsorption and its effect on the colloid stability is one of the most crucial problems. Polymer molecules are increasingly used as stabilizers in many industrial preparations, where stability is needed at a high dispersed phase volume fraction, at a high electrolyte concentration, as well as under extreme temperature and flow velocity conditions.

Understanding how polymer functions as a stabilizer and flocculant is obviously a problem of polymer adsorption and its conformation at the particle/liquid interface(1, 2). The process of polymer adsorption is fairly complicated; the behavior depends on many factors, e.g., the nature of the adsorbent, the molecular weight of the polymer, the temperature, the effect of the solvent,

0097-6156/84/0240-0131$06.00/0

etc. Among these factors, the solvency of the medium liquid can
have an influence on the adsorption in two ways(3). One is the
energetic factor, i.e., since a polymer molecule must replace
solvent molecules to be adsorbed, the difference in energy of
interaction between adsorbent and solvent, and adsorbent and polymer
molecule, will be important in determining the extent of adsorption.
Another is the relative interaction of polymer-solvent and solvent-
solvent, which leads to the expectation that adsorption is best
from a poor solvent. Apart from energetic reasons, the tighter
coiling of the polymers in the poorer solvent would increase the
amount of polymer that could fit into a given area of an adsorbent
surface. The rise in adsorption in reverse order to solvent power
has been confirmed by many researchers(4, 5).
    According to this concept, it is expected that polymer mole-
cules, especially high molecular weight polymers, give an increased
adsorption at a temperature close to the cloud point, and particles
with the thick(or dense) adsorption layer of polymer formed out
of a poor solvent would show strong protection against flocculation.
    In this study, adsorption behavior of water soluble polymers
and their effect on colloid stability have been studied using
polystyrene latices plus cellulose derivatives. As the aqueous
solution of hydroxy propyl cellulose(HPC) has a lower critical
solution temperature(LCST), near 50 °C(6), an increased adsorption
and strong protection can be expected by treating the latices with
HPC at the LCST.
    Also, here, the effect of the adsorption layer of HPC on en-
capsulation of silica particles in polymerization of styrene in
the presence of silica particles has been investigated. Encapsulation is promoted greatly by the existence of the adsorption
layer on the silica particles, and the dense adsorption layer
formed at the LCST makes composite polystyrene latices with silica
particles in the core(7). This type of examination is entirely
new in polymer adsorption studies and we believe that this work
will contribute not only to new colloid and interface science, but
also to industrial technology.

Experimental

Materials
    Polystyrene latices used as an adsorbent were prepared by the
Kotera-Furusawa-Takeda method(8) to reduce the spurious effects of
surface active substances. The average diameter(D) and the surface
charge density(σ_0) of the latex particles were determined: D = 2000
Å and σ_0 = 1.5 μC/cm^2. A silica sample was prepared by the method
described by Stöber et al.(9), and was composed of highly monodisperse spherical particles of 1900 Å in diameter. These colloids
were used after dialyzing exhaustively against distilled water to
remove the ionic impurities.
    The cellulose derivatives used were obtained by the fractional
precipitation method with the use of ethanol as solvent and n-

heptane as a precipitant at 30 °C. The HPC,from Nippon Soda
Industries Co., Japan, and hydroxy ethyl cellulose(HEC), from
Hercules Co., The Netherlands, used in this study have a degree
of ether substitution of 2.4 and 2.5 on each monomer unit,
respectively. The molecular weight of these polymers was determined from the intrinsic viscosity-molecular weight relationship.
The viscosity measurements were carried out by means of a Ubbelohde
viscometer at 25 °C in a 0.1 Mol NaCl aqueous solution for HPC(10)
and in distilled water for HEC(11). The molecular weight distribution of HPC-samples was also analyzed by the Gel Permeation
Chromatography technique. The measurements were carried out with
a Toyosoda-HLC-Model-802 at 25 °C with a 0.1 Mol potassium bi-
phosphate buffer solution as the eluent.
    Polyvinyl alcohol(PVA) was obtained from the Kurarey Co.,Ltd.
Japan; the molecular weight and the degree of hydrolysis were
determined by the supplier as 88,000 and 80 %, respectively. The
molecular weight and the molecular weight distribution data of
the polymer samples are shown in Table 1.

Table 1. Molecular Weight Characterization of Polymer Sample

Sample	M_W	M_W/M_n	Degree of hydrolysis	Degree of ether substitution/monomer
HPC-L	5.3×10^4	2.76	–	2.4
HPC-M	30.3×10^4	1.84	–	2.4
HPC-H	92.5×10^4	2.49	–	2.4
HEC-L	13.0×10^4	–	–	2.5
HEC-H	63.0×10^4	–	–	2.5
PVA	8.8×10^4	–	80 %	–

    The other reagents, commercially available, were of analytical
grade. All the solutions of these materials were made with
deionized and distilled water, using an all-Pyrex apparatus.

Phase Separation Measurements
    The measurements were carried out while increasing the
temperature in 0.5 °C increments at intervals of 30 min., using
an aqueous solution of the polymers in Pyrex tubes(5 ml volume).
Each tube contained a short glass rod which was used to stir the
solution; after being filled with the polymer solution of 0.05 -
2.5 wt %, each tube was evacuated and sealed. The warm up to 70
°C was carried out in a water bath. The cloud point was taken
as the temperature at which phase separation was first noted; it
was compared with the temperature at which the solution first
became clear again while cooling.

Adsorption Measurements
    The amounts of adsorption of the polymer on latex and silica
particles were measured as follows. Three milliliters of the
polymer solution containing a known concentration was introduced
into an adsorption tube(10 ml volume) which contained 2 ml of latex
(C = 4.0 wt %) and silica(C = 2.0 wt %) suspensions. After being
rotated(10 rpm) end-over-end for 1 hr in a water bath at a constant
temperature, the colloid particles were separated from the solution
by centrifugation(25000 G, 30 min.) under a controlled temperature.
The polymer concentration that remained in the supernatant was
measured colorimetrically, using sulfuric acid and phenol for the
cellulose derivatives(12), and potassium iodide, iodine and boric
acid for PVA(13). From these measurements, the number of milli-
grams of adsorbed polymer per square meter of the adsorbent surface
was calculated using a calibration curve.

Flocculation Experiments
    In glass-stoppered vials(8 ml volume), 5 ml portions of $MgCl_2$
solution of various concentrations were taken and on top of the
salt solution, 2 ml of the suspension of polymer-coated particles,
which were prepared by adsorbing a polymer at a controlled temperature, were added carefully in such a way that a sharp boundary
between the dispersion and the salt solution was formed. After
being rotated end-over-end(10 rpm) for 2 hrs, the sample was left
to stand for 10 hrs in order to allow the flocculated particles to
settle. Then, the extinction of the supernatant was measured using
a Jasco Digital Spectrophotometer(Uvidec-410) at a wavelength of
550 nm. The critical flocculation concentration(CFC) was defined
as the salt concentration at which the absorbance of the supernatant was reduced to 50 % of the original. The ionic strength
was varied using $MgCl_2$, while all the experiments were carried out
at a constant temperature of 25 °C.
    As another criterion of stability, a critical flocculation
temperature(CFT) was measured. The measurement of CFT was carried
out as follows: the bare latex suspension was mixed with the polymer
solution of various concentrations at 48 °C by the same procedure
as in the adsorption experiments. Then, the mixture in a Pyrex
tube(8 ml, 4.0 wt %) was warmed slowly in a water bath and the
critical temperature at which the dispersion becomes suddenly
cloudy was measured with the naked eye.

Polymerization in the Presence of Silica Particles
    Radical polymerization of styrene was carried out in the
presence of bare silica particles, and of the HPC-coated silica
particles in water by using potassium persulfate as an initiator.
Table 2 gives the typical ingredients used for these polymerizations. The HPC-coated silica particles were prepared under the
same conditions as in the adsorption experiments. The polymerization temperature was kept at 45 °C to protect the adsorption layer
of HPC, and polymerized for 24 hrs in the same manner as that

Table 2.   Typical Ingredients used for Polymerization of Styrene
in the Presence of Silica particles

Samples	Bare silica particles(wt %)	HPC-coated silica particles(wt %)	Styrene (mol/l)	$K_2S_2O_8$ (mol/l)
HPL(-)	0.2	-	0.83	3.5×10^{-3}
HPL(HPC)	-	0.18_5	0.83	3.5×10^{-3}
SL	-	-	0.83	3.5×10^{-3}

Polymerization temperature: 45 °C; Polymerization time: 24 hrs

described previously(7). The degree of encapsulation of these
particles was examined by comparing the electron micrograph of the
produced particles and by analyzing the molecular weight distribution of the latex polymers utilizing Gel Permeation Chromatography.

Results and Discussion

Phase Diagram of Polymer-water Systems
      The phase diagrams which were obtained for the aqueous solutions
of HPC and PVA samples are shown in Fig.1. (In the case of the
HEC sample, the cloud point was not found in the temperature range

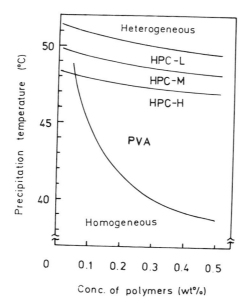

Figure 1.   Phase diagrams of HPC- and PVA-water system.

examined). All the systems show a lower critical solution temper-
ature(LCST) in the 35 - 55 °C range, that is, the phase separation
occurs at a definite temperature on warming, and the systems become
homogeneous again on cooling. It appears that the LCST is influenced extensively both by the polymer concentration, and by its
molecular weight, i.e., the LCST becomes lower both by an increase
in the concentration and in the molecular weight of the polymer.
These phenomena may be explained by the concept of the Flory-Schulz
theory(14) for the critical solution phenomenon.

Adsorption Behavior
        Figure 2 shows adsorption isotherms of HPC, HEC and PVA poly-
mers on the latices at a temperature of 48 °C. It is evident that
the isotherm for HPC is of the high affinity type, with a well-
defined plateau. While the isotherms for HEC and PVA are not high
affinity, their plateaus are influenced by the polymer concentrations
over a wide range. The temperature dependence of the saturated
adsorption(As) of these polymers is shown in Figs.3 and 4 for the
polystyrene latex particles, and in Fig.5 for the silica particles.
The temperature dependence for the HPC-latex systems is shown in
Fig.3 for three molecular weights. After a constant value, there
is a sharp increase in the As values for both HPC and PVA. The
temperature dependence of the As is especially remarkable in the
HPC sample with a high molecular weight, where the As of of HPC-H
at 48 °C is 1.5 times as large as the value at 30 °C. With the
HEC-latex systems, however, no definite temperature trend could
be detected. Moreover, it seems that there is a slight decrease
in the As vs. temperature curve for HEC adsorption on the silica
particles. From a comparison with the phase diagram shown in Fig.1,
it is evident that the trends in the As seen in Figs.3 - 5 are based on
the solvency of the medium, i.e. reduction in the solvency leads
to an increased adsorption at the solid/water interface. Furthermore,
it appears that the temperature dependence of the As is also influenced by the adsorbent, i.e. the dependence is more extensive in
the polymer-silica particle system than in the polymer-latex
particle system. This indicates that some energetic factors (hydrophobic interaction, electrostatic interaction, etc.,) are also playing
a role to some extent in determining the adsorption amounts.
        It is generally accepted that the time required for desorption
of adsorbed polymer is very long, and this process seems to appear
to be irreversible(15). Accordingly, it is expected that the high
adsorption values which appeared near the LCST may be held for a
long time under different temperature conditions. In Table 3,
experimental results for irreversibility of adsorption in the HPC-
latex systems are shown. After the HPC samples and the latex
particles were mixed for 2 hrs at 48 °C under the same condition
as in the case of the adsorption process, one portion of one of
the samples was separated immediately by centrifugation at 48 °C.
The other half portion of the HPC-coated latex suspension was kept
at room temperature for 48 hrs and then centrifuged at 6 °C. As

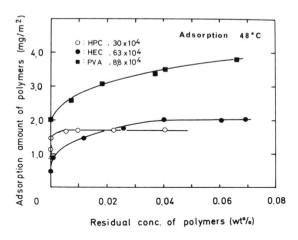

Figure 2.   Adsorption isotherms of HPC-M, HEC-H and PVA onto polystyrene latex particles at 48 °C.

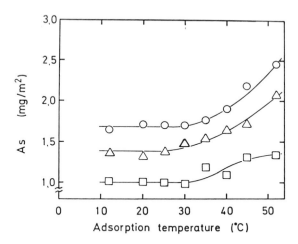

Figure 3.   Temperature dependences of saturated adsorption (As) of HPC onto polystyrene latex particles.

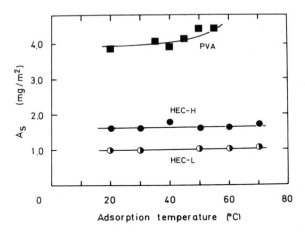

Figure 4. Temperature dependences of saturated adsorption (As) of HEC and PVA onto polystyrene latex particles.

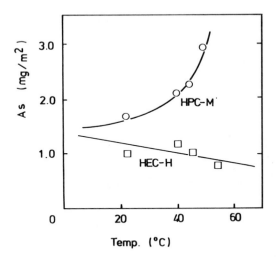

Figure 5. Temperature dependences of saturated adsorption (As) of HPC-M and HEC-H onto silica particles.

Table 3. Irreversibility of Adsorption Layer of HPC on Polystyrene Latices*

Samples	Cooling conditions	Separation temperature($^\circ$C)	Amount of HPC adsorbed(mg/m^2)
HPC-M	–	48	1.66
HPC-M	48°C – 20°C (gradually)	6	1.63
HPC-L	–	48	1.36
HPC-L	48°C – 20°C (gradually)	6	1.38

*adsorbed at 48 $^\circ$C in 0.07 wt % HPC solution.

may be seen in Table 3, the amount adsorbed for both samples is in close agreement. Furthermore, the same irreversibility of adsorption was also confirmed in the system of HPC-silica particles. However, the irreversibility in the adsorption of HEC and PVA polymers is not so complete as in the case of HPC adsorption. Such different behavior in irreversibility of adsorption may be explained by the influence of the substrate on the adsorption affinity and the structure of the adsorbed polymer layer.

In conclusion it can be stated that the high value of the As of HPC obtained at the LCST has been maintained for a long time at room temperature.

Flocculation Behavior against Electrolyte

The stability of polymer-coated particles and the conformation of the adsorbed polymer are closely related(17, 18). In this sense, the study of the stability of polymer-coated particles is instructive with regard to the conformation of the adsorbed polymer. In Fig.6, the dependence of the CFC of $MgCl_2$ on the polymer dosage is given for three HPC-coated latex suspensions. For all systems, an initial decrease of the CFC is observed and after staying for a long time at an extremely low value, the CFC increases strongly again beyond a critical polymer dosage. This is an indication that the flocculation effect of adsorbed polymer changes over to protection against salt. As may be seen, the protection in this system is enormously strong and is dependent to some extent on the molecular weight of the adsorbed polymer, i.e. the CFC increases with increase in the molecular weight from low to medium, which is in accordance with the better protective power and the high As values observed with an increase in the molecular weight(see Fig. 3).

In Fig.7, the effect of the adsorption temperature of HPC in preparing the polymer-coated latices on the flocculation behavior of the system is demonstrated. It was found that both systems show almost the same behavior in flocculation, but evince a fairly different behavior in protection. The HPC-coated latex suspension treated at room temperature flocculated in a 1.2 Mol $MgCl_2$ aqueous

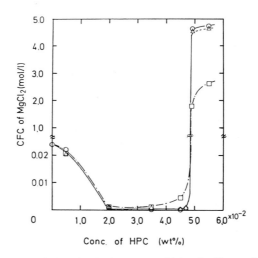

Figure 6. Relationship between critical flocculation
concentration(CFC) and concentration of HPC for HPC-latex
systems.

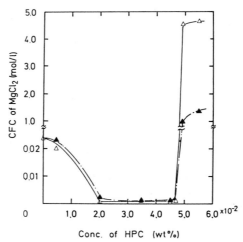

Figure 7. Relationship between critical flocculation
concentration(CFC) and concentration of HPC-M for HPC-latex
systems.

solution. On the other hand, the suspension treated at the LCST (48 °C) displayed a strong protection power and the latex particles resisted direct contact even in a 5 Mol MgCl$_2$ aqueous solution.

Flocculation Behavior against Temperature

One of the characteristic features of sterically stabilized dispersions is the temperature dependence of stability(18, 19). Fig.8 shows the CFT as a function of HPC concentration for a fixed concentration of the latex particles(C = 4 wt %). It was apparent that at a medium polymer concentration, the system flocculates at a lower temperature than the LCST. This means that the system was flocculated with a polymer solution in a solvent better than the theta-solvent. This flocculation may be due to a bridging mechanism, because the CFT that was observed in this region was influenced greatly by the addition of electrolyte(see Fig.9). The addition of electrolyte results in the reduction of the distance of closest approach between particles to about twice the adsorbed polymer layer thickness, and only then does polymer bridging between the two particles become possible. On the other hand, over the range of higher concentrations of HPC the CFT increased steeply and greatly exceeded the LCST of the polymer solution and approached 100 °C. This presumably was associated with the completion of a saturated adsorbed layer on the surface. These high CFT values indicate that HPC molecules are adsorbing in a dense layer built up by multi-point anchoring of the molecule(20). Such a dense adsorbed layer of HPC was inferred from a direct measurement of the layer thickness by using ultracentrifuge analysis(21).

As a result, it was realized that the dense structure of an adsorbed polymer layer is related to high irreversibility of HPC adsorption and strong protection power.

Encapsulation of HPC-coated Silica Particles

It was apparent that the dense adsorption layer of HPC which was formed on the silica particles at the LCST plays a part in the preparation of new composite polymer latices, i.e. polystyrene latices with silica particles in the core. Figures 10 and 11 show the electron micrographs of the final silica-polystyrene composite which resulted from seeded emulsion polymerization using as seed bare silica particles, and HPC-coated silica particles,respectively. As may be seen from Fig.10, when the bare particles of silica were used in the seeded emulsion polymerization, there was no tendency for encapsulation of silica particles, and indeed new polymer particles were formed in the aqueous phase. On the other hand, encapsulation of the seed particles proceeded preferentially when the HPC-coated silica particles were used as the seed and fairly monodisperse composite latices including silica particles were generated. This indicated that the dense adsorption layer of HPC formed at the LCST plays a role as a binder between the silica surface and the styrene molecules.

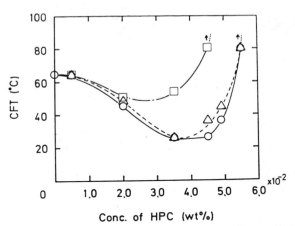

Figure 8.   Relationship between critical flocculation
temperature(CFT) and concentration of HPC for polystyrene
latex.

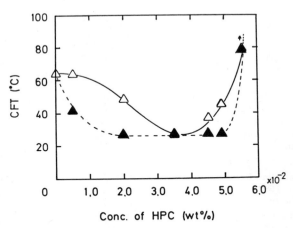

Figure 9.   Relationship between critical flocculation
temperature(CFT) and concentration of HPC-M for polystyrene
latex.

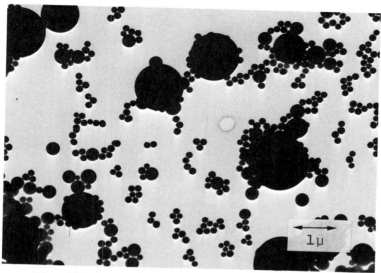

Figure 10. Electron micrograph of composite silica-polystyrene latex system,SPL(-), prepared by using bare silica particles as the seed.

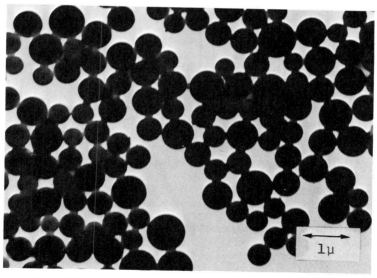

Figure 11. Electron micrograph of composite silica-polystyrene latex system, SPL(HPC), prepared by using HPC-coated silica particles as the seed.

The contribution of the adsorbed HPC layer to the encapsulation was also illustrated by GPC analysis for the latex polymer. The chromatogram of the polymer separated from the HPC-coated silica latex system is shown in Fig.12. The chromatogram is composed of two separated broad peaks(A and B), which indicate that the sample comprises two types of molecules synthesized under different conditions. The latex prepared under similar polymerization conditions, but in the absence of silica particles, gives a single molecular weight peak situated in the range of the peak B(see Fig. 13). Thus, the peak B in the silica-latex composite seems to correspond to the isolated latex particles formed by initiation in the aqueous phase. On the other hand, the higher molecular weight peak A would correspond to encapsulating polymer molecules formed by polymerization in the layer surrounding the solid surface, or perhaps, the product of grafting polymerization(22) with the adsorbed HPC.

All these results indicate that the dense adsorption layer of HPC formed on silica particles at the LCST plays a very important role in the area of particle encapsulation.

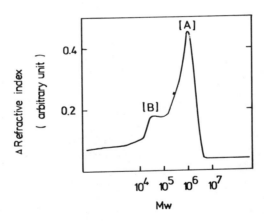

Figure 12. Gel permeation chromatogram of latex polymer separated from composite silica-polystyrene latex system, SPL(HPC).

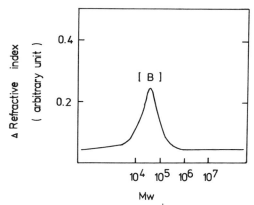

Figure 13. Gel permeation chromatogram of polystyrene latex, (PL), prepared by emulsifier-free emulsion polymerization at 45 °C(in the absence of silica particles).

Literature Cited

1. Vincent B. Advan. Colloid Interface Sci. 1974, 4, 193.
2. Tadros Th. F. Advance Colloid Interface Sci. 1980, 12, 141.
3. Rosoff M. in "Physical Method in Macromolecular Chemistry Vol 1"; Carroll B., Ed.; Marcel Dekker: New York,1969,P.22.
4. Koral J., Ullman R., and Eirich F.R. J. Phys. Chem., 1958, 62, 341.
5. van den Boomgaad Th, King T.A., Tadros Th. F., Tang H., and Vincent B. J. Colloid Interface Sci., 1978, 66, 68.
6. Tagawa T., Yamashita S., and Furusawa K. Kobunshi Ronbunshu 1983, 40, 273.
7. Furusawa K., Kimura Y., and Tagawa T. Kobunshi Ronbunshu (in press).
8. Kotera A., Furusawa K., and Takeda Y. Kolloid Z.u.Z.Polymere 1970, 239, 677.
9. Stöber W., and Fink A. J. Colloid Interface Sci. 1968, 26, 62.
10. Kato T., Tokuya N., and Takahashi A. Kobunshi Ronbunshu 1982, 39, 393.
11. Brown W., Henly D., and Öhman J. Makromol Chem. 1963, 64, 49.
12. Dubois M., Gilles K. E., Hamilton J. K., Rebers P.A., and Smith F. Anal. Chem. 1956, 28, 350.
13. Garvey M. J., Tadros Th. F., and Vincent B. J. Colloid Interface Sci. 1974, 49, 57.
14. Konno S., Saeki S., Kuwahara N., Nakata M., and Kaneko M. Macromolecules 1975, 8, 799.
15. Furusawa K., and Yamamoto K. Bull. Chem. Soc. Japan 1983,56, 1958.

16. Furusawa K., Tezuka Y., and Watanabe N. J. Colloid Interface Sci. 1980, 73, 21.
17. Furusawa K., Sakai H., Watanabe N., and Tomotsu N. Bull. Chem. Soc. Japan 1983, 56, 997.
18. Napper D.H., and Netschey A. J. Colloid Interface Sci. 1971, 37, 528.
19. Evans R., Davison J. B., and Napper D.H. J. Polym. Sci. 1972, B10, 449.
20. Lambe R., Tadros Th.F., and Vincent B. J. Colloid Interface Sci. 1978, 66, 71.
21. Furusawa K, and Kimura Y. (in preparing).
22. Min T.I., Klein A., El-Aasser M.S., and Vanderhoff J.W. Preprints Org. Coatings Plastics Chem., 1982, 46, 314.

RECEIVED October 25, 1983

Segment Density Profiles of Adsorbed Polymers

T. COSGROVE, B. VINCENT, and T. L. CROWLEY—University of Bristol, Cantock's Close, Bristol BS8 1TS, England

M. A. COHEN STUART—Laboratory for Physical and Colloid Chemistry, Agricultural University, De Dreijen 6, 6703 BC Wageningen, The Netherlands

Segment density profiles and hydrodynamic thickness measurements have been made for a series of polyethylene oxides of molecular weights from 25K to 1.3M adsorbed on polystyrene latex in the 'plateau' region of the adsorption isotherm. At high molecular weights the hydrodynamic thickness occurs at the extremity of the density profile. Comparison with a theoretical model based on solvent flow through a porous layer shows that, although the density profile and the hydrodynamic thickness results are consistent, the experimental profile is not sensitive enough to detect the low concentration of segments in tails at large distances from the interface. This is confirmed by further theoretical calculations based on the Scheutjens and Fleer lattice model for an adsorbed polymer.

Several experimental parameters have been used to describe the conformation of a polymer adsorbed at the solid-solution interface; these include the thickness of the adsorbed layer (photon correlation spectroscopy(1) (p.c.s.), small angle neutron scattering (2) (s.a.n.s.), ellipsometry (3) and force-distance measurements between adsorbed layers (4), and the surface bound fraction (e.s.r. (5), n.m.r. (6), calorimetry (7) and i.r. (8)). However, it is very difficult to describe the adsorbed layer with a single parameter and ideally the segment density profile of the adsorbed chain is required. Recently s.a.n.s. (9) has been used to obtain segment density profiles for polyethylene oxide (PEO) and partially hydrolysed polyvinyl alcohol adsorbed on polystyrene latex. For PEO, two types of system were examined: one where the chains were terminally-anchored and the other where the polymer was physically adsorbed from solution. The profiles for these two

cases were markedly different. The former gave a density profile
with a pronounced maximum and the latter a monotonically
decreasing profile. These two cases correspond respectively to a
system consisting of short tails and a system of loops, trains and
tails. The PVA system gave profiles similar qualitatively to the
physically adsorbed PEO. In all the cases, however, the
experimental profiles fell somewhat short of the hydrodynamic
thickness obtained by p.c.s. This suggested that the hydrodynamic
thickness is determined by the tails of the density distribution
and that s.a.n.s. may not be sensitive enough to pick up the
complete density profile at the periphery of the adsorbed layer.

In this paper we present results for a series of PEO
fractions physically adsorbed on per-deutero polystyrene latex
(PSL) in the 'plateau' region of the adsorption isotherm. Hydrodynamic and adsorption measurements have also been made on this
system. Using a porous layer theory developed recently by Cohen
Stuart (10) we have calculated the hydrodynamic thickness of these
adsorbed polymers directly from the experimental density profiles.
The results are then compared with model calculations based on
density profiles obtained from the Scheutjens and Fleer (SF) layer
model of polymer adsorption (11).

Theoretical Calculations

The segment density profile obtained by s.a.n.s. is normalized in
the form,

$$\int_{0}^{\infty} \rho(z)dz = 1 \tag{1}$$

The physical significance of the experimental profile is that
it is the probability that a segment of an adsorbed polymer chain
is at a distance z from the interface. In order to find the
volume fraction $\phi(z)$ at a distance z from the interface we require
the mass/unit area Γ and the partial molar volume of the polymer
ν (12), where $\phi(z)$ is given by

$$\phi(z) = \Gamma\nu\rho(z) \tag{2}$$

For the calculation of the hydrodynamic thickness we divide
the profile artificially into elementary layers, the result being
independent of the division chosen provided it is sufficiently
fine. The s.a.n.s. data is obtained as a function of Q, the wave
vector ($4\pi/\lambda$ sin($\theta/2$), where λ is the neutron wavelength and θ the
scattering angle. The Q resolution corresponds in real space to a
fraction of a bond length which is small enough for defining an
elementary layer.

Following Cohen Stuart ([10]) we choose a semi-empirical continuous function to relate the hydrodynamic permeability, k, to the volume fraction

$$k = \alpha(1 - \phi)/\phi \qquad (3)$$

where α is an experimentally determined constant from sedimentation experiments. k is related to the sedimentation coefficient s of the polymer by ([10])

$$k = \frac{\eta s}{c(1 - \overline{v_i}/\overline{v_o})} \qquad (4)$$

where η is the solvent viscosity, c the polymer concentration and v_i and v_o the partial specific volumes of polymer and solvent respectively. Hence using the equations developed in ([10]) we can calculate the hydrodynamic thickness directly from the experimental density profile.

Experimental

The s.a.n.s. experiments were carried out using the D17 camera at the I.L.L., Grenoble. Data were collected at two wavelengths, 0.8 and 1.4 nm at a sample to detector distance of 1.8 m. The overlapping spectra were combined to give a sufficiently wide Q range to enable the data to be numerically inverted to obtain the density distributions. The latex dispersions were prepared at a solids concentration of 4% and polymer solution concentrations between 200 and 300 ppm.

The sedimentation experiments were carried out using an ultracentrifuge.

The p.c.s. measurements were carried out using a Malvern multibit correlator and spectrometer together with a mode stabilized Coherent Krypton-ion laser. The resulting time correlation functions were analysed using a non-linear least squares procedure on a PDP11 computer. The latex dispersions were first diluted to approximately 0.02% solids after which polymer solution of the required concentration was added.

The samples of the 96% deuterated latex were prepared by a standard surfactant-free procedure which is described fully elsewhere ([13]). The narrow distribution fractions of PEO were obtained from Polymer Labs (Shawbury) and were manufactured by the Toya Soda Co. The details of these samples are given in Table I.

Results

Table I gives details of the adsorbed amounts for the six polymer fractions obtained at an equilibrium concentration of 2000 ppm. Based on the full adsorption isotherm ([2]) these values correspond

Table I. Experimental data for PEO adsorbed on
PSL (diameter 240 ±4nm)

$Mw^{\ddagger}(x10^{-3})$	$2Rg^{\maltese}$/nm	δ_H/nm p.c.s.	δ_H/nm s.a.n.s.	$\Gamma mg/m^{2*}$
25	12.7	5.8 ± 1.5	2.3	0.56 ± 0.5
40	17.5	12.0 ± 3.0	2.8	0.68 ± 0.5
73	23.7	17.3 ± 5.0	5.7	0.89 ± 0.5
150	40.4	28.9 ± 3.0	7.8	0.99 ± 0.5
280	56.9	53.0 ± 3.0	12.3	1.21 ± 0.5
660	91.4	95.2 ±10.0	15.1	1.42 ± 0.5
1290	156.4	160.0 ±10.0	–	1.74 ± 0.5†

‡ maximum polydispersity 1.14
† estimated
* measured at a solution concentration of 2000 ppm at 25°C
$\maltese$ interpolated using the results of Cabane et al. J. Physique
(1982), 43, 1579.

to adsorption in the 'plateau' region. The hydrodynamic thicknesses and 2Rg (Rg radius of gyration of the free coils in solution)
are also given. Also listed are the hydrodynamic thicknesses
calculated from the s.a.n.s. density profiles (δ_H^{sans}).

Figure 1 shows the ultracentrifugation data plotted using
Equation 3. The plot is reasonably linear giving a value for α
of 0.5 ±0.03 nm^2. Figure 2 shows the experimental density
profiles for three of the samples studied (Mw 73K, 150K and 660K)
and the corresponding calculated values of the hydrodynamic
thicknesses. The p.c.s. hydrodynamic thickness (δ_H^{pcs}) is also
shown for the 150K sample.

Discussion

In principle, using the porous layer theory, it is possible to
obtain the hydrodynamic thickness of an adsorbed layer using the
experimental density profile and the permeability function. The
results of this calculation are given in Table I. In figure 2 it
can be seen that the calculated δ_H^{sans} values fall within the tail
of the s.a.n.s. density profiles. However, comparison with the
results obtained by p.c.s. (Table I) show a large systematic
discrepancy.

Values of δ_H^{pcs} in a similar system have been published by
Kato (14) and there is very good agreement with the present values
although their quoted adsorbed amounts are rather large. Klein
and Luckham (4) have used a technique based on the direct measurement of the force separation function between two mica surfaces
covered with adsorbed PEO chains in water. From these results
they infer a 'steric' thickness based on an initial interaction.
Interestingly their measurements correspond almost to 2Rg.
of the free coils in solution. Their results together with the
p.c.s. results and 2Rg are shown in Figure 3. Clearly both
thickness estimates are sensitive to polymer segments at the
periphery of the adsorbed layer.

The experimental thickness measurements may also be compared
with theoretical results based on profiles generated by the S.F.,
Scheutjens Fleer, theory (11). For this calculation we use a value
for χ_s of 1   (net adsorption free energy), for χ of 0.45
(experimental value of the Flory-Huggins parameter) and a polymer
solution concentration of 200 ppm. Although the value for χ_s
seems rather arbitrary it has been shown (10) that δ_H is
insensitive to this parameter.

Figure 4 shows the hydrodynamic thickness calculated for
chains of various lengths, together with 2Rg calculated according
to the relation Rg = $(r/6)^{1/2}$ where r is the number of monomers. The
trends observed in both the experimental (Figure3) and the purely
theoretical (Figure 4) cases are very similar: at low molecular
weights δ_H is less than 2Rg but crosses the 2Rg line at high
molecular weight. The different exponents for 2Rg and δ_H
are due to the increasing importance of tails with increasing

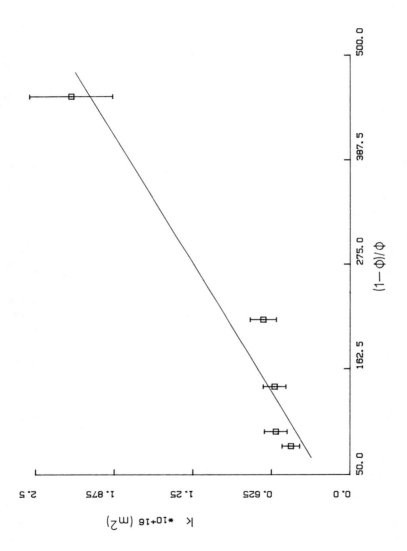

Figure 1. Plot of permeability data using Equation 1.

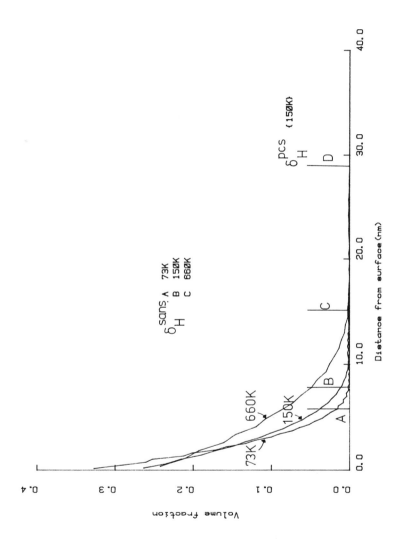

Figure 2. Experimental segment density profiles for PEO adsorbed on PS latex in water. Molecular weights 73K, 150K, and 660K. Vertical lines correspond to estimates of the hydrodynamic thickness (δ_H^{sans}) from the experimental profiles. Also shown is the δ_H^{pcs} value for the 150K sample.

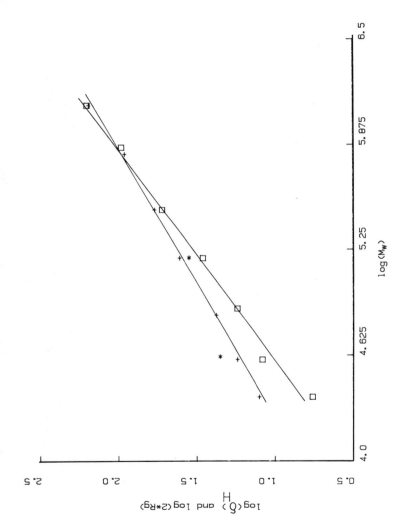

Figure 3. P.C.S. values of the hydrodynamic thickness (□). "Steric" thickness results (*) of Klein and Luckham. +, 2Rg (calculated), against molecular weight.

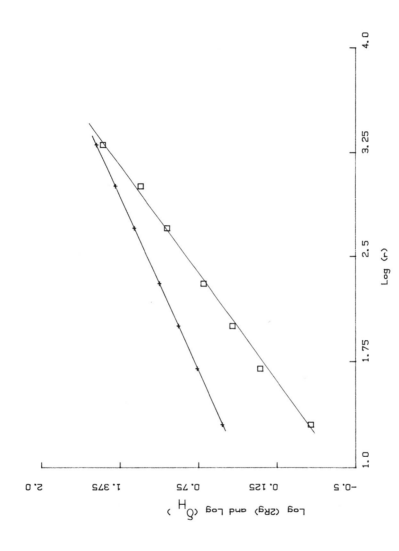

Figure 4.   Hydrodynamic thickness (□) and 2Rg (+) as a function of chain length calculated on the basis of theoretical density profiles using the SF theory.

molecular weight. The agreement between the exponent for the
p.c.s. measurements (0.8 ±0.003) and for the purely theoretical
calculation (0.8 ±0.05) is very close.

It would appear that the p.c.s. results are consistent with
both published experimental data and with this theoretical model.

This must cast some doubt on the hydrodynamic thickness
calculated from the s.a.n.s. profile. From Table I we can see
that the values of δ_H^{pcs} are considerably larger than δ_H^{sans} and
that this discrepancy becomes more pronounced at higher molecular
weights. This is illustrated in Figure 2 where the p.c.s. result
for the 150K sample is found in a region where there is no
detectable intensity from the neutron scattering experiment. This
suggests that the s.a.n.s. experiment is not sufficiently
sensitive to detect the very low segment density (of tails) which
determine the p.c.s. hydrodynamic thickness (10).

To explore this in more detail it is useful to compare the
experimental profiles with those calculated from the S.F. theory.
Figure 5 shows a profile for 2000 segments, using the same
parameters as above. This profile can be qualitatively compared
with the experimental profiles in Figure 2. The major difference
between the theoretical and experimental profiles is the presence
of a small but significant segment density at large distances from
the interface, which is not found experimentally. This difference
in shape is clearly seen when the profiles are superimposed. Also
in Figure 5 we show the hydrodynamic thickness calculated using
the whole profile (δ_H^{total}) and for a distribution from which
tails were excluded (δ_H^{loops}) giving values of 32.0 and 12.0
layers respectively. The ratio of these numbers is similar to the
ratio found between δ_H^{pcs} and δ_H^{sans} from experiment and suggests
that the s.a.n.s. experiment detects most of the distribution
associated with trains and loops but only a small part of the tail
distribution. Although it is difficult to estimate the threshold
of sensitivity of the s.a.n.s. experiment it is estimated to be of
the order of 1% of the segment density.

A simple procedure to demonstrate this effect of sensitivity
is to truncate the theoretical profiles at different layers. In
Figure 5 values of the hydrodynamic thickness are shown when the
profile is truncated at 1% and at 2%. This clearly shows the
effect that reducing the sensitivity dramatically reduces the
hydrodynamic thickness as it eliminates segments at the extremity
of the adsorbed layer.

In a previous paper (15) the segment density of PVA adsorbed
on PS latex in water was presented and it was noted that δ_H^{pcs}
was at the extremity of the s.a.n.s. profile. Calculating δ_H^{sans}
assuming a value of α of $0.5\ nm^2$ gives 13 nm in contrast to the
experimental value of 18 nm. The discrepancy here is much smaller
than in the case of PEO. This effect is difficult to interpret
without further theoretical work but may be attributable to the
fact that the PVA chain is less flexible than PEO and that the
block structure (PVA is a random block copolymer of vinyl acetate.
12%, and vinyl alcohol) makes the formation of tails less likely.

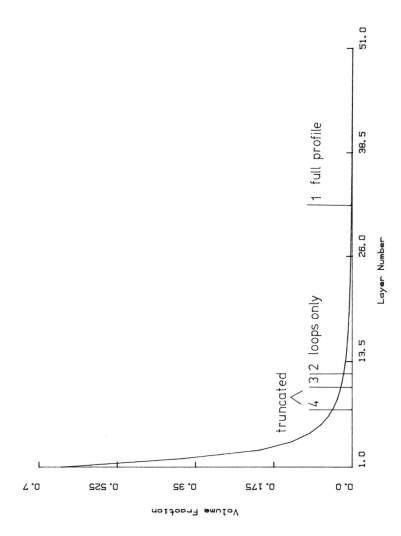

Figure 5. SF theoretical density profile for 2000 segments. $\chi_s = 1$, $\chi = 0.45$ and a polymer solution concentration of 200 ppm. Vertical lines correspond to δ_H values calculated using (1) the full profile, (2) the profile for loops only, (3) the full profile truncated at 1%, and (4) the full profile truncated at 2% volume fraction.

Conclusion

Segment density profiles and hydrodynamic thickness measurements
have been made for polyethylene oxides adsorbed on polystyrene
latex. Comparison with theoretical models shows that the hydrodynamic thickness is determined by polymer segments (tails) at the
extremity of the distribution. It is also concluded that the
sensitivity of the s.a.n.s. experiment precludes the measurement
of segments in this region and that the experimental segment
density profiles are essentially dominated by loops and trains.

Acknowledgments

The authors would like to acknowledge NATO for providing funds to
encourage collaboration between the research groups in Wageningen
and Bristol. The I.L.L. is acknowledged for providing facilities
for carrying out the s.a.n.s. experiments and providing general
facilities. Dr. Derek Cebula is thanked for his assistance during
the experimental runs. J. Bishop and P. Collier are thanked for
obtaining the p.c.s. results. The SERC is acknowledged for grants
for equipment (p.c.s.) and for post-doctoral fellowships for
T.L. Crowley and J. Bishop. Dr. Th.F. Tadros (ICI) is thanked for
his continuing interest in this project. Dr. G.F. Fleer is thanked
for stimulating and enlightening discussions on aspects of the
theory of polymer adsorption.

Literature Cited

1. Garvey, M.J.; Tadros, Th.F.; Vincent, B. J. Coll. and
    Interface Sci. 1976, 55, 440.
2. Cosgrove, T.; Vincent, B.; Crowley, T. L.; Barnett, K. G.;
    King, T. A.; Tadros, Th. F.; Burgess, A. N. Polymer 1981,
    75, 4115.
3. Grant, W. H.; Morrisey, B. W.; Stromberg, R. R. Poly. Sci.
    Tech. 1975, (A)9, 43.
4. Luckham, P.F.; Klein, J.; Nature, 1983, 300, 429.
5. Robb. I.D.; Smith, R. Eur. Poly. J. 1974, 10, 1005.
6. Cosgrove, T.; Vincent, B.; Barnett, K.G.; Cohen Stuart,M.A.;
    Macromolecules 1981, 14, 1018.
7. Killmann, E.; Korn, M. J. Coll. and Interface Sci. 1980,
    76, 19.
8. Cohen Stuart, M.A.; Fleer, G.J.; Bijsterbosch, B.H. J. Coll.
    Interface Sci. 1982, 90, 321
9. Cosgrove, T.; Vincent, B.; Crowley, T.L. Faraday Symposia
    1981, 16, 101.
10. Cohen Stuart,M.A;Cosgrove, T.; Vincent, B. Macromolecules
    (submitted).

11.   Scheutjens, J.M.H.M.;   Fleer, G.J. J. Phys. Chem. 1979, 83, 1619;   1980, 84, 178.
12.   Brandrupt, J.;   Immergut, E.H. "Polymer Handbook";   J. Wiley 1975.
13.   Barnett, K.G. Ph.D. Thesis, Bristol University, 1982.
14.   Kato, T.;   Nakamura, K.;   Kawasuchi, M.;   Takahashi, A. Poly J. 1981, 13, 1037.
15.   Cosgrove, T.;   Vincent, B.;   Crowley, T. in "Adsorption from Solution"; Ottewill, R.H.;   Rochester, C.H.;   Smith, A.L., Eds.;   Academic: New York, 1983, 287.

RECEIVED October 7, 1983

Thickness of Adsorbed Protein Layers on Glass: Adsorption of Proteins in Multilayers

A. SILBERBERG

Weizmann Institute of Science, Rehovot 76100 Israel

When proteins are "irreversibly" adsorbed in layers thicker than 1000 Å it becomes possible to use an ordinary Ostwald viscometer (time of flow about 700 sec) to determine the layer thickness precisely. It is important, however, to remove the protein layer from the surface over which the air/liquid meniscus is displaced during the measurement so as to assure that the conditions of flow with and without the layer in the capillary are totally comparable. Using this method we find that in the case of bovine serum albumin very thick layers are formed; layers whose thickness grows in direct proportionality to albumin concentration up to 15% w/v, at least. We also find a reversible doubling of layer size as temperature is raised from 7.7 to 15°C in the case of triple helical soluble collagen adsorbed end on to glass. There is no influence of pH on these results over a wide range (pH 3-8). The process by which such multi-layer formation might be caused is discussed.

Macromolecules are highly surface active. If a group which is frequently repeated along the chain possesses an interaction energy with a solid/liquid interface which is favorable, even if only slightly so, the large number of contacts that can be taken up simultaneously by the large molecule will effectively attach it to the surface. If the act of adsorption involves a conformation change this will not in general lower the tendency to adsorb, but will slow down the process enormously and will even more drasti-cally delay the process of desorption; to the point, in fact, where adsorbed macromolecules will not tend to detach at all, or at least not within reasonable times, though put into contact with pure solvent (irreversible adsorption) (1). If, for example, the macromolecule is an open chain, flexible homopolymer the mean equilibrium configuration of the chains at the surface will depart significantly from the conformation in bulk solution. A sizable

fraction p of the segments in the deformed conformation will contact the solid surface and saturate it almost completely. The
extent of individual contact will vary. In principle all macromolecules which have at least one segment contacting the surface
constitute this first layer, this "monolayer" of adsorbed macromolecules. Further adsorption is possible in this case if the
concentrated polymer segment region existing near the surface
proves to be a sufficiently attractive environment for other
macromolecules. Up to an amount of one segment per segment of the
first layer can in principle be bound in such a second layer if
the solvent is sufficiently poor (2).

   This, however, is not the only way multilayers of polymers
can be formed. If the macromolecule is a compactly folded copolymer, such as a protein, its collapsed state will be determined by
internal compensation of energetically favorable interactions.
This produces a molecule whose outside is on the whole well soluble
in the solvent, (water in the case of proteins) but which may
nevertheless bear patches of groups which will be energetically in
a poor solvent environment in water. Such patches will then preferentially adsorb to surfaces less hydrophilic than water and an
oriented surface layer of macromolecules will result. Should the
pull of the surface be strong enough, the conformation of the protein, compact though it is, may alter, in order to improve the
attachment to the surface. It is likely, however, that in this
process the upper surface of the macromolecule will also rearrange
and that a patch of groups becomes exposed to which protein molecules from solution now can adsorb to form a second layer. This
layer in turn may then become activated in a similar way to add a
third layer and so forth. Presumably the level of activation will
gradually decrease with layer number. Overall adsorption will
stop when the chemical potential of the polymer in the surface
matches that in solution.

   We shall describe two cases where this phenomenon seems to
happen.

Materials and Methods

Bovine Serum Albumin Fraction V (Sigma). The desired quantity of
albumin was dissolved in the appropriate buffer and stored in the
cold.

Soluble Calf Skin Collagen (Worthington). ($\sim$7 mg/ml in Tris buffer,
pH 3.7).
   The desired amount of this collagen solution was diluted (0.2
ml to 10 ml) with citrate buffer, pH 4.0 and then dialyzed overnight against the buffer to be used. 2 ml of that solution were
then diluted to 10 ml with the appropriate buffer, centrifuged in
the cold (40000 g for one hour) and the supernatant immediately
decanted into the viscometer in the cold room (10°C)

Citrate buffer (.055 M Citrate; 0.395 N NaCl) was made up and the pH adjusted with concentrated NaOH or HCl. Buffer was stored in the cold.

Time of Flow Measurements

The measurements were performed in an Ostwald Cannon-Fenske visco-meter (No. J-627-25) using the method described by Silberberg and Klein (3). This involves determining the time of flow as a func-tion of the amount of liquid in the viscometer. Amounts between 7 and 8 g are chosen and the viscometer weighed to determine the exact amount. Buffer replacements were undertaken by dilution. At no time subsequent to the original filling was an air/liquid meniscus allowed to enter the capillary. Protein was removed from the surface of the measuring bulb by inverting and treating the measuring bulb surface with sulfochromic acid for 30 min. Details are as given previously (3).

The glass surface is then washed with buffer and finally an appropriate amount of buffer is added. The time of flow, as a function of amount of buffer in the viscometer is then determined.

Results

The results for Albumin are shown in Figure 1. Times of flow were measured at 15°C ± 0.01°C. It is seen that the surface treatment with sulfochromic acid had only a small effect on the time of flow. On the other hand we have the surprising result that layer thickness increases in direct proportion to albumin concentration up to the highest concentration (15% w/w) which was tested. This is true both at pH 4.0 and pH 7.0 with approximately the same slope. Layers which are very thick result.

The data with soluble collagen are shown in Figure 2. Adsorp-tion here was performed at ∿10 µg/ml in the cold (10°C). We know, from a separate study, that at this concentration the surface saturates within several hours. A tremendous effect of removing the collagen from off the flow part of the viscometer is found. As a function of pH, however, there is no change. This is demons-trated even more clearly in Figure 3. Note that, unlike with albumin, the measurements were performed at 7.7°C in the case of these experiments.

When the adsorption of collagen was allowed to occur overnight at 10°C, and the collagen solution was replaced by buffer still in the cold (10°C) using the dilution procedure, but the viscometer was subsequently transferred to a thermostat at 15°C, the results of Table I are obtained. Raising the temperature from 7.7°C to 15°C has roughly doubled the measured film thickness.

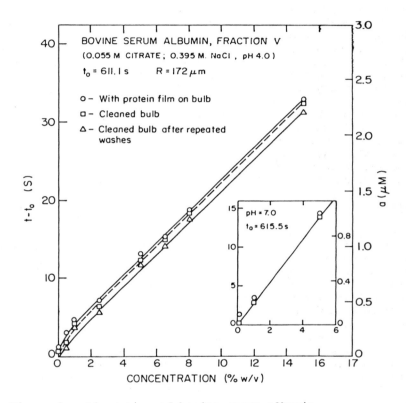

Figure 1. Adsorption of bovine serum albumin.
            t : time of flow with layer on capillary wall
            t_o: time of flow of buffer at 15°C
            R : radius of glass capillary
            a : layer thickness

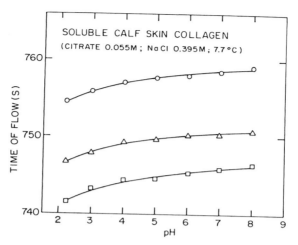

Figure 2.   Adsorption of soluble calf skin collagen.
   o: Collagen layer over entire surface
   Δ: Collagen layer removed from measuring bulb
   ⊔:   No layer anywhere

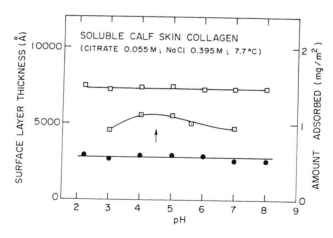

Figure 3.   Adsorption of soluble calf skin collagen.
   ⊓:   Apparent layer thickness; collagen layer on
        measuring bulb not removed.
   ●:   Correct layer thickness
   ⊡:   Amount adsorbed (4)

Table I.   Adsorbed Layer Thickness of Soluble Calf Skin Collagen
           on Glass as a Function of pH and Temperature.
           (thicknesses [a]7.7°C and [a]15°C are given in Å)

pH	3	4	5	6	7	8
[a]7.7°C	2840	2770	2890	2940	2880	2820
[a]15°C	6630	7250	7310	7290	7270	7250

Discussion

If we consider multilayer formation to be the result only of
sequential desorption (adsorption) of polymers one on top of the
other at each surface site, we can write the following partition
function for one such "chain"

$$\xi = 1 + C_1 X + C_2 C_1 X^2 + C_3 C_2 C_1 X^3 + \cdots \cdots \tag{1}$$

where

$$X = \exp[\mu/kT) \tag{2}$$

and where μ is the chemical potential of the macromolecule in solution. k is the Boltzmann constant, T is the absolute temperature
and C_i is the partition function of the macromolecule in layer i
from the surface. The state of a bare site on the surface is given
weight 1. Assuming that there are M sites on the surface for such
vertical chains, the partition function of the surface will be
given by ξ^M and the average number of layers m by

$$m = \frac{d\ln\xi}{d\ln X} \tag{3}$$

Equation (1) can also be written

$$\xi = 1 + C_1 X[1 + C_2 X[1 + C_3 X [1 + C_4 X [1 \cdots \cdots$$

where eventually at some C_j we will have

$$c_j X < 1$$

If we then assume that

$$C_k = C_j \qquad k \geq j$$

the series is easily summed and the result substituted into (3).
It will be found that m will lie close to j, the exact value
depending on the actual value of the coefficients.
        If we assume that

$$1 \simeq C_j X = C_1 \delta^j X$$

and write $\quad \delta = \dfrac{1}{1-\epsilon} \quad$ with $\quad \epsilon \ll 1$ we have,

$$X \simeq \frac{1}{C_1}(1 + j\epsilon) \simeq \frac{1}{C_1}(1 + m\epsilon)$$

so that m grows linearly with X which is proportional to concentration. The linear relationship of Fig. 1, in the case of albumin could be understood along these lines.

In the case of the 3000 Å long soluble collagen molecules, the thickness has been shown to be a function of temperature. It is one layer of vertically aligned collagen molecules thick at 7.7°C (3) and roughly two layers at 15°C. These changes are reversible and independent of the temperature at which the collaagen was adsorbed from solution. The equilibration with the collagen was done both at 10°C and at 15°C. The same readings are obtained when the films which so resulted, were subsequently measured, using pure buffer, at 7.7°C or at 15°C. Hence it is the temperature of measurement which determines the adsorbed layer structure. Since these changes occur in contact with a collagen free buffer medium they can only involve a reversible re-arrangement of the molecules on the surface.

The intrinsic viscosity of the collagen preparation supports the notion that a significant fraction of the adsorbed collagen is present in the form of the dimer, i.e. of two triple helical, 3000 Å long cylinders, flexibly joined together. Whereas at 7.7°C these dimers may mainly be folded and have two of the non-helical ends on the surface. It is conceivable that one end is permitted to lift off at the higher temperature and that the doubling in thickness is thus produced by a mechanism not related to a BET-like multilayer formation.

Acknowledgment

These measurements were performed with remarkable care, patience and accuracy by Haviva Meltzer to whom great thanks are due.

Literature Cited

1.   Silberberg, A. J.Phys. Chem. 1962, 66, 1884-1907.
2.   Silberberg, A. J. Colloid Interface Sci. 1972, 38, 217-226.
3.   Silberberg, A., Klein, J. Biorheology 1981, 18, 589-599.
4.   Penners, G.; Priel, Z.; Silberberg, A. J. Colloid Interface Sci. 1981, 80, 437-444.

RECEIVED November 1, 1983

Steric Considerations in Protein Adsorption

D. R. ABSOLOM and A. W. NEUMANN

Research Institute, The Hospital for Sick Children, Toronto, Ontario, Canada M5G 1X8

C. J. VAN OSS

Department of Microbiology, State University of New York, Buffalo, NY 14214

Pure delipidated bovine serum albumin (BSA) adsorbs onto ethanol-cleaned glass at a (Langmuir-type) plateau value of $\simeq 1.8$ $\mu g/cm^2$, at bulk BSA concentrations > 2.5 mg/ml. The shape of the adsorption isotherm, the irreversibility of the adsorption, the continuing diffusion of BSA along the plane of adsorption, and the ease and speed with which BSA could be electrophoretically transported along the plane of adsorption without detaching from the glass, agree best with adsorption of a monolayer of tightly packed, partly dehydrated BSA molecules with their longitudinal axes perpendicular to the glass plate. The most likely conformation of the adsorbed BSA molecules is a close vertical stacking with alternating polarities, allowing a certain degree of electrostatic attraction between protein molecules, and causing a loss of water of hydration. A monolayer of vertically stacked BSA molecules also conforms well to the dimensions of dehydrated BSA derived from hydrodynamic data, and offers a satisfactory explanation for the strong increase in the diffusion coefficient of BSA in the adsorbed state. The observed 50% increase in electrophoretic mobility of adsorbed BSA (as compared to dissolved BSA) also agrees well with the mobility of cylindrical molecules oriented perpendicularly to the electric field. The dimensions of large unhydrated BSA molecules that most reasonably fit these observations and the other known data are: 22 Å x 29 Å x 135 Å.

The use of prosthetic devices in the circulation or in contact with blood extracorporeally is seriously limited by thromboembolic phenomena that occur at the blood-foreign material inter-

0097–6156/84/0240–0169$06.00/0
© 1984 American Chemical Society

face. The most striking difference between a foreign surface and the natural intima is the very rapid adsorption and accumulation of blood proteins on the surface of the material. The adsorption of proteins not only modifies the surface of the foreign material but also, probably due to conformational changes or restricted mobility, gives rise to altered biological activities of the adsorbed species. In addition, the adsorption of proteins modifies the subsequent interaction of the cellular elements with artificial surfaces, e.g., albumin serves to depress the level of cell adhesion [1] whereas fibrinogen or immunoglobulin G [2] increases the extent of cell adhesion.

We have attempted to develop a detailed understanding of the mechanism governing the interaction of the major blood proteins and cells with polymer materials [1-6]. During the course of these studies, we have had occasion to examine extensively the adsorption behaviour of various serum proteins to different polymer surfaces [3]. In addition, we have investigated the lateral movement of bovine serum albumin (BSA) adsorbed onto a glass surface in the plane of adsorption, i.e. bidimensional diffusion, as well as the electrophoretic mobility of the adsorbed protein molecules [7,8]. This work was undertaken in an attempt to gain further insight into the conformational state and the nature of the packing of the adsorbed protein molecules. For this purpose, observations were made of: 1) the extent of albumin adsorption onto ethanol-cleaned glass as a function of bulk protein concentration; 2) the electrophoretic transport of BSA, initially adsorbed onto part of the surface, along hitherto unoccupied region of the glass surface; and 3) the diffusion rate of a protein boundary produced by initially covering one part of the glass surface with (BSA) while leaving the rest of the surface free of protein.

MATERIALS AND METHODS

Complete experimental details have been published elsewhere [3,7,8] and are therefore only briefly described here.

Bovine Serum Albumin (BSA)

BSA (Cohn's Fraction V, five times crystallized, fatty acid-free, 99.4% pure) was purchased from Calbiochem-Behring Corporation (La Jolla, CA). The BSA was further delipidated by treatment with activated charcoal [9] and then radiolabelled with ^{125}I by the chloramine-T method [10]. Unbound ^{125}I was removed by means of Sephadex-G-200 (Pharmacia Piscataway, N.J.), gel filtration followed by extensive dialysis against phosphate buffered saline (PBS). The final radioactive BSA (BSA*) had an activity of $\simeq 0.6$ mCi/100 mg BSA*. One part of BSA* was then added to 9 parts of BSA. The PBS used throughout this study had a pH 7.2 and an ionic strength, $\mu = 0.15$.

Glass

Glass slides of 15.2 x 2.5 cm of Corning-Pierce glass were
purchased from Gelman Instrument Company (Ann Arbor, MI). The
glass slides were washed in 96% ethanol for 30 min prior to use.

Adsorption Isotherms

Adsorption isotherms of albumin on glass were established at
bulk BSA concentrations from 0.1 to 5% (w/v) in PBS. The
cleaned glass slides were immersed in the bulk protein solution
for 30 min at 23°C and then rinsed by dilution/displacement.
The surface concentration of adsorbed albumin was then
determined by comparing the radioactivity of an aliquot of
solution of known protein concentration as described previously
[3,4]. For this purpose, a Beckman Instrument (Palo Alto, CA)
γ-counter was used.

Electrophoresis

Ethanol-cleaned glass slides were immersed for 30 min in 0.25,
0.138, 0.105, and 0.064% (w/v) BSA-BSA* solution to a height of
2.5 cm (leaving 15.2 - 2.5 = 12.7 cm of the glass surface
unexposed), care being taken not to expose the adsorbed
BSA-surface to an air interface. The glass slides were rinsed 3
times by dilution and displacement. The plates were then
immersed again, by volume displacement, in the desired
electrophoresis buffer (barbital acetate, pH 8.7 at μ = 0.05,
0.025, or 0.01). The glass slides (with adsorbed BSA on 2.5 cm,
at one end of their total length of 15.2 cm) were then immersed
in buffer to a liquid level of $\approx$ 3 mm above the glass surface,
in an electrophoresis chamber with Pt electrodes (Gelman
Instruments, Ann Arbor, MI), and constant voltage was supplied
(for times and voltages, see Tables 1 and 2). The temperature
at which the electrophoresis stabilized was $\approx$ 30°C. Voltage
was measured (while the slides were immersed) between the ends
of the glass (at a distance of 15.2 cm). After completion of
the electrophoresis, the slides were removed and were hot-air
dried, and subsequently: (1) autoradiographically developed
using Lanex (Kodak) high intensity film sheets, to determine the
distance migrated, and (2) cut into four sections of 3.5 cm each
(leaving an anodic end-piece of 1.2 cm for handling purposes) to
determine the amount of protein adhering to each section by
determining the amount of radioactivity associated with each
portion (cf Fig. 1). For autoradiography purposes, the slides
were placed on X-ray film (Kodak No-Screen) and held between
Lanex intensifying screens (Kodak) for 16 hrs at -80°C [11].
The films were then developed for 5 min at 20°C in Kodak liquid
X-ray developer, rinsed in 3% acetic acid and fixed for 10 min
in Kodak Rapid Fixer.

TABLE 1 Electrophoresis of BSA adsorbed on glass at various ionic strengths. Initial adsorption (at 0.25% w/v, BSA) at 1.96 μg/cm², and electrophoretic mobility U.

Ionic strength μ of buffer	BSA concentration in μg/cm²				t in seconds	V/15.2 cm	Distance migrated in cm	Electrophoretic mobility U in μM/sec/V/cm
	Section 1a)	Section 2a)	Section 3a)	Section 4a)				
0.05	1.22	0.56	0.23	–	5400	150	8.36	1.57
	1.63	0.31	–	–	3600	150	5.7	1.60
	1.02	0.64	0.29	0.05	5400	220	12.4	1.59
0.025	1.28	0.46	0.17	–	3600	150	7.9	1.84
	0.92	0.51	0.38	0.13	3600	220	11.8	1.87
	0.99	0.74	0.21	0.08	5400	150	12.1	1.86
0.01	1.06	0.64	0.29	–	3600	150	8.31	2.34
	0.80	0.54	0.35	0.16	5400	150	12.8	2.41
	0.66	0.57	0.47	0.24	3600	220	12.5	2.40

a) See Fig. 1

TABLE 2   Electrophoresis of BSA adsorbed on glass at various densities and ionic strengths

Density of initial BSA adsorption in μg/cm²	Concentration of BSA solution from which adsorption took place in % (w/v)	Ionic strength μ of buffer	t in seconds	V/15.2 cm	Distance migrated in cm	Electrophoretic mobility U in μM/sec/V/cm
1.38	0.20	0.05	5400	150	5.97	1.12
			3600	150	4.10	1.15
			5400	220	8.80	1.13
		0.025	3600	150	5.67	1.62
			3600	220	8.49	1.62
			5400	150	8.47	1.59
		0.01	3600	150	6.31	1.77
			5400	150	9.60	1.80
			3600	220	9.10	1.75
1.05	0.15	0.05	5400	150	4.68	0.88
			3600	150	3.31	0.83
			5400	220	6.45	0.82
		0.025	3600	180	4.65	1.09
		0.01	3600	150	4.49	1.27
			5400	150	6.78	1.27
			3600	220	6.56	1.26
0.64	0.075	0.05	5400	150	3.73	0.70
			3600	150	2.51	0.71
			5400	220	5.70	0.73
		0.025	3600	150	3.24	0.91
			3600	220	4.96	0.95
			5400	150	5.05	0.95
		0.01	3600	150	3.49	0.98
			5400	150	5.10	0.96
			36.00	220	5.38	1.02

Electrophoresis on cellulose acetate strips (Sepraphore III, Gelman Instrument, Ann Arbor, MI) was done in the conventional manner [12] in order to obtain a comparative electrophoretic mobility of non-adsorbed albumin. For this purpose, BSA-BSA* (2.5% w/v) was deposited on the cellulose acetate paper twice in volumes of 10 μl each. Electrophoresis was again performed in the Gelman Chamber with Pt electrodes at 20°C (see Table 3). After completion, the strips were stained with Ponceau S protein stain (Gelman Instruments) and washed with 5% acetic acid. The stained cellulose acid strips were subsequently cut into 3 mm wide pieces which were monitored for protein content γ-counting.

Diffusion

Following immersion of the glass slides in a 1.0% (w/v) BSA-BSA* solution to a depth of 2.1 cm for 30 min at 21°C, the slides were thoroughly rinsed in PBS by dilution/displacement. The slides were then completely immersed in PBS, where they were kept for different lengths of time, i.e., for 1, 2, 4, and 16 hrs. Thereafter, the slides were removed and air-dried and placed on X-ray film between Lanex Intensifying Screens as described above. The supernatants from these diffusion experiments were then concentrated 10 times by evaporation in order to establish their radioactive content.

RESULTS

Adsorption

Figure 2 shows the adsorption isotherm of albumin on ethanol-cleaned glass. Two plateaus are visible: the first from 0.5 to 2.2% (w/v) bulk BSA concentration, and a second from 3 to 5% BSA.

Electrophoresis

Influence of Ionic Strength. As shown in Tables 1 and 2, the electrophoretic mobility (U) of BSA, adsorbed onto glass as well as supported on cellulose acetate, in all cases is highest at the lowest ionic strengths μ. For any given ionic strength, it is clear from Tables 1 and 2 that greatest increases in electrophoretic mobility were observed at the highest surface concentrations of adsorbed BSA, as compared to the electrophoretic mobility of BSA in cellulose acetate under the same conditions of pH and ionic strength (Table 3).

Permanence of Adsorption of BSA. By determining the total amount of protein adsorbed on the four sections (cf Fig. 1) of the glass slide (Table 1), it can be seen that within experimental error, that all the initially adsorbed BSA was accounted for

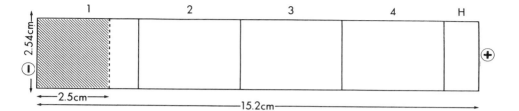

Figure 1. Scale drawing of glass plates. BSA was adsorbed into
the left position (2.5 cm long) of the plates, which
subsequently was the cathodal end. After electrophoresis the plates were cut up into 4 equal pieces, each
3.5 cm long (numbered 1 to 4) for γ-counting plus an
anodal end (H), used for handling, which remained un-
counted. Reproduced from Absolom et al. (8) with
permission from Verlag Chemie Gmb H.

TABLE 3 Electrophoresis of BSA on cellulose acetate strips

Ionic strength μ of buffer	t in seconds	V/15.2 cm	Distance migrated in cm	Electrophoretic mobility U in μ/sec/V/cm
0.05	5400	220	6.02	0.63
	5400	150	4.40	0.67
	3600	220	4.20	0.66
	3600	150	2.81	0.64
0.025	3600	220	5.34	0.83
	3600	150	3.50	0.81
	0054	220	8.80	0.84
0.01	3600	220	6.18	0.97
	3600	150	4.54	1.05
	5400	220	9.50	1.00

at the completion of each run, thereby, suggesting that the
protein molecules remained adsorbed to the glass surface during
the electrophoretic migration.

Comparison with Cellulose Acetate and Moving Boundary Electrophoresis. Due to experimental constraints, electrophoresis of
BSA adsorbed on glass was performed at the equilibrium temperature of 30°C (Tables 1 and 2) whilst electrophoresis of BSA on
cellulose acetate was done at 20°C. Finally, we wished to compare the electrophoretic mobilities of BSA, adsorbed on glass
(at 30°C) and on cellulose acetate (at 20°C) with the electrophoretic mobility values of BSA in free solution obtained with
the moving boundary (Tiselius) method. For this comparison, it
is pertinent to note that, again due to experimental limitations,
the moving boundary value of U = 0.65 µm/sec/V/cm [13] is
obtained at µ = 0.1 and at 4°C. By taking into account
changes in dielectric constant and viscosity, as a function of
temperature [14], it is possible to extrapolate the moving boundary value at µ = 0.1 to the lower ionic strengths, dictated
by experimental design, that were employed in this work. Thus,
the values from Tables 1 and 2 can be compared directly with the
values shown in Table 3 (adjusted to 30°C), as well as with
moving boundary standards [13]. From Table 4, it can be seen
that at the highest surface concentration of BSA studies (1.96
µg/cm^2), the electrophoretic mobility of adsorbed BSA is
almost twice as fast as the mobility obtained on cellulose
acetate (adjusted to 30°C), and from ≈ 20 to 70% faster than
the (extrapolated) values of free liquid moving boundary electrophoresis of BSA.

Influence of the Surface Concentration of BSA. Compared to the
corrected moving boundary electrophoretic mobility of BSA in
solution, the mobility of BSA adsorbed onto glass is considerably faster at all ionic strengths at 1.96 µg/cm^2 and somewhat faster at lower ionic strengths 1.38 µg/cm^2. However,
at lower adsorption densities (1.05 and 0.64 µg/cm^2), the
adsorbed BSA moves more slowly in the applied electric field
than BSA in moving boundary electrophoresis under otherwise
identical conditions, and at the lowest surface adsorption (0.64
µg/cm^2) the mobility of the adsorbed BSA are even somewhat
slower than in cellulose acetate gel at all conditions of ionic
strength investigated.

Diffusion

Figure 3 shows an autoradiograph of the extent of adsorbed BSA
diffusion, in a lateral direction, as a function of time. The
height to which BSA had progressed after immersion in PBS
(having initially been exposed to BSA* to a height of 21 mm) was
26, 28, 33 and 38 mm after 1, 2, 4, and 16 hrs, respectively.

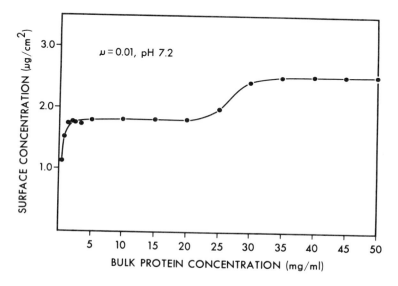

Figure 2.   Isotherm of BSA adsorption on ethanol-cleaned glass, with plateaus at $\simeq 1.8$ g/cm^2 and at $\simeq 2.6$ μg/cm^2. Reproduced from Absolom et al. (8) with permission from Verlag Chemie Gmb H.

TABLE 4   Comparison of the adsorbed BSA electrophoresis results of Tables 1 and 2, with cellulose acetate electrophoresis (Table 3) and moving boundary electrophoresis [6], extrapolated to 30°C (as in Tables 1 and 2) and to the appropriate ionic strengths (Tables 1-3)

Ionic strength μ of buffer	Electrophoretic mobility of BSA					
	Adsorbed on glass at				On cellulose acetate	In moving boundary
	1.96 μg/cm²	1.38 μg/cm²	1.05 μg/cm²	0.64 μg/cm²		
0.05	1.59a)	1.13	0.84	0.71	0.7b)	1.35c)
0.025	1.86	1.64	1.09	0.9c)	1.80	1.42
0.01	2.38	1.77	1.26	0.99	1.21	1.45

a) Averages from Tables 1 and 2

b) Extrapolated from averages from Table 3 for 30°C

c) Extrapolated to appropriate ionic strength and to 30°C from U = 0.65 μm/sec/V/cm [13] at μ = 0.1 and 4°C

Figure 3. Autoradiograph of radio-iodinated bovine serum albumin (BSA), adsorbed onto glass and subsequently immersed in phosphate-buffered saline for (from left to right) 0, 1, 2, 4, and 16 h. Reproduced from Michaeli et al. (7) with permission of Academic Press.

Following 10 times concentration of the supernatants of the
various immersion periods no BSA could be detected in the bulk
solution in contact with the glass slide. No BSA could initially be detected in the surface region, originally devoid of BSA,
beyond the moving front. In addition, there was no blurring of
the advancing front due to possible desorption and redistribu-
tion of adsorbed BSA over the whole surface via the bulk
liquid. A plot of the observed progression of BSA in a straight
front along the glass surface vs the square root of the time
elapsed (in seconds) yields a striking straight-line relationship. That progression, however, is remarkably enough, approximately 100x faster ($\approx$ 18 µm/min) than the diffusion rate of
diluted albumin in solution ($\approx$ 0.2 µm/min) measured by means of
a synthetic boundary in a three dimensional aqueous medium [15].

DISCUSSION

Mode of Adsorption of BSA

From the bimodal adsorption isotherm of BSA onto ethanol-cleaned
glass (Fig. 2), a first plateau value of a surface concentration
of $\approx$ 1.8 µg/cm^2 prevails at a comparatively wide bulk
concentration, between 0.3 to 2.2% (w/v) protein. Other bimodal
adsorption isotherms of BSA onto polystyrene latex have been
reported previously [16]. However, at the concentrations
employed in this work (Fig. 2) adsorption of albumin onto a wide
selection of polymer materials with a range of surface properties have generally given rise to a single plateau in the
adsorption isotherm [3]. Thus, the present bimodal characteristics appear to be unique to glass and BSA. The fact that at
$\approx$ 1.8 µg/cm^2 (at 0.25% (w/v) BSA), no further BSA could be
adsorbed (on a second exposure to 0.25% BSA), indicating that at
these concentrations, BSA does not adsorb to itself, points
rather strongly to BSA being adsorbed as a monolayer in the
first plateau region. From a consideration of the molecular
dimensions of BSA which have been characterized as prolate
ellipsoids, for a monolayer of surface concentration of 1.8
µg/cm^2 implies that these molecules (140 x 40 Å, hydrated
[17,18]) must be closely packed with their major axis
perpendicular to the plane of adsorption. This allows $\approx$ 640
Å^2/BSA molecule or 29 x 22 Å, a surface area which would
suffice to accommodate the short ends of the dehydrated, ellipsoid molecules. At $\approx$ 140 Å in length, such molecules would
not be able to form a monolayer if they adsorbed with their long
axis parallel to the surface until the surface concentrations
had decreased to $\approx$ 0.4 µg/cm^2. Thus, since a surface
density of 1.8 µg/cm^2 is readily achieved and since no further BSA adsorbs (on a second exposure to 0.25% (w/v) BSA), the
indications are that during the first plateau, the BSA has
adsorbed as a monolayer. It is only at the lowest surface con-

approach a random orientation of the ellipsoid BSA molecules.
Although BSA molecules have a rather strong overall negative
charge, at the neutral to slightly alkaline pH used, albumin
also has a sizeable dipole moment [19], which together with
other adsorptive driving forces (e.g., bulk protein concentration, van der Waals attraction between the BSA molecules and the
glass surface) contribute to the formation of a monolayer of BSA
molecules stacked perpendicular to the surface in a regular way,
as well as to an at least partial decrease in their full hydrated state.   Finally, the second plateau of the adsorption
isotherm occurs at a bulk fluid concentration greater than 35
mg/ml giving rise to a surface density of 2.6 µg/cm^2.   The
increase in surface adsorption of 0.8 µg/cm^2 indicates that
a second monolayer has formed on top of the first.   The height
of the second plateau would suggest that whilst the first monolayer consists of tightly packed, somewhat hydrated molecules
adsorbed with their long axis perpendicular to the surface, the
second monolayer, which builds up on top of the first only at
high bulk BSA concentrations, consists of molecules adsorbed
with their long axis parallel to the plane of the surface.

Electrophoretic Mobility

The electrophoretic mobility of cylindrical molecules is considerably influenced by the orientation of the molecules in the
electric field.   Cylindrical molecules which are perpendicular
to the electric field may have a mobility that is 100% faster
than that of cylinders orientated parallel to the electrical
field [20], whilst cylinders perpendicular to the electric field
would be 50% faster than when randomly orientated [14,20].
According to Overbeek and Wiersema [20], orientation of asymme-
trical particles in an electric field does not occur to any
significant degree in the relatively weak electric fields
generally used in electrophoresis.   However, depending on the
mode of adsorption of the BSA molecules onto glass (see above),
an initial orientation of the molecules perpendicular to the
electric yields is the most probable situation at a surface
concentration of 1.96 µg/cm^2.   This orientation may well be
the main cause of the observed increase in the electrophoretic
mobility of BSA at the highest density of adsorption as compared
to moving boundary electrophoresis (Table 4).   Thus, when
adsorbed perpendicularly to the glass surface, the BSA molecules
are orientated perpendicularly to the electric field, and thus
can be expected to migrate ≈ 50% faster than randomly oriented, adsorbed BSA molecules (cf Table 4).   When adsorbed at
lower surface concentrations most of the molecules will adsorb
with their long axis parallel to the surface and thus are randomly oriented in the electric field, which would imply that
they should have the same electrophoretic mobility as in the
moving boundary mode.   However, when adsorbed in this mode, the

energy of attachment per BSA molecule is considerably increased (7.4 to 10 kT) [8] and the freedom of lateral movement should be accordingly diminished. Indeed this is what is observed experimentally: see the decrease in electrophoretic mobility, as compared to the moving boundary mode of BSA at the lower adsorption surface concentrations (cf Table 4).

At the highest adsorption densities evaluated, the surface concentration pressures, which also enhanced the surface diffusion rate of adsorbed BSA [7], may play an additional role. However, whilst the diffusion rate of adsorbed BSA is greatly accelerated, the actual transport of adsorbed BSA due to diffusion ($\simeq$ 5 mm in the first hour) [7] still is negligible compared to the distance adsorbed BSA migrates in an electric field ($\simeq$ 50-100 mm/hour) (cf Table 1). Thus, the increased diffusiveness of adsorbed BSA cannot contribute significantly to its enhanced electrophoretic mobility. The relative constancy of the electrophoretic mobilities (at a given ionic strength) regardless of the duration of the electrophoretic run or of the applied voltage, would suggest that as long as the electric field is applied, the perpendicular orientation of the absorbed BSA molecules is maintained.

Consideration of the three sets of data presented above (absorption isotherms, electrophoretic mobility, and diffusion rates) suggest that at high bulk protein concentrations a monolayer of tightly packed, partly dehydrated BSA molecules is adsorbed onto the glass surface with their longitudinal axis perpendicular to the glass surface. The most likely conformation of the adsorbed BSA molecules is a close vertical stacking with alternating polarities, permitting a certain degree of electrostatic attraction between molecules, resulting in a loss of water of hydration.

Acknowledgments

Supported in part by The Medical Research Council of Canada (MT5461, MA8024), The Natural Science and Engineering Research Council of Canada (A8278), and The Ontario Heart Foundation (4-12). One of the authors (D.R.A.) acknowledges the support of The Ontario Heart Foundation through a Senior Research Fellowship.

Literature Cited

1. Absolom, D.R., Neumann, A.W., Zingg, W., and van Oss, C.J. Trans. Am. Soc. Artif. Intern. Organs 1979, 25, 152.
2. Chang, S.K., Hum, O.S., Moscarello, M.A., Neumann, A.W., Zingg, W., Leutheusser, M.J., and Reugsegger, B. Med. Prog. Technol. 1977, 5, 57.
3. van Oss, C.J., Absolom, D.R. Neumann, A.W., and Zingg, W. Biochim. Biophys. Acta 1981, 670, 64.

4. Absolom, D.R., van Oss, C.J., Zingg, W., and Neumann, A.W. Biochim. Biophys. Acta 1981, 670, 74.
5. Absolom, D.R., van Oss, C.J., Genco, R.J., Francis, D.W., and Neumann, A.W. Cell Biophys. 1980, 2, 113.
6. Neumann, A.W., Hum, O.S., Francis, D.W., Zingg, W., and van Oss, C.J. J. Biomed. Mater. Res. 1980, 14, 449.
7. Michaeli, I., Absolom, D.R., and van Oss, C.J. J. Colloid. Interface Sci. 1980, 77, 586.
8. Absolom, D.R., Michaeli, I., and van Oss, C.J. Electrophoresis 1981, 2, 273.
9. Chen, R.F. J. Biol. Chem. 1967, 242, 173.
10. Hunter, W.M., and Greenwood, F.C. Nature 1962, 194, 495.
11. Swanstrom, R., and Shank, P. Anal. Biochem. 1978, 86, 184.
12. Hudson, L., and Hayes, F.C., in "Practical Immunology", Blackwell: London, 1976, p. 122.
13. Bronson, P.M. Personal Communication 1960, Run 019.
14. van Oss, C.J. Separ. Purif. Methods 1975, 4, 167.
15. Creeth, J.M. Biochem. J. 1952, 51, 10.
16. Fair, D.B., and Jamieson, A.M. J. Colloid. Interface Sci. 1980, 77, 525.
17. Squire, P.G., Moser, P., and O'Kouski, C.T. Biochemistry 1968, 7, 4261.
18. Wright, A.K., and Thompson, M.R. Biophys. J. 1975, 15, 137.
19. Oncley, J.L., Dintzis, H.M., and Hollies, N.R.S. Abstr. Amer. Chem. Soc. 1952, 122, p. 12.
20. Overbeek, J. Th. G., and Wiersema, P.H., in "Electrophoresis", Bier, M., Ed., Vol. 2, Academic Press: New York, 1967, pp. 1-52.

RECEIVED October 7, 1983

Dynamic Behavior of Hydrophobically Modified Hydroxyethyl Celluloses at Liquid/Air and Liquid/Liquid Interfaces

SHU-JAN LIANG and ROBERT M. FITCH[1]

Institute of Materials Science and Department of Chemistry, The University of Connecticut, Storrs, CT 06268

A new class of amphiphilic, surface-active graft co-polymers, hydrophobically modified hydroxyethyl celluloses (HM-HEC's), are comprised of a cellulose backbone with short polyethylene oxide (PEO) and grafted alkyl side chains. They are excellent steric stabilizers of O/W emulsions.

Polymer monolayers, formed by adsorption from solution at various liquid interfaces, were compressed and expanded in a modified Langmuir trough with a Wilhelmy plate. Variables included polymer molecular weight, alkyl chain length and degree of grafting. The monolayers generally exhibited large hystereses in dynamic pressure/area curves.

A quantitative model is proposed for the dynamic response, which is based on the hypothesis that the elastic part is due to thermal motions, while the viscous part is due to adsorption and desorption of chain segments and molecules.

The rheological properties of a fluid interface may be characterized by four parameters: surface shear viscosity and elasticity, and surface dilational viscosity and elasticity. When polymer monolayers are present at such interfaces, viscoelastic behavior has been observed (1,2), but theoretical progress has been slow. The adsorption of amphiphilic polymers at the interface in liquid emulsions stabilizes the particles mainly through osmotic pressure developed upon close approach. This has become known as steric stabilization (3,4,5). In this paper, the dynamic behavior of amphiphilic, hydrophobically modified hydroxyethyl celluloses (HM-HEC), was studied. In previous studies HM-HEC's were found to greatly reduce liquid/liquid interfacial tensions even at very low polymer concentrations, and were extremely effective emulsifiers for organic liquids in water (6).

[1]Current address: S. C. Johnson & Son, Inc., 1525 Howe Street, Racine, WI 53403

0097-6156/84/0240-0185$06.00/0

The HM-HEC monolayer at such an interface was found to strongly
retard the rate of transport of small organic molecules across the
interface (7). Considerable relaxation-reorientation of the HM-
HEC chains slowly occurs at room temperature for as long as ten
days. The desorption from the interface of HM-HEC molecules
resulting from such reorientations leads to an apparently thinner
and more permeable monolayer.

Because the adsorbed HM-HEC molecules exhibit such slow rates
of chain reorientation, the effects of molecular weight, amount of
hydrophobic substitution and chain lengths of the hydrophobes on
the interfacial properties of HM-HEC monolayers can be investigated by two kinds of dynamic experiments: hysteresis and stress-
jump, using a Langmuir trough film balance.

Experimental

Materials. Hydrophobically modified hydroxyethyl cellulose (HM-
HEC) research samples were supplied by the Hercules Research
Center. The compositions of the samples determined according to
the preparation recipes, rather than by analysis, are summarized
in Table I.

Table I

HM-HEC Samples

Code	$\bar{M}$	Hydrophobe	Weight % of Hydrophobe	No. Hydrophobes per Molecule
30-20-1.0-11	300,000	C_{20}	1.0	11
30-16-1.5-20	300,000	C_{16}	1.5	20
30-16-1.0-13	300,000	C_{16}	1.0	13
30-16-0.5-6	300,000	C_{16}	0.5	6
10-16-1.0-4	100,000	C_{16}	1.0	4
5-16-1.0-2	50,000	C_{16}	1.0	2
5-8-2.5-11	50,000	C_8	2.5	11

Langmuir Trough Film Balance. A Langmuir trough, designed by Th.
F. Tadros of ICI Jealott's Hill Research Station and custom-
constructed by Bailey Engineering of Windsor, England, was
employed. A reversible driving motor with continuously variable
speed was used to move the barrier within a hydrophobically

treated glass frame which enclosed the monolayer. Movable micro-switches were placed so as to stop or reverse the movement of the barrier at any predetermined position automatically.

A Perkin-Elmer microbalance, modified to give an analog out-put to a continuously recording strip-chart recorder, was employed to obtain the surface tension force acting on a platinum Wilhemy plate immersed in the interface. The platinum plate was cleaned by heating to white heat in a flame and subsequently wet with water prior to immersion. The contact angle at either air/aqueous or organic/aqueous interfaces was always observed to be 0°. The buoyancy correction was calculated by measuring the depth of immersion with a cathetometer, and from a knowledge of the densities of the fluids involved. The P-E microbalance main-tains the plate at a fixed position regardless of the force acting upon it.

An HM-HEC monolayer at the air/aqueous interface was formed by adsorption from an aqueous solution of the polymer placed in the Langmuir trough overnight. In "stress-jump" experiments, HM-HEC monolayers were placed under rapid compression to a large degree and surface pressure was measured as a function of time after compression was stopped. (The compressional "jumps" required a minute or two to complete, and in some cases were on the order of the polymer monolayer relaxation times. See later section for discussion). In hysteresis experiments, the adsorbed monolayers were subjected to continuous compression-expansion cycles at a specific speed, while surface pressure was determined as a function of surface area.

Mathematical Model

When a monolayer at equilibrium, with surface pressure π_o, is subjected to compression at a speed of v cm^2/sec, the surface pressure, π, is increased because of the reduction of surface area, A. The increase in surface pressure will change the free energy of the adsorbed molecules and lead to a desorption of whole molecules or segments of molecules if these are reversibly adsorbed. The relationship between surface pressure and surface area for a monolayer may be given by an equation of state:

$$(\pi + \pi^o) \ (A - A^o) = nRT \tag{1}$$

where n is the number of moles of adsorbed segments, and π^o and A^o are constants to account for deviations from ideal behavior. For an ideal monolayer, equation 1 would become

$$\pi A = nRT \tag{2}$$

The rate of relaxation caused by desorption or readsorption is assumed to follow a simple first order function with a rate constant α: (8)

$$\frac{\partial n}{\partial t} = \alpha(\pi - \pi_o) \tag{3}$$

When an ideal monolayer is compressed, $A = A_o - vt$, where t is the time after the experiment begins. At $t = 0$, $A = A_o$, the uncompressed area of the monolayer, and $\pi_o A_o = n_o RT$ at equilibrium. From equations (2) and (3), a simple relationship for the surface pressure as a function of area, compression rate and time is obtained:

$$\left(\frac{\pi}{\pi_o}\right)_t = \frac{q + (1 - \frac{vt}{A_o})^{-(q+1)}}{q + 1} \tag{4}$$

$$\text{where } q = \frac{\alpha RT}{v}, \text{ and} \tag{5}$$

where the quantity vt/A_o is the degree of compression. The parameter q is a measure of the ratio of the desorption rate to the compression rate, and can be calculated from the results of stress-jump experiments.

In a stress-jump experiment, after a certain degree of compression, the surface area of the monolayer is held constant at a predetermined value, A_1. Then from equations (2) and (3):

$$\frac{\partial(\pi A_1/RT)}{\partial t} = \alpha (\pi - \pi_o)$$

$$\frac{\frac{\partial(\pi - \pi_o)}{\pi - \pi_o}}{\partial t} = \frac{\partial(\ln(\pi - \pi_o))}{\partial t} = \frac{\alpha RT}{A_1} \tag{6}$$

$\frac{\alpha RT}{A_1}$, defined as a relaxation rate constant, can be calculated from the slope of a plot of $\ln(\pi - \pi_o)$ versus time. There exist two limiting cases:

$$(1) \qquad q = 0; \left(\frac{\pi}{\pi_o}\right)_t = (1 - \frac{vt}{A_o})^{-1} \tag{7}$$

where no desorption occurs during the compression process; and

$$(2) \qquad q = -\infty: \left(\frac{\pi}{\pi_o}\right)_t = 1$$

where the rate of desorption is very fast compared to the rate of compression.

For a non-ideal monolayer, in which lateral interactions among molecules and chain segments within the monolayer are significant, a modification of equation (4) can be employed:

$$\left(\frac{\pi + \pi^o}{\pi_o + \pi^o}\right)_t = \frac{q + (1 - \frac{vt}{A_o + A^o})^{-(q + 1)}}{q + 1} \qquad (8)$$

In a hysteresis experiment, the movable barrier would be reversed at a time, designated as t_1, so that the monolayer comes under an expansion process at the same speed, v. The increase of surface area causes a reduction in the surface pressure. For a reversibly adsorbed monolayer, the desorption of segments may continue during the first period of expansion until the surface pressure is reduced to its equilibrium value. On further expansion, readsorption occurs because the surface pressure is below its equilibrium value.

At $t = t_1$,

$$\left(\frac{\pi}{\pi_o}\right)_{t_1} = \frac{q + (1 - \frac{vt_1}{A_o})^{-(q + 1)}}{q + 1} \qquad (9)$$

At $t = 2t_1$, the area has returned to its original value: $A = A_o$.
For intermediate times, i.e., $t_1 \leq t \leq 2 t_1$,

$$A = A_o + v(t - 2t_1) \qquad (10)$$

and

$$\left(\frac{\pi}{\pi_o}\right)_t = \frac{q}{q-1} + [(\frac{\pi}{\pi_o})_{t_1} - \frac{q}{q-1}] \ [1 + \frac{v(t-t_1)}{A - vt_1}]^{q-1} \qquad (11)$$

During the nth cycle of a hysteresis experiment, on compression:

$$2(n-1)t_1 \leq t \leq (2n-1)t_1; \ A = A_o - v(t-2(n-1)t_1), \text{ and} \qquad (12)$$

$$\left(\frac{\pi}{\pi_0}\right)_t = \frac{q}{1+q} - \left[\frac{q}{1+q} - \left(\frac{\pi}{\pi_0}\right)_{2(n-1)t_1}\right]\left[1 - \frac{v(t-2(n-1)t_1)}{A_0}^{-(1+q)}\right] \quad (13)$$

on expansion:

$$(2n-1)t_1 \overset{\le}{} t \overset{\le}{} 2nt_1; \quad A = A_0 + v(t - 2nt_1) \quad (14)$$

$$\left(\frac{\pi}{\pi_0}\right)_t = \frac{q}{q-1} + \left[\left(\frac{\pi}{\pi_0}\right)_{2(n-1)t_1} - \frac{q}{q-1}\right]\left[1 + \frac{v(t - (2n-1)t_1)}{A_0 - vt}^{q-1}\right] \quad (15)$$

In Figures 1-3, theoretical curves of surface pressure are plotted against area for various q-values. In Figure 1, only the first compression is plotted for various q-values in ideal cases, and for two additional non-ideal cases when q = 0: $A^0 = 0.1\ A_0$ and $\pi^0 = 0.1\ \pi_0$. The value of π/π_0 increases as the value of A^0 or π^0 increases. This indicates that the ideal model tends to underestimate π/π_0 if lateral attractions are significant. The theoretical curves also show that surface pressure decreases when the compression rate, v, is decreased for a given monolayer, i.e. as q becomes more negative. In Figure 2, surface pressure vs. area curves are plotted for q = -0.8, with values of vt_1/A_0 equal to 0.5 (for two cycles) and 0.6 (for three cycles). In Figure 3 similar sets of curves are plotted for q = -5. As the absolute value of q increases, the area of hysteresis increases, reaches a maximum, and then decreases: in the two limiting cases of q = 0 and q = -∞, corresponding to conditions of irreversible adsorption and infinitely rapid desorption/adsorption, respectively, there is no hysteresis.

Furthermore, we employ the same assumptions to describe a different set of hysteresis experiments: a monolayer with surface pressure π_0 at equilibrium is subjected to expansion at a constant speed of v cm^2/sec. The theoretical curves of surface pressure are plotted against area for various q-values in Figure 4. The curves show that the reduction of surface pressure decreases when the expansion rate is decreased for a given monolayer, i.e. as q becomes more negative. In Figure 5, curves are plotted for q = -2 with the two different modes: initial compression and initial expansion. Because the theoretical curves of the second and subsequent cycles in both modes almost coincide, we can expect that the surface pressure vs. area curves will be independent of how the hysteresis experiment starts after about two initial cycles.

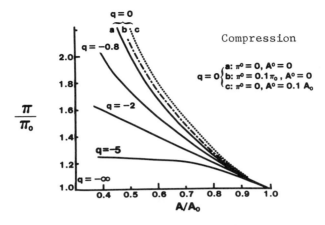

Figure 1.   Theoretical dependence of π/π_0 as calculated from equations (4) and (8); solid lines: ideal monolayers; dashed lines: non-ideal.   Parameter is q.

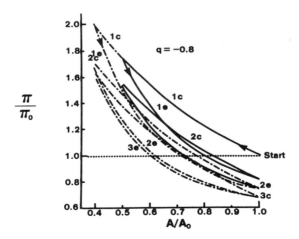

Figure 2.   Theoretical curves of π/π_0 vs. A/A_0 for q = -0.8 with maximum degree of compression = 50% (solid lines) and 60% (dashed lines).

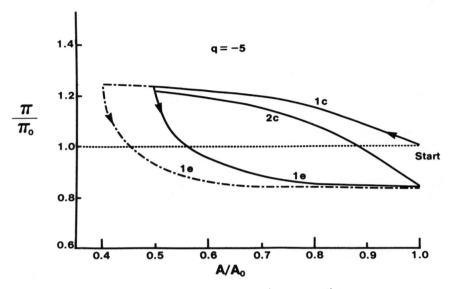

<u>Figure 3..</u> Theoretical curves of π/π_o vs. A/A_o for q = -5 with maximum degree of compression = 50% (solid lines) and 60% (dashed lines).

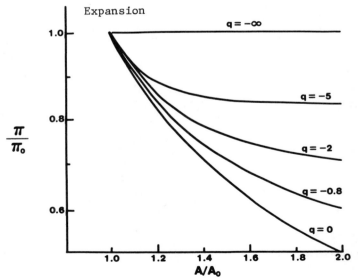

<u>Figure 4.</u> The effect of q on π/π_o vs. A/A_o as the monolayer is expanded.

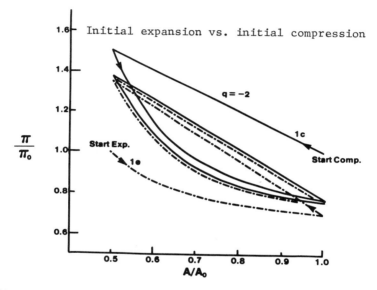

Figure 5.   Theoretical curves of π/π_0 vs. A/A_0 for $q = -2.0$ for two different hysteresis experiments: compression followed by expansion (solid line) and expansion followed by compression (dashed line).

Results and Discussion

Stress-Jump Experiments. The results of stress-jump experiments for HM-HEC monolayers with various compositions are shown in Table II, where the relaxation rate constants, $\frac{\alpha RT}{A_1}$, were calcu- from the initial slopes of the plots of ln $(\pi - \pi_o)$ vs. time curves.
    The dependency of the value of the corrected relaxation rate constant, $\frac{\alpha RT}{A_o}$, on the degree of compression found in HM-HEC 30-16-0.5-6 monolayers indicates that the relaxation process is not a simple first order function. Because of strong lateral interactions, the polymer monolayers possess both elastic and viscous properties. It has been found in separate experiments on the diffusional barrier properties of HM-HEC monolayers that a very slow process occurs over a period of several days. This probably involves both reorientation of chain segments within the interface as well as adsorption/desorption of molecules (7). The characteristic relaxation rate constant for this process is on the order of k $\approx 10^{-5}$ s^{-1}. From these relaxation rate constants, we may compare the dynamic properties of HM-HEC monolayers:

1) The segmental mobility of the polymer in the monolayer is enhanced by the solvation of the hydrophobes with toluene (9): the relaxation rate constant at the toluene/aqueous interface was three times that at the air/aqueous interface, as shown by Experiments Numbers 1 and 2 in Table II.

2) The dynamic behavior of HM-HEC monolayers depends on the concentration in bulk solution (10, 11, 12): the monolayer obtained from dilute solution, having a higher relaxation rate constant, is more flexible and presumably thinner (Experiments Numbers 1 and 3).

3) An increase in the amount of hydrophobic modification restricts segmental mobility by an increase of viscosity within the monolayer: for the same molecular weight (300,000) and hydrophobe chain length (C_{16}), the polymer monolayer with the higher amount of hydrophobe has a smaller relaxation rate constant (Experiments Numbers 3 and 7).

4) Relaxation rates are strongly dependent on molecular weights: for a given amount (1%) and chain length (C_{16}) of hydrophobes: polymer 5-16-1-2, having one-sixth the M.W. of 30-16-1-13, has a relaxation rate constant approximately 100 times as great (Experiments Numbers 1 and 9). This result implies a great difference in configurations of the adsorbed molecules at the interface, as a result of different surface activities (13). As the polymer molecules adsorb at the interface, the hydrophobic moieties are held within the

Table II

The Relaxation Rate Constants of HM-HEC Monolayers

Exp. No.	Monolayer	Interface	Concentration of Bulk Solution	Degree of Compression vt_1/A_0	Relaxation Rate Constant $\alpha RT/A_1$ (sec-1)	Corrected Relaxation Rate Constant $\alpha RT/A_0$ (sec-1)
1	30-16-1-13	air/aqueous	100 ppm	49%	2.24×10^{-4}	1.14×10^{-4}
2		toluene/aqueous	100 ppm	49%	7.63×10^{-4}	3.89×10^{-4}
3		air/aqueous	5 ppm	49%	1.55×10^{-3}	7.91×10^{-4}
4	30-16-0.5-6	air/aqueous	10 ppm	36%	1.42×10^{-3}	9.06×10^{-4}
5				55%	2.44×10^{-3}	1.10×10^{-3}
6		air/aqueous	5 ppm	23%	6.80×10^{-4}	5.25×10^{-4}
7				44%	1.80×10^{-3}	1.00×10^{-3}
8				55%	2.50×10^{-3}	1.12×10^{-3}
9	5-16-1-2	air/aqueous	50 ppm	60%	2.39×10^{-2}	1.17×10^{-2}
10	5-8-2.5-11	air/aqueous	50 ppm	60%	4.08×10^{-2}	1.63×10^{-2}

interfacial zone, while the cellulosic parts form loops & tails
solvated by water. A thicker monolayer is expected for a
higher M.W. polymer (14).

5) The chain length of hydrophobes has a greater effect on the
   dynamic behavior of the polymer monolayer than the number of
   hydrophobes, when the side chains are short: the 5-8-2.5-11
   molecules with eleven C_8 hydrophobes per chain have a higher
   relaxation rate constant than the 5-16-1-2 molecules with
   only two C_{16} hydrophobes. Many short side chains per molecule
   result in a greater degree of adsorption, as evidenced by a
   lower surface tension (see Figure 9), but a smaller energy
   per adsorbed segment. The chain length of the hydrophobes
   determines their degree of secondary bonding in the air phase
   so that the 5-16-1-2 molecules have less tendency to desorb,
   a smaller value of α (Experiments Numbers 9 and 10,
   Table II).

Hysteresis Experiments. The dynamic behavior of a 30-16-1-13
monolayer at the air/5 ppm aqueous interface was studied at two
different speeds, 3.17 cm/min and 0.353 cm/min, and is shown in
Figure 6. These may be compared with the theoretical curves in
Figures 2 and 3. Comparing the π-A curves at these two speeds,
we found that the surface pressure was not only a function of
area, but also of speed, especially in the high compression
regions. The results indicate that the rates of desorption and
readsorption, α, of HM-HEC 30-16-1-13 are of somewhat the same
order of magnitude as the rates of compression and expansion we
employed. At slow speeds, during compression the adsorbed 30-16-
1-13 molecules have much more time to reorient themselves; and in
expansion, some of the desorbed segments can be readsorbed, possibly along with molecules from the bulk solution.
     Similar results were observed for the monolayers of 30-16-
0.5-6 and 10-16-1-4, when the speeds of compression and expansion
were properly chosen. In Figure 7, the dynamic behavior of the
monolayer 30-16-0.5-6 at the air/10 ppm aqueous interface, with
two speeds: 3.1 and 0.225 cm/min, are shown. That for 10-16-1-4
at the air/10 ppm aqueous interface, is shown in Figure 8.
Toluene was subsequently poured carefully onto this same monolayer, and after standing 20 hours, the hysteresis experiments
were repeated. The results are also shown in Figure 8. In
Figure 9, the dynamic behaviors of two low M.W. HM-HEC monolayers,
5-16-1-2 and 5-8-2.5-11, at air/50 ppm aqueous interfaces, both
studied at 3.6 cm/min, are presented. From the relatively high
speed ($\approx$ 3.0 cm/min) π-A curves, one may make the following
observations: In Figures 6 through 9, the effect of molecular
weight on the dynamic behavior of HM-HEC monolayers can be seen
in the changes from concave to convex in the shape of the π-A
curves of initial compression as the M.W. decreases. This result
agrees with the prediction using the model, where the absolute

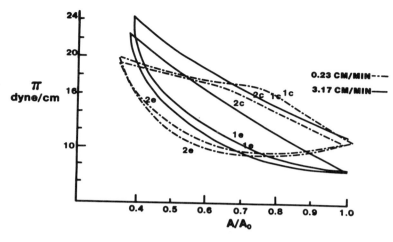

Figure 6. Dynamic behavior of HM-HEC 30-16-1-13 monolayer at air/5 ppm aqueous solution interface, two hysteresis cycles at speeds of 3.17 cm/min and 0.23 cm/min.

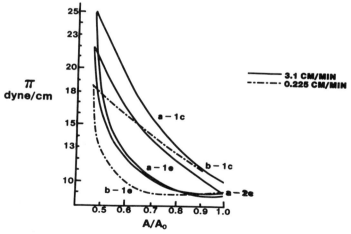

Figure 7. Dynamic behavior of HM-HEC 30-16-0.5-6 monolayer at air/10 ppm aqueous solution interface, (a) and (b): hysteresis experiments with speeds of 3.1 cm/min and 0.225 cm/min, respectively.

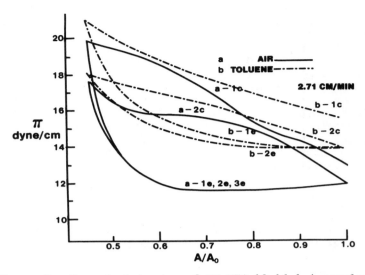

Figure 8. Dynamic behavior of HM-HEC 10-16-1-4 monolayer
at 10 ppm aqueous solution interfaces, at air (a) and
toluene (b): hysteresis experiments at compression speed
of 2.71 cm/min.

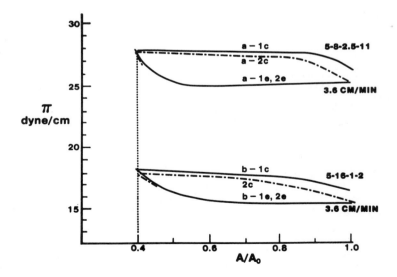

Figure 9. Dynamic behavior of low M.W. HM-HEC monolayers
at air/50 ppm aqueous solution interface, (a): 5-8-2.5-11
(b): 5-16-1-2.   Speed: 3.6 cm/min.

value of q, the ratio of the desorption to the compression rate, increases with decreasing M.W. at constant v (see Figure 1).

Among the monolayers, we found that 10-16-4 at the air/10 ppm aqueous interface had the largest area of hysteresis as shown in Figure 8. During its second cycle of the high speed compression, the monolayer became relatively incompressible, manifested in an increase of slope in the π vs A curve at high compression. In the presence of toluene the interactions among hydrophobes would be reduced, thereby decreasing the internal viscosity of the monolayer, so that both compressional modulus and hysteresis area are reduced (6). The compressional moduli for 10-16-1-4 at air/ and toluene/10 ppm aqueous interfaces were found to be 14.5 and 5.5 dyne/cm, respectively.

Test of the Mathematical Model. In the mathematical model, behavior of the polymer monolayer was related to two parameters: the degree of compression, $(1-A/A_o)$, and the ratio of the relaxation rate to the compression (expansion) rate, q. The results from three typical hysteresis experiments with three different polymers were chosen for comparison to the theory. Their q-values, either calculated from the experimental conditions or chosen for best fit, and their corresponding relaxation rate constants, obtained from separate stress-jump experiments, are listed in Table III.

Table III

Monolayer	Experimental π-A Curve	Speed of Compression/cm min^{-1}	Corrected Relaxation Rate Constant/ sec^{-1}	q
30-16-1-13	Figure 6	3.17	7.91×10^{-4}	-0.257
30-16-0.5-6	Figure 7, curve (b)	0.225	1.00×10^{-3}	-4.80
		0.225	$4.17 \times 10^{-4*}$	-2.0^*
		0.225	$3.13 \times 10^{-4*}$	-1.5^*
5-16-1-2	Figure 9, curve (b)	3.60	$1.17 \times 10^{-2\dagger}$	-3.50
		3.60	$3.34 \times 10^{-2*}$	-10.0^*

† Compressional speed during stress-jump too slow to avoid some stress relaxation
* Assumed values

In Figure 10, the π-A curves, both experimental and theoretical, of the initial compression are plotted. We found good agreement with monolayer 30-16-1-13 (curves (a) and (a')) where the absolute value of q is small and the hysteresis areas of the

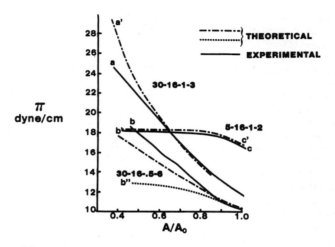

<u>Figure 10</u>.   The comparison of the theoretical (dashed
lines) and experimental (solid lines) π vs. A curves of the
first compression for three monolayers: (a) HM–HEC 30–16–
1–13 monolayer at air/5 ppm aqueous solution interface with
compression speed of 3.17 cm/min; (b) HM–HEC 30–16–0.5–6
monolayer at air/10 ppm aqueous solution interface with
compression speed of 0.225 cm/min and (c) HM–HEC 5–16–1–2
monolayer at air/50 ppm aqueous solution interface with
compression speed of 3.6 cm/min.

theoretical curves are also small. For monolayer 30-16-0.5-6, the calculated value of q = -4.8 and an assumed value of -1.5 were used to plot the theoretical π-A curves, as shown in curves (b') and (b"), respectively. The results indicate that the model underestimates the surface pressures at high compressions under these conditions. Several reasons may account for this lack of agreement: (1) The theoretical curves are highly sensitive to values of q between -1 and -5 (see Figure 1). The experimental q, in turn, relies on the relaxation rate constant estimated from a stress-jump experiment. (2) The relaxation process of the polymer is not a simple first order function. The relaxation rate constant measured from a stress-jump experiment with a high speed precompression thus might not apply to the system with a low speed compression. (3) In the real system, the relaxation rate constant is related not only to adsorption/desorption, but also to the internal viscosity of the HM-HEC monolayer, which depends on the extent of micellar aggregation, both intra- and inter-molecular, resulting from hydrophobic interactions.

For low M.W. monolayer 5-16-1-2, the value of q = -10 (instead of the experimental value of -3.5) was chosen to obtain the best fit to the theoretical curve. The relaxation process in this low molecular weight polymer was very fast, so that the stress induced during the so-called stress-"jump" was to a large extent relieved during the initial compression. The "jump" was at the maximum available speed of 3.60 cm min^{-1}, not nearly fast enough under these conditions to avoid this source of error. This was not a problem for the high molecular weight polymers in which the relaxation process continued for more than 24 hours. It is probable, therefore, that the actual rate of relaxation is at least three times faster than that measured from our stress-jump experiment. However, despite these difficulties, the model provides a good explanation for surface pressure vs. area relationships which depend upon the nature of the polymer and the experimental conditions.

Conclusion

Hydrophobically modified hydroxyethyl celluloses exhibit considerable surface activity, the magnitude of which depends on the chain length of the hydrophobes, the percentage of hydrophobic modification, and the molecular weight. The hysteresis and stress-jump experiments together permit one to obtain the viscoelastic properties of polymer monolayers, characterized by a parameter q, the ratio of relaxation rate to the compression (or expansion) rate. Under conditions of rapid compression (small negative q), the elastic properties of the polymer monolayer dominate, and one obtains the elastic modulus from the slope of the π-A curve. At relatively slow speeds ($-1 \gtrsim q \gtrsim -5$), viscous properties are measured, and a large hysteresis area is observed. We found that for high M.W. HM-HEC, the rate of segmental orientation and the exchange rate between monolayer and the bulk phase are extremely slow, with a relaxation rate constant on the order of 10^{-4}sec^{-1}, such that the polymer monolayers could be regarded as insoluble, even though they are formed by adsorption from solution..

Acknowledgment

Financial support was provided by Hercules, Inc.

Literature Cited

1. Dimitrov, D. S., Panaoilov, I., Richmond, P., Ter-Minassian-Seraga, L., J. Colloid Interface Sci. (1978), 65, (3), 483.
2. Graham, D. E., Phillips, M. C., J. Colloid Interface Sci. (1980), 76, (1), 227.
3. Hesselink, F. Th., Vrij, A., Overbeek, J. Th. G., J. Phys. Chem. (1971), 75, 2094.
4. Napper, D. H., J. Colloid Interface Sci. (1977), 58, 390.
5. Tadros, Th. F., Ed., "The Effect of Polymers on Dispersion Properties"; Academic Press: London, (1982).
6. (a) Azad, A. R. M., Fitch, R. M., private communication (1981).
    (b) Landoll, S., J. Poly. Sci. Chem. Ed. (1982), 20, 443.
7. Liang, Shu-Jan, Fitch, R. M., J. Colloid Interface Sci. (1982), 90, (1), 51.
8. Veer, F. A., van den Tempel, M., J. Colloid Interface Sci. (1973), 42, (2), 418.
9. Glass, J. E., J. Poly. Sci. (1971), Part C, 34, 141.
10. Nakamae, K., Shimatami, S., Fujimura, Y., and Matsumoto, T., J. Adhesion Soc. Japan (1981), 17, (8), 312.
11. Graham, D. E., Phillips, M. C., J. Colloid Interface Sci. (1979), 70, (3), 427.
12. Steller, K., Hercules Research Center, private communication.
13. Cohen-Stuart, M. A., Scheutjens, J. M. H. M., and Fleer, G. J., J. Poly. Sci. (1980), 18, (3), 559.
14. Fleer, G. J., Scheutjens, J. M. H. M., Advances in Colloid and Interface Sci. (1982), 16, 341.

RECEIVED October 20, 1983

POLYMERS BETWEEN SURFACES

Statistical Thermodynamics and Configurational Structure of Chains Confined Between Surfaces

The Effect of Concentration and Segment/Surface Attraction on the Behavior of Chains Bounded by a Pair of Surfaces

MOTI LAL and GILL M. WATSON

Unilever Research, Port Sunlight Laboratory, Bebington, Wirral, L63 3JW, England

The effects of chain segment concentration and the segment/surface interaction energy on the configurational and thermodynamic behaviour of tetrahedral lattice chains confined between a pair of impenetrable surfaces is investigated. The concentration effect has been accounted for in terms of the mean field approximation. The present study involves the application of Di Marzio and Rubin's probability matrix formalism in a suitably modified form which allows the introduction of the mean field approximation in the interfacial region and takes a partial account of the intrachain excluded volume effect by disallowing immediate reversals of bond directions in the chain. This study shows that while the qualitative behaviour of the properties of the chain is essentially governed by the segment/surface interactions, the concentration effect can bring about significant quantitative changes in those properties. In particular, it is found that the segment density distribution is markedly affected by the changes in the mean segment concentration in the interfacial region. This finding calls into question the validity of the assumption that the free energy of the confined chain can be resolved into the linearly additive volume restriction and osmotic terms, the former being independant of composition.

The problem of chains confined to the region bounded by a pair of surfaces is the subject of a great deal of interest to both theoreticians and experimentalists. Such an interest derives mainly from the desire to acquire a molecular understanding of the role of polymers as stabilising and flocculating agents for colloidal dispersions. It is generally held that the phenomena of polymer induced colloid stability and flocculation follow from the thermodynamic and configurational changes in the adsorbed

NOTE: This is Part V in a series.

0097–6156/84/0240–0205$06.25/0
© 1984 American Chemical Society

region brought about by the collision of a pair of particles.
The object is, therefore, to seek a quantitative interpretation
of these phenomena in terms of such changes. The older
treatments, advanced by Meier (1), Hesselink et al (2, 3, 4) and
others (5), have attempted to evaluate the free energy
changes arising from the compression of chains as the two surfaces
approach closer separations. Those treatments involve the
division of the free energy into linearly additive contributions
(volume restriction term and osmotic term) assumed to be mutually
independent. More recent studies are based on the self
consistent field model and have tackled the problem of terminally
anchored chains confined between parallel plates (6, 7). Most
recently, Scheutjens and Fleer have extended their statistical
mechanical treatment for chains adsorbed on a single surface (8)
to chains between two surfaces (9). Configurational and
statistical mechanical studies of excluded volume chains lying
between surfaces have been pursued using Monte Carlo and exact
enumeration methods (10-14).

   The present computational study involves the modification
of the probability-matrix approach of Di Marzio and Rubin (15)
so as to include the effect of concentration and to take a
partial account of the intramolecular excluded volume effect by
disallowing immediate reversals of bond directions in the chain
configurations. The aim of these calculations is to evaluate the
effects of interchain interactions and segment/surface binding
energy on the segment-density distribution and the configurational free energy of chains in the region bounded by a pair
of parallel planes. The results should enable us to estimate the
importance of these factors in the modification of the
configurational and thermodynamic state of the interfacial region
as the two planes are brought to closer distances.

THE MODEL

In line with our previous computations (10, 11, 16), we assume
a tetrahedral lattice to represent the present systems. A chain
is formed by linearly joining successive sites on the lattice, a
site in the chain denoting a segment and the vector joining a
pair of consecutive sites a bond. The bond length (ℓ) and the
bond angle are, respectively, equal to $\sqrt{3}$ lattice units and
109.48°. It is stipulated that a bond in the chain cannot assume
a direction opposite to that of its immediate predecessor. In
this way, the overlap between segments i and i+2 is avoided, and
so the excluded volume condition is partially fulfilled. A bond
can assume three conformational states corresponding to the
(bond) rotational angles $\phi = 0°$ (trans), 120° (gauche$^+$) and
240° (gauche$^-$).

The chains are confined in the region bounded by a pair of parallel planes

$$y - x = A$$
and $$y - x = B$$

with $(B-A)/2 = D$, where $\underline{D}$ is the width of the interfacial region in units of $d = \sqrt{2}$ lattice units $(= \sqrt{\frac{2}{3}} \ell)$.
The confining planes make an angle of 45° with the $z = A$ plane. The rationale underlying the choice of the above lattice planes as bounding surfaces resides in their ability to allow the occurrence of a configurational state in which all the segments of the chain are adsorbed (ie. located on the surface). Geometrical constraints prevent the chain from lying flat on the $z=A$ surface, and it may be readily seen that such a surface cannot accommodate more than 50% of the chain segments.

The model is characterised by the following three energy parameters:

i) $\Delta \epsilon_1$, which represents the change in energy accompanying the formation of a non-bonded segment/segment pair, specifies the solvent condition. $\Delta \epsilon_1 > 0$ (repulsion between segments) corresponds to good solvent condition, whereas $\Delta \epsilon_1 < 0$ prescribes poor solvent condition.

ii) $\Delta \epsilon_{t \rightarrow g}$ is the energy difference between a gauche and a trans state. It is related to bond flexibility, $\oint$, which may be defined as (17)

$$\oint = e^{-\Delta \epsilon_{t \rightarrow g}} \tag{1}$$

so that for $\Delta \epsilon_{t \rightarrow g} = 0$, $\oint = 1$ (completely flexible chain) and for $\Delta \epsilon_{t \rightarrow g} = \infty$, $\oint = 0$ (completely rigid chain assuming the all-trans state).

iii)   Segment/surface binding energy parameter, $\Delta \epsilon_s$, denotes the change in energy resulting from the formation of a segment/surface bond. Negative values of $\Delta \epsilon_s$ correspond to segment/surface attraction. Adsorption of a chain would occur only if $-\Delta \epsilon_s$ exceeds the critical value which is ≈ 0.45 kT for the chain confined to a single surface (18).

In the present model the co-ordination number for the first bond of the chain is 4 and for the remaining bonds it is 3. Thus the configurational partition function of an N-bond, isolated chain (ie. in the limit of zero concentration) is

$$\Omega_{(o)} = 4 \times 3^{N-1} \tag{2}$$

neglecting the interchain interactions. Now consider the system
at a finite concentration. For bonds of a chain in the system,
the (effective) co-ordination number is no longer 3 but is
reduced due to the occupancy of segments of other chains on
lattice sites. Let the fraction of sites occupied by the
segments be ϕ. Therefore the fraction of unoccupied sites will
be $(1-\phi)$. According to the mean field approximation, the
fraction $(1-\phi)$ represents the factor by which the co-ordination
number is reduced. Therefore, the partition function of the
chain at ϕ is

$$\Omega_{(\phi)} = 4 \times 3^{N-1} \times (1-\phi)^N \tag{3}$$

Equation (3) will readily enable the chemical potential of the
chain to be determined as a function of ϕ. The foregoing
approximation has been applied to account for the concentration
effect in the interfacial region. Extension of the mean field
theory to this region must be consistent with two essential
features of the system, namely, the presence of segment/surface
interactions and variation of segment concentration normal to the
confining planes. Below, we give an outline of the computational
method which not only allows the theory to be applied in accord
with the conditions embodied in the above two features but also
incorporates the short range excluded volume effect mentioned
earlier in the section.

THEORETICAL FRAMEWORK

Rubin (19) originally developed the probability matrix formalism
for a random-walk, lattice chain confined to an impenetrable
barrier represented by a lattice plane. This formalism was
subsequently extended by Di Marzio and Rubin (15) to a chain
confined between two lattice planes. Rubin's approach is
essentially a mathematical device which provides a convenient
method for the computation of the configurational partition
function and other properties of the system. It divides the
interfacial region into planes parallel to the bounding surfaces
(Fig 1) such that the chain segments can be located only on these
planes - there exists no possibility for a segment lying in the
region between two consecutive planes. Let there be M such
planes including the confining surfaces which are labelled as 1
and M in the figure. The probability, $p_n(i)$, that a chain
segment i lies in a plane n is a sum of 3 terms which are related
to the probability of segment i-1 being located in planes n-1, n
and n+1.

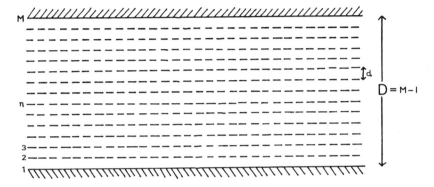

Figure 1. Schematic representation of the model for the interfacial region. The region is composed of M parallel planes including the bounding surfaces which are labelled as 1 and M. The distance between a pair of adjoining planes is $d = \sqrt{2}$ lattice units. The width of the interfacial region $D = M-1$ (in units of d).

One may write

$$p_n(i) = \psi_{-1}p_{n-1}(i-1) + \psi_o p_n(i-1) + \psi_{+1}p_{n+1}(i-1) \qquad (4)$$

where $p_{n-1}(i-1)$, $p_n(i-1)$ and $p_{n+1}(i-1)$ are the probabilities of segment $i-1$ residing in planes $n-1$, n and $n+1$ respectively. The coefficients ψ_{-1}, ψ_o and ψ_{+1} denote the conditional probabilities for segment i being in plane n if segment $i-1$ was located, respectively, at $n-1$, n and $n+1$. ψ's are related to the lattice co-ordination number as

$$\psi_o = 'z/z, \text{ where } 'z \text{ is the co-ordination in two} \qquad (5)$$
$$\text{dimensions}$$

and $\quad \psi_{-1} = \psi_{+1} = \dfrac{1}{2} \dfrac{(z-'z)}{z}$

$$\left.\begin{array}{l} \text{For } n = 1, \; p_{n-1} \; (i-1) = 0 \\[2mm] \text{and for } n = M, \; p_{n+1} \; (i-1) = 0 \end{array}\right] \begin{array}{l} \text{since the confining} \\ \text{surfaces are impenetrable (6)} \end{array}$$

Further, for planes 1 and M the segment/surface interactions will necessitate the introduction of the Boltzmann factor in the probability equation. Thus:

$$\begin{array}{ll} & p_1(i) = \psi_o p_1(i-1) \; e^\theta + \psi_+ p_2(i-1)e^\theta \quad) \\ \text{and} & p_M(i) = \psi_{-1}p_{M-1}(i-1)e^\theta + \psi_o p_M(i-1)e^\theta \quad) \end{array} \qquad (7)$$

where $\theta = -\Delta\varepsilon_2/kT$

The foregoing formalism can be presented succinctly in the matrix notation as

$$\underset{\sim}{P}(i) = \Psi\underset{\sim}{P}(i-1) \qquad (8)$$

with

$$\underset{\sim}{P}(i) = \begin{bmatrix} p_1(i) \\ p_2(i) \\ " \\ " \\ " \\ p_n(i) \\ " \\ " \\ p_{M-1}(i) \\ p_M(i) \end{bmatrix}, \quad \underset{\sim}{P}(i-1) = \begin{bmatrix} p_1(i-1) \\ p_2(i-1) \\ " \\ " \\ " \\ p_n(i-1) \\ " \\ " \\ " \\ " \\ p_{M-1}(i-1) \\ p_M(i-1) \end{bmatrix} \qquad (9)$$

and

$$
\Psi=
\begin{bmatrix}
\psi_o e^\theta & \psi_+ e^\theta & 0 & 0 & 0 & 0 & 0 & 0 & 0 \\
\psi_- & \psi_o & \psi_+ & 0 & 0 & 0 & 0 & 0 & 0 \\
0 & \psi_- & \psi_o & \psi_+ & 0 & 0 & 0 & 0 & 0 \\
0 & 0 & \psi_- & \psi_o & \psi_+ & 0 & 0 & 0 & 0 \\
0 & 0 & 0 & \cdot & \cdot & \cdot & 0 & 0 & 0 \\
0 & 0 & 0 & 0 & \cdot & \cdot & \cdot & 0 & 0 \\
0 & 0 & 0 & 0 & 0 & \cdot & \cdot & \cdot & 0 \\
0 & 0 & 0 & 0 & 0 & 0 & \psi_- & \psi_o & \psi_+ \\
0 & 0 & 0 & 0 & 0 & 0 & 0 & \psi_- e^\theta & \psi_o e^\theta
\end{bmatrix}
\tag{10}
$$

Rubin termed Ψ as the transition probability matrix. It can be readily established that

$$
\underset{\sim}{P}(N) = \Psi^{N-1}\underset{\sim}{P}(1)
\tag{11}
$$

Vector $\underset{\sim}{P}(1)$ sets the conditions relating to the position of the first segment. For a chain whose first segment may reside in any of the M planes,

$$
\underset{\sim}{P}(1) =
\begin{bmatrix}
e^\theta \\
1 \\
1 \\
1 \\
' \\
' \\
' \\
' \\
' \\
e^\theta
\end{bmatrix}
\tag{12}
$$

A component $p_n(N)$ of $\underset{\sim}{P}(N)$ represents the relative probability of an N-segment chain terminating at a plane n with first segment located in any of the M planes. Therefore, the sum of the components of $\underset{\sim}{P}(N)$ may be identified with the configurational partition function of the chain confined between 1 and M

$$\Omega_M = \sum_{n=1}^{M} P_n(N) = \underset{\sim}{u}^T \cdot \underset{\sim}{P}(N) \tag{13}$$

where $\underset{\sim}{u}^T$ is the row sector $(1,1,---,1)$

The configurational free energy of the chain, G_M, is simply equal to $-kT \ln \Omega_M$. The mean number of segments bound to the confining surfaces can be obtained by differentiating the free energy with respect to θ

$$\left.\begin{array}{c}\langle N(1)\rangle \\ \langle N(M)\rangle\end{array}\right\} = -\frac{\delta(G_M)}{\delta\theta} \tag{14}$$

In general,

$$\langle N(n)\rangle = -\frac{\delta(G_M)}{\delta\theta_n} \tag{15}$$

where θ_n is the interaction energy of a segment with plane n. It should be remarked that although θ_n for $1<n<M$ is zero in the present model, $\delta(G_M)/\delta\theta_n$ will not normally be zero.

In the application of the above treatment to the present model, account must be taken of the condition of fixed bond angle which disallows the overlap between two successive bonds in the chain. This feature can be accommodated in the scheme by replacing the quantities ψ_{-1}, ψ_o and ψ_+ in the transition probability matrix by 4x4 sub-matrices.

$$\{\psi_{-1}\} = \begin{pmatrix} 0 & 0 & 0 & 0 \\ 0 & 0 & 0 & 0 \\ 0 & 0 & 0 & 0 \\ 1 & 0 & 1 & 1 \end{pmatrix}$$

$$\{\psi_o\} = \begin{pmatrix} 1 & 1 & 0 & 1 \\ 0 & 0 & 0 & 0 \\ 0 & 1 & 1 & 1 \\ 0 & 0 & 0 & 0 \end{pmatrix} \tag{16}$$

$$\{\psi_+\} = \begin{pmatrix} 0 & 0 & 0 & 0 \\ 1 & 1 & 1 & 0 \\ 0 & 0 & 0 & 0 \\ 0 & 0 & 0 & 0 \end{pmatrix}$$

It is possible to include in the above the effect of trans/gauche energy difference, but this will entail conditional probability matrices of much greater complexity, leading to severe computational difficulties.

At finite concentration, the conditional probabilities will be modified to include a factor, ω, which takes account of the presence of other chains in the system. According to the mean field approximation,

$$\omega_n \simeq (1 - \phi_n) \tag{17}$$

at the athermal solvent condition ($\Delta\epsilon_1 = 0$). ω_n is the modifying factor corresponding to the plane n, and ϕ_n is the segment concentration at n. For non-athermal solvent conditions ($\Delta\epsilon_1 \neq 0$), ω_n must contain the Boltzmann factor corresponding to the segment/segment interactions. Thus

$$\omega_n \simeq (1-\phi_n)e^{(-\Delta\epsilon_1/kT)\phi_n"z} \tag{18}$$

where "z is the number of non bounded nearest neighbours of a chain segment, which is 2 on the tetrahedral lattice (except for the end segments for which it is 3).

The modified transition probability matrix assumes the following structure

$$\Psi_\phi =$$

$$
\begin{bmatrix}
\omega_1\{\psi_o\}e^\theta & \omega_1\{\psi_+\}e^\theta & 0 & 0 & 0 & 0 & 0 \\
\omega_2\{\psi_-\} & \omega_2\{\psi_o\} & \omega_2\{\psi_+\} & 0 & 0 & 0 & 0 \\
0 & 0 & 0 & \cdot & \cdot & \cdot & 0 \\
0 & 0 & 0 & 0 & \cdot & \cdot & 0 \\
0 & 0 & 0 & 0 & 0 & \cdot & 0 \\
0 & 0 & 0 & 0 & 0 & \omega_M\{\psi_-\}e^\theta & \omega_M\{\psi_o\}e^\theta
\end{bmatrix}
\tag{19}
$$

Vector $\underset{\sim}{P}(1)$ also undergoes the corresponding modification and we have

$$
\underset{\sim}{P}(1) =
\begin{bmatrix}
\begin{pmatrix} 1/4 \\ 1/4 \\ 1/4 \\ 1/4 \end{pmatrix} \omega_1 e^\theta \\[1em]
\begin{pmatrix} 1/4 \\ 1/4 \\ 1/4 \\ 1/4 \end{pmatrix} \omega_2 \\[1em]
\vdots \\[1em]
\begin{pmatrix} 1/4 \\ 1/4 \\ 1/4 \\ 1/4 \end{pmatrix} \omega_M e^\theta
\end{bmatrix}
\tag{20}
$$

COMPUTATIONAL DETAILS

The computation is directed to the evaluation of:

i) the configurational partition function, Ω_ϕ, using relations (11) and (13) with Ψ_ϕ and $\underset{\sim}{P}(1)$ given by equations (19) and (20)

and ii) $\dfrac{1}{\Omega_\phi} \dfrac{\delta(\Omega_\phi)}{\delta\theta_n}$ = $<N(n)>$, n = 1 to M.

It can be shown that for the present model

$$
\frac{\partial(\Omega_\phi)}{\partial\theta_n} = \sum_{j=1}^{4} \left(\sum_{r=0}^{N-1} \underset{\sim}{u}^T \Psi_\phi^r \; \underset{\sim}{\upsilon}_{4(n-1)+j} \; \underset{\sim}{\upsilon}^T_{4(n-1)+j} \; \underset{\sim}{P}(N-r) \right)
\tag{21}
$$

$$
+ \frac{1}{4} \omega e^{\theta_n} \underset{\sim}{u}^T \Psi_\phi^N \; \underset{\sim}{\upsilon}_{4(n-1)+j}
$$

where $\underset{\sim}{\upsilon}_k$, k = 4(n-1)+j, is a column vector consisted of 4M components with the kth component equal to unity, the remaining components being zero. $\underset{\sim}{\upsilon}^T_k$ is the transpose of $\underset{\sim}{\upsilon}_k$.

The factors ω_n, n = 1 to M, are expressible in terms of $<N(n)>$, N, ϕ and M as

$$
\omega_n = 1 - <\phi>_I \frac{<N(n)>M}{N} \; \exp \; \left[\Delta\varepsilon_1/kT \right] \frac{"z<\phi>_I <N(n)>M}{N}
\tag{22}
$$

where $\langle\phi\rangle_I = \frac{1}{M} \sum_{n=1}^{M} \phi_n$

is the mean segment concentration in the interfacial region. ω's are initially unknown quantities, as their determination requires the knowledge of $\langle N(n)\rangle$ at a given value of $\langle\phi\rangle_I$. So it is necessary to pursue an iterative procedure whereby using an arbitrary set of $\langle N(n)\rangle$ values, initial values of ω_n are obtained from equation (22). These values are substituted in equations (19) and (20) to construct a trial probability matrix and an initial vector in order to compute a new set of $\langle N(n)\rangle$ values from equation (21). Substituting the new values of $\langle N(n)\rangle$ in equation (22), one would obtain an improved set of ω_n values. The procedure is continued until the difference between successive sets of ω_n values becomes negligibly small. The final set of ω_n values is then used to compute the partition function. For given $\langle\phi\rangle_I$ and M, the interation may be conveniently started with values of $\langle N(n)\rangle$ obtained for a system of a single chain residing in the interfacial region ie. $\phi_n \to 0$, hence $\omega_n = 1$, $n = 1$, M.

As is clear from equations (11), (13) and (21), the main computational task is to successively raise the transition probability matrix to powers ranging from 1 to N in steps of 1. A computer program was developed to accomplish this and to carry out the iteration procedure described above. Computational facilities at our disposal (Harris 500) allowed the consideration of matrices of order not exceeding 60. Considering that the order of the transition probability matrix is 4 times the width (M) of the interfacial region, the computational limitation restricts the present investigation to the systems in which the distance between the confining the surfaces is less than 15 units (1 unit $= \sqrt{\frac{2}{3}}\ell = $ d).

The successive iteration scheme adopted here proved satisfactory for $\langle\phi\rangle_I < 0.2$, $\theta < 0.75$ and M < 12. At higher values of $\langle\phi\rangle_I$, θ and M, the solution of ω's oscillated between two sets of values. The mean of the two solutions was used as a starting value in a new iteration which sometime yielded a single solution and at other times degenerated into two solutions again.

RESULTS AND DISCUSSION

The calculations were performed for 100-segment chains lying between surfaces with M ranging from 2 to 10. The mean segment concentration in the interfacial region, $\langle\phi\rangle_I$, was varied in the range 0-0.2. The athermal solvent condition ($\Delta\epsilon_1 = 0$) was assumed, and the values of the segment/surface binding energy, $\Delta\epsilon_1/kT$, were taken to be 0, -0.25, -0.5 and -0.75. The

properties computed include the mean fraction of segments
attached to the surfaces (ie. the bound fraction, $\langle v \rangle$), segment-
density distribution in the interfacial region and the configurational free energy of the chains.

The Bound Fraction $\langle v \rangle$

The behaviour of $\langle v \rangle$ with respect to the change in the mean
segment concentration, $\langle \phi \rangle_I$, at fixed M is shown in Figure 2 at
various values of $\Delta \varepsilon_\ell$. It is observed that under the condition
of zero or weak segment/surface attraction, $\langle v \rangle$ increases with
$\langle \phi \rangle_I$, whereas for strong segment/surface attraction, $\langle v \rangle$ is a
decreasing function of the segment concentration. At or close to
the critical energy of adsorption, $\langle v \rangle$ is found to vary little
with $\langle \phi \rangle_I$. It is well established that below the critical
energy of adsorption, layers close to the surface are depleted
and the maximum concentration of segments occurs aways from the
surface. The effect of increasing $\langle \phi \rangle_I$ is to increase the
intersegmental repulsions which will be greatest in the layers
around the maximum, causing the transfer of segments from those
layers into the depleted layers: hence the increase in the bound
fraction. In the case of strong segment/surface attraction, the
maximum concentration occurs at the surface. The increase of
intersegmental repulsions arising from the increase in $\langle \phi \rangle_I$
will be somewhat alleviated if segments move away from the
surface layer, leading to the reduction in the bound fraction,
which is indeed found to be the case.

Figures 3 and 4 show the variation in $\langle v \rangle$ with intersurface
distance D (= M-1) at θ = 0 and 0.75. At large D, $\langle v \rangle$ approaches
the value for the chain adsorbed on a single surface. The
reduction in D brings about an increase in $\langle v \rangle$, which becomes
progressively rapid as the confining surfaces approach closer
separations. At D = 1, $\langle v \rangle$ will assume the upper limiting value
of 1, since at this distance all segments of the chain must be in
contact with either surface. We observe that the introduction of
the concentration effect does not bring about any qualitative
changes in the dependence of $\langle v \rangle$ on D. However, the quantitative
differences are appreciable, especially under the condition of
strong segment/surface attraction. The effect of concentration
is marked at large separation, becoming gradually less pronounced
with the reduction in D and finally disappearing at D=1 when $\langle v \rangle$
is unity at all values of $\langle \phi \rangle_I$.

Segment-density Distributions

The distribution of segment density normal to the surfaces is an
important configurational property which serves to characterise
the structure of the interfacial region. It is described in
terms of the mean fraction of segments of the chain in each of

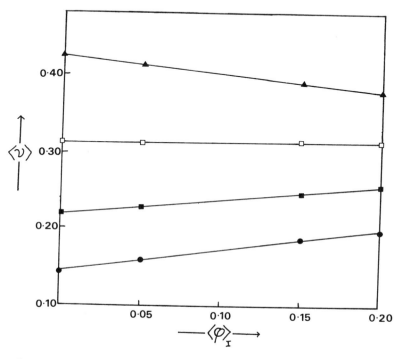

Figure 2.   The bound fraction, $\langle \nu \rangle$, as a function of
mean segment concentration, $\langle \phi \rangle_I$, in an
interfacial region of width equal to 5d
(6 lattice planes).

● : $\theta = 0$;   ■ : $\theta = 0.25$;   □ : $\theta = 0.5$;   ▲ $\theta = 0.75$

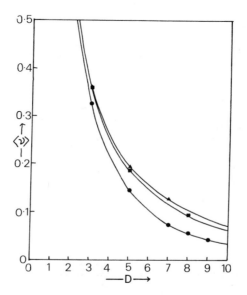

Figure 3.   The bound fraction, $\langle\nu\rangle$, versus the width of
              the interfacial region D, at $\theta=0$
              ● : $\langle\phi\rangle_I \simeq 0$; ■ : $\langle\phi\rangle_I = 0.15$; ▲: $\langle\phi\rangle_I = 0.20$

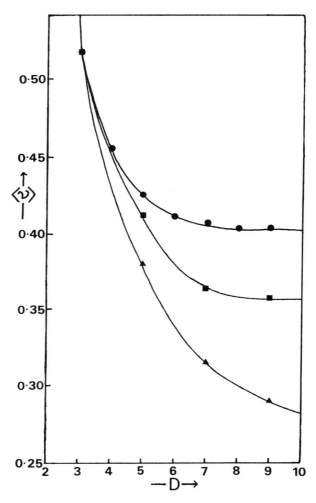

Figure 4.   The bound fraction, <ν>, versus the width of the interfacial region, D, at θ = 0.75. The significance of the various symbols is the same as in Figure 3.

the planes forming the interfacial region. The computed
distributions at θ = 0, 0.25 and 0.75 are presented in Figures 5,
6 and 7 for the interfacial region comprised of 6 planes.

Below the critical energy of adsorption (θ < 0.45), the
distributions possess a maximum occurring at the mid plane. With
the increase in segment/surface attraction, the surface layers
become richer in segments, lessening the degree of non uniformity
in the distribution, and finally at the critical point the non
uniformity is minimised (but may not disappear). As the
segment/surface attraction exceeds the critical value, the
distribution is reversed in that instead of a maximum, it
possesses a minimum. The existence of these features in the
distribution was first established by Di Marzio and Rubin (15)
for a single chain ($<\phi>_I \simeq 0$). The present study confirms that
such features are retained at finite concentration. Inclusion of
the concentration effects in the model gives rise to broader
distributions both below and above the critical energy of
adsorption. The broadening results in the plateau of uniform
density around the mid-plane. The width of the plateau increases
with $<\phi>_I$, which is most clearly seen in Fig (6).

The shape of the segment density distribution is a result
of the two forces producing opposite effects in the system. The
intersegmental repulsion produces in the system the tendency to
assume uniform distribution. But the segment/surface
interactions bring about non-uniformity in it. This is because
such interactions, depending on whether they are repulsive or
attractive, will either enhance or diminish the probability for
the location of segments in the surface layers, thereby leading
to lower or higher concentration in the immediate vicinity of the
surfaces. At low concentration ($<\phi>_I$ = 0) the interchain
interactions are negligible, so the distribution is largely
determined by the segment/surface interactions, and, therefore,
has a high degree of non-uniformity. At increased concentration,
the interchain repulsion becomes significant, giving rise to a
sub region of uniform density between the surfaces.

Configurational Free Energy

The behaviour of the configurational free energy of the chain as
a function of the intersurface distance at low and high segment
concentration ($<\phi>_I \simeq 0$ and 0.2) is compared in Figure 8 where
$\Delta\mu/_{kT}$ is plotted against D. $\Delta\mu$ is the change in the free
energy of the chain due to the confinement between the surfaces D
units apart, at constant composition. The results shown
correspond to θ = 0 and 0.75. At θ = 0, the change in the free
energy is occasioned by the reduction of the entropy of the chain
due to the physical constraint imposed by the surfaces. In the
limit of D → ∞, $\Delta\mu$ must be zero at all concentrations. The

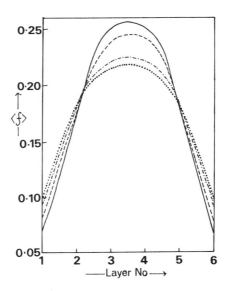

Figure 5.   The distribution of chain segment density, at $\theta = 0$, in an interfacial region with M = 6.
———: $\langle\phi\rangle_I \simeq 0$; ----: $\langle\phi\rangle_I = 0.05$;
–·–·–· : $\langle\phi\rangle_I = 0.15$; ...... : $\langle\phi\rangle_I = 0.20$

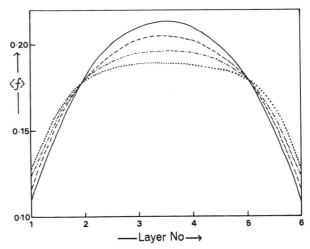

Figure 6.   The distribution of chain segment density at $\theta = 0.25$, in an interfacial region with M = 6. The various curves correspond to the same values of mean segment concentration as in Figure 5.

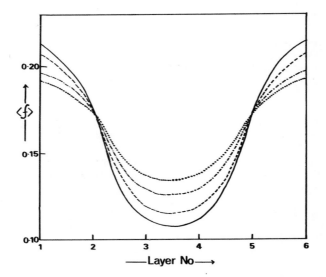

Figure 7.   The distribution of chain segment density, at
             $\theta = 0.75$, in an interfacial region with M = 6.
             The various curves correspond to the same
             values of mean segment concentration as in
             Figure 5.

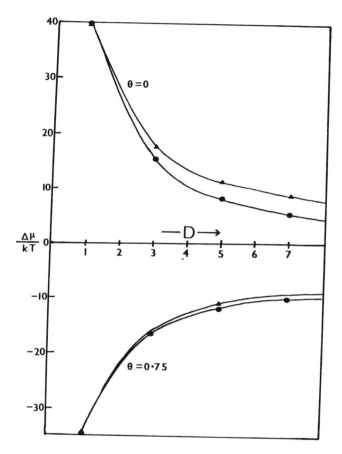

Figure 8.   The free energy of confinement of the chain,
$\Delta\mu/_{kT}$, at constant composition, as a
function of the width of the interfacial
region, D, at θ = 0 and 0.75.
● : $\langle\phi\rangle_I \simeq 0$;   ▲ : $\langle\phi\rangle_I$ = 0.2

reduction in D leads to an increase in $\Delta\mu$ which becomes steeper
as the two surfaces come closer. It is found that $\Delta\mu$ is an
increasing function of $<\phi>_I$.

At $\theta = 0.75$, $\Delta\mu/_{kT}$ derives from two contributions: the
entropy reduction and the segment/surface attraction. The first
term increases the free energy, whereas the second term reduces
it. The net effect is that $\Delta\mu$ decreases with the intersurface
distance. At this value of θ also, we find that $\Delta\mu$ is greater at
the higher concentration, although the difference between the two
curves is much smaller than at $\theta = 0$. In the limit of $D \to \infty$, $\Delta\mu$
will approach the value for the chain on a single surface, which
will not be the same for the two concentrations.

CONCLUDING REMARKS

The present study shows that although the incorporation of the
concentration effect in the model leads to few qualitative
changes in the configurational and thermodynamic behaviour of the
confined chains, the quantitative changes arising from this
effect can be significant. It is found that below the critical
energy of adsorption, the bound fraction is an increasing
function of the mean segment concentration, but above the
critical point, $<\nu>$ decreases with the increase in concentration.
The segment density assumes a broader distribution at finite
concentrations, and at higher concentration the distribution
contains a plateau of uniform density around the mid plane. The
entropic and the segment/surface interaction terms of the free
energy of the chain depend appreciably on the segment
concentration.

Standard theories of steric stabilisation assume that the
free energy of the system can be expressed as a sum of two terms,
volume restriction and osmotic, which are mutually independent.
It is now well recognised (6,20) that such a division of the free
energy is valid only if the segment density distribution is
independent of the mean concentration in the interfacial region.
Figures 5, 6 and 7 show that the distributions are markedly
affected by the changes in concentration. This casts a serious
doubt on the plausibility of the fundamental assumption
underlying these theories.

Acknowledgment

One of the authors (ML) greatly appreciates the assistance
rendered by Miss Christine Smith of this Laboratory in the
preparation of this manuscript.

Literature Cited

1. Meier, D.J.; J. Phys. Chem., 1967, 71, 1981.
2. Hesselink, F. Th., J. Phys. Chem., 1969, 73, 3488.
3. Hesselink, F. Th., J. Phys. Chem., 1971, 75, 65.
4. Hesselink, F. Th., Vrij. A.; Overbeek, G. J. Phys. Chem., 1971, 75, 2094.
5. Napper, D.J.; Evans, R.; Koll. Z. u. Z. Polym., 1973, 251, 329.
6. Dolan, A.K.; Edwards, S.F.; Proc. Roy. Soc., 1974, A337, 509; 1975, A343, 427.
7. Levine, S.; Tomlinson, M.M.; Robinson, K. Faraday Discuss Chem. Soc., 1978, 65, 202.
8. Scheutjens, J.M.H.M.; Fleer, G.J. J. Phys. Chem. 1979, 83, 1619.
9. Scheutjens, J.M.H.M.; Fleer, G.J. Adv. Colloid Interface Sci., 1982, 16, 361.
10. Clark, A.T.; Lal, M. J. Chem. Soc., Faraday Trans. 2, 1981, 77, 981.
11. Clark, A.T.; Lal, M. in "The Effect of Polymers on Dispersion Properties"; Tadros, Th. F., Ed.; Academic Press: New York, 1982; p.169.
12. Webman, I.; Lebowitz, J.L., Kalos, M.H., J. Physique, 1980, 41, 579.
13. Wall, F.T.; Seitz, W.A.; Chin, J.C.; de Gennes, P.G. Proc. Nalt. Acad. Sci., 1978, 75, 2069.
14. Middlemiss, K.M.; Torrie, G.M.; Whittington, S.G. J. Chem. Phys., 1977, 66, 3227.
15. Di Marzio, E.A.; Rubin, R.J. J. Chem. Phys., 1971, 55, 4371.
16. Clark, A.T.; Ph. D. Thesis, C.N.A.A., 1980.
17. Clark, A.T.; Lal, M. J. Phys., 1978, A11, L11.
18. Lal, M.; Richardson, K.A.; Spencer, D.; Turpin, M.A. in "Adsorption at Interfaces"; Mittal, K.L., Ed., American Chemical Society: Washington, 1975, Vol.8, p.16.
19. Rubin, R.J. J. Chem. Phys., 1965, 43, 2392.
20. Gaylord, R.J. J. Colloid & Interface Sci., 1982, 87, 577.

RECEIVED November 10, 1983

Interactions Between Polymer-Bearing Surfaces

JACOB KLEIN and YAACOV ALMOG

Polymer Department, Weizmann Institute of Science, Rehovot 76100, Israel

PAUL LUCKHAM

Cavendish Laboratory, Madingley Road, Cambridge CB3 0HE, England

The forces acting between atomically smooth mica surfaces immersed in both organic and aqueous liquid media
have been determined in the range of surface separations
0 - 300 nm, both in the absence and the presence of adsorbed polymer layers. In this way the interactions
between the adsorbed macromolecular layers themselves
were determined. We present results for the following
cases: i) Poor solvent, ii) θ - solvent, iii) good
solvent, iv) polyelectrolytes in aqueous media. Our
results show that interactions between the adsorbed
layers may be either attractive or repulsive, depending
on the nature of the solvent and the extent of adsorption. For the polyelectrolyte case the interactions are
a combination of field-type (electrostatic) and steric
forces.

The forces acting between colloid particles in dispersed systems
may be strongly modified by adsorption of polymeric or macromolecular layers onto the particle surfaces (1). This effect
has been utilized empirically since historical times (as for
example by the ancient Egyptians, who stabilized aqueous carbon-
black dispersions by adsorbed layers of gum arabic, a water-soluble, naturally occurring polysaccharide, to form stable inks):
nowadays such adsorbed layers are commonly used both for stabilization and destabilization in a wide range of synthetic (1)
and naturally occurring (2) colloidal systems. The criteria for
colloidal stability depend on several factors, such as hydrodynamic interactions, kinetics of Brownian collisions and the
extent to which the surface regions are in a state of thermodynamic equilibrium, in addition to the basic nature of the
surface-surface forces. Nonetheless, it is the latter which
is in general the dominant factor in determining the behaviour

0097–6156/84/0240–0227$06.00/0

of systems with large surface-to-volume ratios, and which must
be understood in order to have fundamental insight into the
question of stability in such systems.

Steric stabilization and the related phenomenon of polymer
adsorption have been intensively studied over the past thirty
years (1). However, it is only in a very few relatively recent
cases that attempts were made to measure directly the forces
between surfaces bearing adsorbed macromolecular layers. Sur-
face-balance (3) and compression-cell (4) techniques have been
used to measure the pressure between colloidal particles(bearing
adsorbed polymers) in two- and three-dimensional arrays. More
recently the disjoining pressure between layers of polymer adsorbed at the two liquid-air interfaces of a film of polymer
solution was measured as a function of film thickness (5); and
the force between layers of polymer adsorbed onto smooth rubber
spheres was determined as a function of the distance between
the spherical surfaces (6). All these methods were limited by
not being able to measure attraction, if any, between the adsorbed layers. Israelachvili and co-workers (7), modifying an
approach pioneered by Tabor and co-workers (8,9) measured the
interaction force (F(D) as a function of distance D between two
smooth mica sheets immersed in an aqueous solution of a commer-
cial-grade resin consisting of highly polydisperse polyethylene
oxide (PEO). Their results showed strong hysteretic effects,
and a continuous build up with time of adsorbed layer thickness,
and could not be described in terms of an equilibrium force law.

Over the past few years, both at the Weizmann Institute and
in the Cavendish Laboratory, we have used a modification of the
'mica approach' to measure the interaction forces F(D) between
two mica surfaces,a distance D apart,immersed in organic and
aqueous liquid media, both in the absence and in the presence
of polymer layers absorbed onto the mica from the liquid. We
have studied a number of model systems covering a wide range of
conditions, using monodispersed, well characterized polymers.
In this paper we briefly describe the apparatus and experimental
method, then consider the interactions between i) layers of
polystyrene in cyclohexane under poor-solvent and ii) θ - solvent conditions,iii) the interactions between adsorbed PEO
layers in a good (aqueous) solvent and iv) the surface forces
between layers of adsorbed poly-L-lysine, a cationic polyelectrolyte, in aqueous salt solutions. We consider briefly the implications of our results for the current theoretical understanding.

Apparatus and Method

Muscovite mica may be cleaved to provide thin (~2 µm) sheets
that are molecularly smooth on both sides and which can be used
as substrates in studying surface forces (8). Figure 1 shows
schematically the essential features of the apparatus (10)
(used at W.I.). Two smooth curved mica sheets are glued on

cylindrical lenses and mounted opposite each other in a crossed
cylinder configuration (to avoid problems of alignment associated
with two parallel surfaces): the top sheet is rigidly mounted
(via arm B, figure 1) on a piezocrystal while the bottom surface
is mounted onto the rigid, movable arm A via a flexible leaf-
spring of spring constant K. The closest distance D between the
surfaces is measured by an optical method involving multiple beam
white-light interferometry (10) between the mica sheets (which
are half-silvered on their glued side) and may be determined to
within ± 0.3 nm. D is controlled via a three-stage mechanism,
of which the piezocrystal is the fine control stage (to ± 0.3 nm).
The force F(D) between the surfaces is measured by applying a
known relative displacement ΔD_O between the two rigid supports A
and B, (by applying a known voltage to the piezocrystal, say) and
at the same time observing - using the optical interferometry
technique - the actual motion ΔD of the surfaces relative to each
other. If there is no force between the surfaces then we expect
$\Delta D = \Delta D_C$, and if they attract, $\Delta D > \Delta D_O$; if the surfaces repel
each other, their relative displacement ΔD will be less than ΔDo,
and if they attract, $\Delta D > \Delta D_C$ (the difference in both cases being
taken up by the leaf spring). In general,

$$F(D + \Delta D) + K(\Delta D_O - \Delta D) \qquad (1)$$

(K being the leaf-spring constant) and by starting measurements
with the surfaces far apart, where $F(D) \simeq 0$, force profiles may
be determined. The method also allows the measurement of the
mean refractive index n(D) of the medium between the surfaces (9),
and from this the amount Γ of adsorbed species per unit area of
mica may be evaluated. Finally the mean radius of curvature R
of the cylindrically curved mica surfaces near the contact area
may also be calculated from the shape of the interference fringes.

Procedure. Prior to an experiment all parts of the apparatus com-
ing in contact with solution are thoroughly cleaned and dried
(glass parts by standing in sulphachromic acid overnight, metal
and Delrin parts by sonication in degreasing agents and dilute
acid, and all parts finally rinsed in filtered ethanol and dried
in a laminar flow cabinet). The apparatus is then assembled,
closed and mounted in a vibration-free, thermally insulated box.
The mica surfaces are brought to contact in air, and the optical
parameters of the system are noted: pure solvent is added to the
glass cell (figure 1) so as to immerse the surfaces, and F(D) is
measured (in the absence of polymer). At this stage the presence
of dust or other contaminant on the surface may be noted, and
only experiments free of such artefacts are taken to the next
stage. Polymer is then added to the required concentration, and
the surfaces allowed to incubate in the solution for (generally)
several hours, to permit adsorption to take place. F(D) is then
again measured, and if necessary the polymer solution may be re-

placed by solvent (to leave only the surface adsorbed polymer in
in the system), and F(D) measured once more. Variations on this
procedure for the different systems studied will be described in
the 'Results and Discussion' Section.

Materials. Unless otherwise stated, all chemicals and solvents
were analytical grade materials (Fluka and B.D.H.), and were used
as received. The water used for washing and preparation of aqueous electrolyte solutions was deionized and freshly double-distilled in a fused-silica still. All liquids are filtered (0.22 μm
Millipore or Fluoropore filters) prior to introduction into the
glass cell. The mica used throughout was Best Quality FS/GS grade
2 Muscovite Ruby mica, mined in Kenya (Mica and Micanite Ltd.,
U.K.).

Results and Discussion

The force-distance profiles presented in the following sections
are generally plotted as F(D)/R v. D, i.e. the force axis is 'normalized' by dividing F(D) by the mean radius R of the mica sheets.
In the Derjaguin approximation ($\underline{11}$),

$$F(D)/R = 2\pi E(D) \tag{2}$$

where E(D) is the interaction energy per unit surface area between
two flat, <u>parallel</u> plates a distance D apart, obeying the same
force law. In this way the effect of different curvature of the
mica surfaces in the different experiments is eliminated. Where
this is not done, the value of R is given explicity in the figure
caption.

Polystyrene in Cyclohexane at T < Θ

The force profile between bare mica surfaces immersed in pure cyclohexane at 24°C is shown in figure 2. No force (within error) is
detected as the surfaces approach from large D down to D $\simeq$ 12 nm.
when attraction sets in. At the point J (figure 2) the surfaces
jump into their air contact position (within error). Such jumps
are due to a mechanical instability whenever $\partial F(D)/\partial D \geqslant K$, the
spring constant of the lower leaf-spring (figure 1). The broken
line is the theoretical van der Waals attraction $F(D) = -AR/6D^2$,
expected between crossed cylinders of radius R (R = 0.66 cm) where
A is the appropriate Hamaker constant (estimated as 1 x 10^{-20} J
for mica in cyclohexane ($\underline{12}$)). The data of figure 2 could be con-
strued as indicating a van-der-Waals-like interaction between the
mica surfaces, though we note that Horn et al ($\underline{12}$) have recently
presented data indicating <u>oscillating</u> forces between mica surfaces
in dried cyclohexane from which water had been thoroughly removed.
These oscillations disappeared, however, when the solvent was not
especially dried, in accord with the present observations. Polystyrene was then introduced into the cell to a concentration of

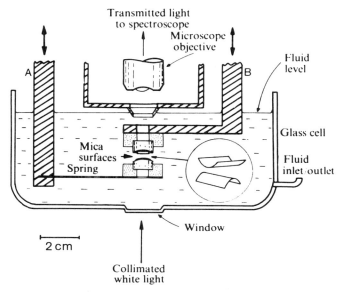

Figure 1.   Section of apparatus used to measure surface-surface forces between mica sheets.   (Reproduced with permission from reference 10, Copyright 1983, Royal Society of Chemistry).

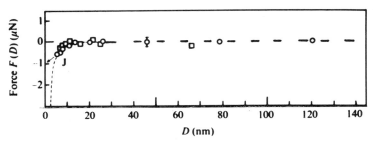

Figure 2.   Force between curved, bare mica surfaces (radius R) a distance D apart in Cyclohexane.   □, R = 0.35 cm.; 0, R = 0.66 cm.   Broken line is theoretical van der Waals attraction (see text).   (Reproduced with permission from reference 10, Copyright 1983, Royal Society of Chemistry).

7 ± 2 µg ml^{-1} and the surfaces left to incubate in the polymer
solution for some 10 hours, a long way apart (D $\simeq$ 3mm). Two
anionically polymerized polystyrene samples (Pressure Chemicals)
were used, PS1 (M_w = 6.10^5) and PS2 (M_w = 1.0 x 10^5. $M_w/M_n \leqslant 1.1$
for both polymers).
      Following incubation F(D) was measure (at 24° ± 2°C), and
the solution was then replaced by pure cyclohexane and F(D) measured again. The results are shown in figure 3, for PS1. Once
again there is little interaction between the surfaces as they
approach from a long way apart, but at around D $\simeq$ 60 nm an attraction is observed, which increases until the surfaces jump in
from the point A to a new equilibrium position at B. Further approach results in increasing repulsion as shown (also inset to
figure 3). On separation, the force decreases, becoming attractive again (F(D) < 0), until the surfaces jump apart from the
point C out to a new equilibrium position at E; further separation shows little interaction beyond E. Further compression-de-
compression cycles fully reproduced the above F v. D behaviour.
The jumps at A and C, as noted earlier, are due to instabilities,
and occur because at these points $\partial F(D)/\partial D \geqslant K$, the leaf-spring
constant. The refractive index n(D) of the medium separating the
mica surfaces, both before and after adsorption of polymer, was
also determined, and the results are shown in figure 4. Within
error n(D) does not change on replacing the polymer solution by
pure solvent, nor following several compression/decompression
cycles. This strongly indicates a quasi-irreversible adsorption
of the polymer onto the mica surfaces, in accord with independent
micro-balance experiments of polystyrene adsorption onto mica
(13). The value of the adsorbance Γ (for PS1) deduced from n(D)
is 6 ± 1 mg m^{-2} of mica surface, again in accord with independent
adsorbance measurements (13).
      The F(D) v. D profiles following incubation of PS2 (M = 10^5)
are not shown, but followed the same qualitative trend: no interaction down to D $\simeq$ 25 nm, when attraction set in, and finally,
on closer approach, a strong repulsive wall at D $\leqslant$ 6 nm.
      The main features of the force-distance profiles are i) an
effective extension δ from the surface of some 1.5 R_g for each adsorbed layer, where R_g is the unperturbed radius of gyration for
the respective polymers. These values of δ are comparable with
ellipsometric (14) and viscometric (15) studies of absorbed layer
thicknesses in various systems under Θ-conditions; ii) an initial attraction followed ultimately by a strong repulsion. This
may be understood by considering the interactions between opposing
segments as they come into overlap (10): in the poor solvent conditions (T = 24°C < Θ = 35°C) of the present investigation the osmotic interactions are attractive so long as the concentration of
overlapping segments is within the range of concentrations expected for the biphasic region, i.e. the range of concentrations for
which polystyrene in cyclohexane would flocculate. For PS1 at
24°C this corresponds to concentrations of up to 25% polymer (10):

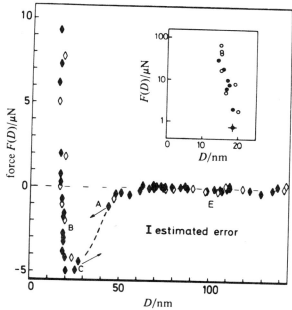

Figure 3   Force v. Distance D between curved mica surfaces
(R = 0.66 cm) following 10 hrs. incubation in PS1 solution at 24°C.
◇,0 - in solution;◆, ● - following replacement of solution by
pure cyclohexane. (Reproduced with permission from reference 10,
Copyright 1983, Royal Society of Chemistry).

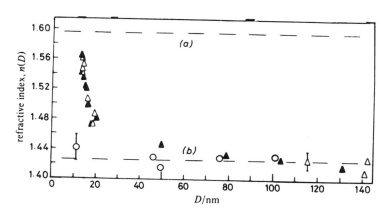

Figure 4.   Variation of refractive index n(D) of medium separating mica surfaces D apart. 0 - in pure cyclohexane; Δ-follow-
ing incubation in PS1 solution; ▲ - after replacing solution by
pure cyclohexane. (a) - n(bulk polystyrene); (b) - n(pure cyclohexane). (Reproduced with permission from reference 10, Copyright
1983, Royal Society of Chemistry).

for concentrations higher than this the osmotic interactions are
once again <u>repulsive</u>. Since the adsorption of polymer onto the
mica is essentially irreversible, compression of the surfaces
(i.e. reducing D) eventually increases the polymer concentration in
the gap beyond this limit, and the interaction changes from attraction to <u>repulsion</u>. Reference to the refractive index profile
n(D) shows that the mean polymer volume fraction in the gap for
D ~ 20 nm, i.e., at the point where the changeover begins from
attraction to repulsion (figure 3), is in fact about 25%, in support of the qualitative explanation above.

A more quantitative model for the form of the force-distance
profile between adsorbed polymer layers in poor solvent conditions,
based on the above ideas, has recently been presented by Pincus
and one of us (<u>16</u>). This is an approach (first described by De
Gennes (<u>17</u>) for the case of adsorbed polymers in good- and Θ-
solvents) whereby the excess free energy E(D) of adsorbed polymer
in the gap between two surfaces a distance D apart is calculated
with respect to the polymer segmental distribution across the
gap. By minimizing E(D) it is possible to deduce the equilibrium
segmental distribution and the value of E(D) for any D, and hence
the disjoining pressure $\pi d = - \partial E(D)/\partial D$. The predictions of
these calculations (<u>16</u>) are in good qualitative and quantitative
accord with the present results for $T < \Theta$.

Polystyrene in Cyclohexane at $T \geqslant \Theta$

By mounting a small heating element within the glass cell (figure
1) it becomes possible to heat the polymer solution, monitoring
the temperature via a small thermocouple close to the mica surfaces.
Because of the extreme sensitivity of the present approach to
changes in D, it is not practicable to <u>thermostat</u> the system, but
rather one allows a steady-state temperature to be reached, where
the power provided by the heating coil equals the heat losses
from the system. In this way sufficiently steady temperatures
may be attained over the time of the force measurements. Figure
5 shows the force-distance profile between layers of PS1 adsorbed
on mica: following overnight adsorption at room temperature F(D)
was measured at 23°C (curve (a), figure 5); the resulting profile
is very similar to that obtained previously (figure 3) under the
same conditions. The cell was then heated to 37.2°C and F(D)
was again measured (curve (b), Fig. 5). The resulting force-distance profile at the higher temperature still shows a persistent
(though considerably weaker) attractive region, of similar range
to the profile at room temperature (curve (a)). However, the
distance of closest approach on strongly compressing the surfaces
is now about half (6.5 nm) of its previous value (~ 12 nm) for an
equivalent compression. On re-cooling the system to room temperature, the behaviour indicated in curve (a) was recovered, and on
re-heating, curve (b) was again obtained.

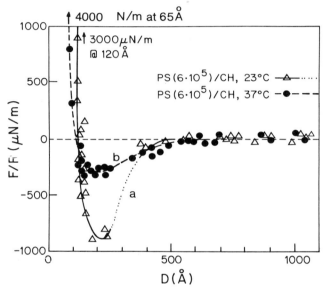

Figure 5.   F(D)/R v. distance D between mica surfaces bearing adsorbed PS1 layers, at 23°C and 37°C.   (Adapted from reference 18).

The persistent attraction between the adsorbed PS1 layers at
37.2°C (higher than the Θ-temperature for the system, 34.5°C) is
at first sight puzzling, in view of our previous interpretation
of the attraction at room temperature being due to osmotic effects
resulting from the T < Θ conditions. There are two possible explanations for this: the concept of a Θ-temperature derives from
a condition in free solution, when the net van der Waals atractions
between the segments of a polymer exactly 'compensate' the repulsive 'hard-core' excluded volume interactions. It may not be
justified to assume that the effective 'Θ-temperature' in the
close vicinity of a wall is identical to the bulk value (35°C),
and in that case one may need to increase the temperature beyond
the present value of 37°C in order to entirely eliminate osmotic
attraction effects (18). The other possibility is suggested by
the fact that the strong repulsive 'wall' at 37°C, at D ~ 6.5 nm,
(figure 5 curve (b)) is much closer in than at 23°C (figure 5
curve (a)). This implies some desorption of polymer has occurred
due to raising the temperature: qualitatively one may imagine
that such desorption has released surface binding sites on both
mica surfaces, and thus facilitated attractive 'bridging' effects
by adsorbed polymer across the inter-surface gap. In fact some
calculations by Scheujtens and Fleer (19) seem to predict such
attraction at T = Θ, but since their model assumes thermodynamic
equilibrium conditions (i.e. the surface-adsorbed polymer may exchange with a free polymer solution, so that complete desorption
at D = 0 is possible), and in fact predicts attraction even in
good solvent conditions, it is probably not appropriate in the
present case of irreversibly adsorbed polymer. A more promising
approach is via the generalized van der Waals approach used by
De Gennes (17), and Pincus and Klein (16), where the condition of
irreversible adsorption may be explicitly included.

Experimental support for the suggestion that depleted surface
layers result in attractive forces (at T ⩾ Θ) has come from recent
experiments (J.K. and Y.A., submitted) where mica surfaces partially covered by polystyrene in cyclopentane above the Θ-temperature show a clear mutual attraction, which disappears when full
surface coverage by the polymer is attained.

Polyethylene Oxide (PEO) in a Good Aqueous Solvent

The interaction between bare mica surfaces in 0.1 M KNO_3 (pH 5.5)
aqueous electrolyte is shown in figure 6a. The straight line
(curve (a)) indicated on the logarithmic-linear plot is in accord
with the exponential relation

$$F/R \propto \Theta^{-\kappa D} \qquad (3)$$

expected due to overlap of the electrostatic double-layers associated with the mica surfaces as they approach each other, where
κ is the Debye-Huckel parameter (9); the corresponding surface

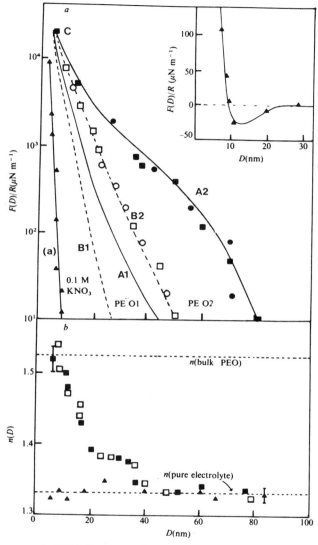

Figure 6.   a) F(D)/R v. D between mica surfaces in 0.1 M KNO₃ (▲) and following incubation in PEO1 and PEO2 solutions. ■/● - slow compression/slow decompression (also solid line). O/□ - rapid decompression/immediate recompression (also broken line). b) Refractive index n(D) of medium separating surfaces in 0.1 M KNO₃ (▲); ■ - following incubation in PEO1 solution, and subsequent replacement by pure electrolyte (□). (Reprinted with permission from reference 20, Copyright 1982, Macmillan Journals Ltd.).

potential   of the mica is about 100 mV. The inset shows the attractive well ('secondary minimum') at 10 nm $\leqslant$ D $\leqslant$ 20 nm, on a
linear-linear scale, where the van der Waals forces dominate the
interaction. This behaviour, as well as the values of κ ($9 \times 10^8 m^{-1}$)
and ψ, is similar to that previously reported for the same system
(9).

Polyethylene oxide (Toyo Soda, Japan) was added to the system to concentrations of 10 and 150 $\mu g\ ml^{-1}$, and allowed to incubate for 16 $\pm$ 2 hrs. Two samples were used: PEO1, M = 1.6 x
10^5, (Rg = 13 nm) and PEO2, M = 4 x 10^4 (Rg = 6.5 nm), both with
narrow molecular weight distributions (M_w/M_n $\leq$ 1.08). Figure
6(a) shows the force-distance profiles following adsorption of
the polymer. The behaviour on first approach following adsorption is indicated by solid lines A1 and A2, for PEO1 and PEO2
respectively; for the case of PEO2 experimental points are not
included, to avoid cluttering the figure. Little interaction
is detectable between the surfaces as they approach from a long
way away down to D $\simeq$ 80 nm and D $\simeq$ 45 nm for PEO1 and PEO2, respectively, when a monotonically increasing repulsion is observed,
down to D $\simeq$ 5 nm. (point C, figure 6a). Subsequent behaviour
depends on the <u>rate</u> of the compression/decompression cycles, but
may be summarized as follows:
i)   Compression of the surfaces after they had been apart for
      an hour or more followed the behaviour of the first-approach
      profiles A1, A2.
ii)   <u>Slow</u> decompression (taking $\geqslant$ 1/2 hour in moving outward
      from the point C), and subsequent compression, also fol-
      lowed the A curves.
iii) Rapid decompression (taking $\leqslant$ 5 min to move outward from C
      to where interaction was no longer detectable), and also
      immediate subsequent compression, followed the broken
      curves B1, B2.
For rates of compression or decompression intermediate to these,
the data fell in the region between the A and B lines. No <u>attrac-</u>
<u>tion</u> or <u>adhesion</u> between the PEO bearing mica surfaces was ob-
served (within error) in any of the experiments in the present
study.

The data of figure 6a is for an incubation concentration of
150 $\mu g\ ml^{-1}$ of the respective polymers, but is essentially unchanged for the lower (10 $\mu g\ ml^{-1}$) polymer concentrations, and
also following replacement of the solution by pure electrolyte.

The variation of refractive index n(D) of the medium separating the mica surfaces is shown in figure 6b (for PEO2), both
before and after adsorption of polymer, as well as following replacement of the polymer solution by pure electrolyte after adsorption. The results show that adsorption of the PEO is essentially irreversible, and that little polymer appears to desorb
either following compression/decompression cycles, or in pure
solvent. The value of the adsorbance Γ estimated from the n(D)
profiles is 4 $\pm$ 1.5 mg m^{-2} for both polymers.

The force-distance profiles A1, A2 appear to show the 're-laxed', or 'quasi-equilibrium' limit for the interaction between the mica plates bearing the PEO in the good solvent conditions of the present study. The adsorbed layer thicknesses δ are then about half the value of D at which onset of repulsion (A curves) is first noted. δ thus corresponds to some $3R_g$ for both poly-mers in the present investigation, a value comparable to that ob-tained for hydrodynamic layer thickness of PEO absorbed on latex particles in water, for similar molecular weights, from light scattering studies.

The repulsive interactions between the polymer-bearing mica surfaces are probably osmotic in origin, in the present good sol-vent conditions. An important feature in interpreting the results is the quasi-irreversible adsorption of the polymer: at the simplest level, one may assume that as the adsorbed layers come into overlap (with no desorption) the effective mean concentra-tion in the gap increases, with consequent increasing osmotic re-pulsion. This picture may be over simplified, as it is possible that, on compression, more polymer segments in the gap will ad-sorb at the surface, thereby reducing the total free energy and resulting in an attractive component in the interaction. In any case, equilibrium models of steric interactions (17, 19) (in which desorption can take place as D decreases) are not appro-priate for comparision with the present study, and in fact pre-dict attraction even in good solvent conditions. The calculations based on minimization of E(D) with respect to the segmental dis-tribution profile, noted earlier, can however be modified to the case of fixed adsorbance, and in this limit De Gennes has cal-culated (17) a repulsion at all overlap separations in a good solvent; a detailed comparison of the present results with his predictions will be presented elsewhere.

The effect of rapid withdrawal on the magnitude of the F(D) curves B — which is essentially to reduce the repulsive inter-action for a given D, relative to the quasi-equilibrium curves A — can be understood as follows: on compression (to the point C, figure 6a) more polymer segments are forced onto the mica sur-face, and do not have time to move off the surface during a rapid decompression. The net result is less segments in the gap (as opposed to segments actually in contact with the surface — the overall Γ, consisting of (surface + gap) segments, is unchanged) and hence a lower repulsive osmotic interaction, as observed.

Finally we note that our results differ from those reported by the Australian group (7), who measured F(D) between mica plates in an aqueous solution of a commercial resin of highly polydis-persed PEO. Their results indicated short- and long-time hysteret-ic effects as well as a continuous build up of adsorbed material (up to 1000 nm over 24 hrs.), and may be due to impurities in the sample they used (20).

Poly-L-lysine in aqueous salt solutions

The interactions between bare mica surfaces in 10^{-1} and 10^{-3} M KNO_3 solutions were determined at pH = 3.5. In both cases an exponential type relation $F(D) \propto \Theta^{-\kappa D}$ was indicated, with decay lengths $1/\kappa$ = 1.4 nm and 8 nm for the two salt concentrations, respectively, but with an effective surface potential $\psi \simeq 40$ mV, considerably lower than its value at the higher pH used in the PEO experiments (figure 6a, curve (a)). The lower value of ψ is probably the result of a lower net degree of ionization of the mica surface in the presence of the large H^+ concentration (the low pH was used to ensure full ionization and polyelectrolyte).

Poly-L-lysine, of $M_w = 9 \times 10^4$, $M_w/M_n \simeq 1.2$, and structure

$$\left\{ \begin{array}{c} \\ N - \overset{\displaystyle H}{\underset{\displaystyle |}{C}} - \overset{\displaystyle O}{\underset{\displaystyle }{C}} \\ | \\ (CH_2)_4 \\ | \oplus \\ NH_4 \end{array} \right\}_n$$

was obtained from Miles Yeda, and added to the cell to concentrations of 10 and 100 $\mu g\ ml^{-1}$ of polyelectrolyte; force-distance profiles were determined in the usual way following overnight (16 ± 2 hrs) incubation. Figure 7 shows the force-distance profiles between the mica surfaces in 10^{-1} m KNO_3 (pH 3.5) following incubation in 10 $\mu g\ ml^{-1}$ poly-L-lysine solution. The data is shown on a semi-log plot to allow inclusion of the large variation in $F(D)$, while the inset shows the interaction around $F \simeq 0$ on a linear scale. The broken line (figure 7) indicates the interactions prior to addition of polymer. Measurements commenced at a separation of D ~ 300 nm; within error, no forces were detected down to D ~ 120 nm when a monotonically increasing repulsion was observed. Log F(D) varied approximately linearly with D down to D ~ 100 nm (decay length ≃ 1.4 nm). At this separation the force profile 'levels out' (at least on a logarithmic scale), down to 5 nm when a steeper rise was again observed.

The F v. D profile measured on first approach was not reversible: on separating the surfaces F(D) dropped sharply, as shown, until for D ≳ 20 nm no further force could be detected. Subsequent compression and decompression of the surfaces gave rise to a reversible and reproducible force profile, figure 8, closely following that obtained on the first separation of the surfaces after the initial approach (figure 7). From figure 8 we note that the force decays approximately exponentially with D (decay length 1.5 nm). This short range repulsive interaction (figure 8) was time independent: in particular, overnight standing (16 hrs) of the surfaces following the first compression/decompression

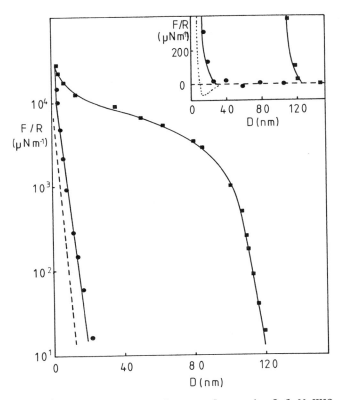

Figure 7. F/R v. D between mica surfaces in 0.1 M KNO_3 (broken or dotted line) and following incubation in poly-L-lysine solution. ■ - first approach, ● - first withdrawal. Inset — F/R v. D on linear scale.

cycle did not lead to a change in the profiles shown in figure 8.

The form of the force-distance profiles following incubation at the higher polyelectrolyte concentration (100 µg ml^{-1}) was the same (21) (within error) as that shown in figure 7 and 8. For the lower salt concentration, 10^{-3} M KNO$_3$, the general features of the F(D) v. D curves were similar to those in figures 7 and 8, except that the values for D for onset of interactions were generally larger, (D ≃ 140 nm), and the exponential decay of F(D) with D following the first approach was considerably slower (decay length ~ 10 nm). The range of interactions following compression in 10^{-3} M KNO$_3$ was also considerably further out at D ≃ 70 nm (compared with D ≃ 20 nm in 10^{-1} M KNO$_3$, figure 8) (21).

Refractive index measurements indicated an adsorbance of 2 ± 0.5 mg m^{-2} of the polymer onto the mica surfaces.

The main features of the results are (i) a long range repulsion on first approach, which varies exponentially with D in its initial stages, with a decay length close to the Debye-Huckel length 1/κ in the absence of polymer; (ii) an irreversible compression of the adsorbed layers following the first approach, resulting in a short range exponentially decaying repulsion with a decay length again quite close to 1/κ. These features suggest that the initial stages of the interaction are due to overlap of electrostatic double-layers associated with the adsorbed polyelectrolyte, followed by an irreversible 'steric' compression of the (initially extended) poly-L-lysine onto the mica surface to form a dense, tightly bound surface phase. The final form of the interaction (figure 8) following this irreversible compression also appears to be of the electrostatic double-layer overlap type (by comparing its decay length with 1/κ). The final 'squashed' state of the polyelectrolyte would appear to be the equilibrium one: the highly extended initial configuration prior to a first approach appears to be metastable, and may be prevented from reaching the equilibrium state by energy barriers associated with a net 'space-charge' within the original extended adsorbed layer.

Acknowledgments

We thank Professors S. F. Edwards, P. J. Flory, P. G. De Gennes, J. N. Israelachvili, P. Pincus, A. Silberberg and D. Tabor for useful discussions and comments. This work was supported in part by the United States-Israel Binational Science Foundation (BSF), Israel (Y.A.) and by the Science and Engineering Research Council, (U.K.).

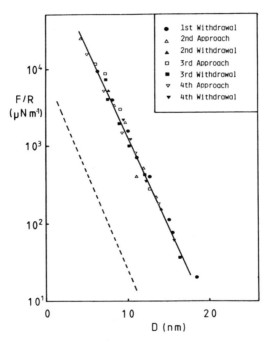

Figure 8.   F/R v. D following first approach after incubation
in poly-L-lysine solution (broken line - forces in absence of
polyelectrolyte).

Literature Cited

1. Vincent, B. Adv. Colloid Interface Sci. 1974, 4, 193.
2. "The Chemistry of Biosurfaces"; Hair, M., Ed.; Marcell Decker, New York, 1971.
3. Doroszkowski, A.; Lambourn, R. J. Colloid Interface Sci. 1973, 43, 97.
4. Cairns, R. J. R.; Ottewill, R. H.; Osmond, D. W.; Wagstaff, L. J. Colloid Interface Sci. 1976, 54, 45.
5. Lyklema, H.; Van Vliet, T. Faraday Disc. Chem. Soc. 1978, 65, 25.
6. Cain, F. W.; Ottewill, R. H.; Smitham, J. B. Faraday Disc. Chem. Soc. 1978, 65, 33.
7. Israelachvili, J. N.; Tandon, R. K.; White, L. R. J. Colloid Interface Sci. 1980, 78 432.
8. Tabor, D.; Winterton, R. H. S. Proc. Roy. Soc. London 1969, A312, 435.
9. Israelachvili, J. N.; Adams, G. E. JCS Faraday 1 1978, 74, 975.
10. Klein, J. JCS Faraday 1, 1983, 79, 99.
11. Derjaguin, B. V. Kolloid Zh. 1934, 69, 155.
12. Horn, R. G.; Israelachvili, J. N. J. Chem. Phys. 1981, 75, 1400.
13. Terashima, H.; Klein, J.; Luckham, P. in "Adsorption from Solution"; Ottewill, R. H.; Rochester, C. H., Eds.; Academic, London, 1982.
14. Stromberg, R. R.; Tutas, D. J.; Passaglia, E. J. J. Phys. Chem. 1965, 69, 3955.
15. Rowland, F.; Bulas, R.; Rotstein, E.; Eirich, F. Ind. Eng. Chem. 1965, 57, 49.
16. Klein, J.; Pincus, P. Macromolecules 1982, 15, 1129.
17. De Gennes, P. G. Macromolecules 1982, 15, 429.
18. Israelachvili, J. N.; Tirrell, M.; Klein, J.; Almog, Y. Macromolecules - submitted.
19. Scheutjens, J. M. H. M.; Fleer, G. J. Adv. Colloid Interface Sci. 1982, 16, 361.
20. Klein, J.; Luckham, P. Nature, 1982, 300, 429.
21. Luckham, P.; Klein, J. JCS Faraday 1 - submitted.

RECEIVED October 7, 1983

The Stability of Dispersions of Hard Spherical Particles in the Presence of Nonadsorbing Polymer

G. J. FLEER and J. H. M. H. SCHEUTJENS—Laboratory for Physical and Colloid Chemistry, Agricultural University, De Dreijen 6, 6703 BC Wageningen, The Netherlands

B. VINCENT—School of Chemistry, University of Bristol, Cantock's Close, Bristol BS8 1TS, England

We present an improved model for the flocculation of a dispersion of hard spheres in the presence of non-adsorbing polymer. The pair potential is derived from a recent theory for interacting polymer near a flat surface, and is a function of the depletion thickness. This thickness is of the order of the radius of gyration in dilute polymer solutions but decreases when the coils in solution begin to overlap. Flocculation occurs when the osmotic attraction energy, which is a consequence of the depletion, outweighs the loss in configurational entropy of the dispersed particles. Our analysis differs from that of De Hek and Vrij with respect to the dependence of the depletion thickness on the polymer concentration (i.e., we do not consider the polymer coils to be hard spheres) and to the stability criterion used (binodal, not spinodal phase separation conditions).

Comparison of our theory with experimental data shows excellent agreement, both with respect to the molecular weight dependency and to the effect of particle radius and particle concentration.

Our model predicts restabilisation at very high polymer concentrations. It is shown that this restabilisation is a thermodynamic effect, resulting from a decreased interparticle attraction, and is not kinetically determined, as proposed by Feigin and Napper.

In recent years much attention has been paid to the stability of colloids in the presence of free, nonadsorbing polymers. It is generally found that at relatively low polymer concentrations

0097-6156/84/0240-0245$06.00/0

destabilisation of colloidal dispersions occurs (1-8). In some
instances restabilisation at high polymer concentrations has been
reported (1-5). So far, this restabilisation has only been observed for "soft" particles, i.e., particles carrying anchored polymer chains.

Several theoretical models have been proposed to explain
these phenomena. The first crude model is due to Vincent et al.
(3). It applies specifically to soft spheres and discusses the
flocculation in terms of interpenetration of free polymer coils
with the polymer sheaths surrounding the particles. Beyond a certain polymer concentration, the interpenetration of two polymer
sheaths is easier than the mutual interpenetration of free polymer and attached polymer, resulting in attraction between the
soft particles.

The other approaches are all based on the concept of depletion of chain polymers near a nonadsorbing hard surface, leading
to an osmotic attraction between two particles when two such
depletion layers overlap. Joanny et al. (9) used scaling arguments to predict qualitatively that phase separation may occur
if the distance between the particles becomes smaller than the
so-called correlation length. Feigin and Napper (10, 11) presented a more sophisticated model accounting for the segment profile
in the depletion layer, and predicted not only the destabilisation
but also the restabilisation. The latter phenomenon is, in their
model, associated with an energy barrier and is, therefore, a kinetic effect which does not correspond to thermodynamic stability.
De Hek and Vrij (6) developed a model for a mixture of hard dispersed particles and hard (but mutually permeable) polymer
spheres and predicted phase separation conditions at the spinodal
point, in terms of the second virial coefficient of the particles.
Finally, Sperry (12) used a very simple geometric model for the
calculation of the osmotic force between two particles. Both the
treatments of De Hek and Vrij and of Sperry are based on an earlier model by Asakura and Oosawa (13).

In this paper, we present the outline of a general approach
for the interaction of hard spheres in the presence of nonadsorbing polymer. The pair potential is derived from a recent lattice
theory for interacting polymer near a surface (14-16). Preliminary results for two hard plates in a polymer solution have been
reported previously (17). Here we extend these results to the
interaction between hard spheres. The depletion thickness turns
out to be of the order of the radius of gyration in dilute polymer solutions, but decreases when the chains in solution begin to
overlap. Qualitatively, this behaviour agrees with the findings
of the scaling theory (9). Our model gives a simple analytical
expression for the depletion thickness and the pair potential between two hard spheres. For dilute polymer solutions, the pair
potential resembles closely that used by De Hek and Vrij (6) (and,
for that matter, that of Sperry (12)) but our theory calculates
the phase separation concentration for binodal, rather than spino-

dal conditions. For reversible flocculation, the binodal criterion
should be applied. Excellent agreement is found between the new
theory and the measurements of De Hek and Vrij (6). Moreover, the
present model also predicts a thermodynamic restabilisation at
very high polymer concentrations. Extension of the theory to soft
particles is, in principle, possible but the numerical data are,
as yet, lacking. Qualitatively, it may be expected that restabilisation for soft spheres occurs at lower polymer concentrations
than for hard spheres.

Interaction between two hard plates

The principle of depletion is illustrated in Figure 1. If a surface is in contact with a polymer solution of volume fraction ϕ_*,
there is a depletion zone near the surface where the segment concentration is lower than in the bulk of the solution due to conformational entropy restrictions that are, for nonadsorbing polymers, not compensated by an adsorption energy. The effective
thickness of the depletion layer is Δ. Below we will give a more
precise definition for Δ.

When two plates are at a separation H which is much larger
than 2Δ, the depletion layers do not overlap, the concentration
halfway the plates equals ϕ_*, and the interaction energy is zero
(Figure 1, a). If, on the other hand, H $<<$ 2Δ, the conformational
restrictions are such that there is no polymer between the plates
(Figure 1, b) and the osmotic pressure of the solution drives the
plates together. An equivalent description is that, upon decrease
of H, solvent is transferrred from the gap between the plates
(pure solvent) towards the solution, thereby decreasing the free
energy of the system. Each solvent molecule going from pure solvent to the solution contributes a free energy change μ^o, the
solvent chemical potential, which is negative. Note that μ^o is
defined as the chemical potential of solvent in the polymer solution with respect to the reference state (pure solvent). In the
region where there is no polymer between the plates the decrease
in H is proportional to the number of solvent molecules which are
transferred. When the plates are brought closer over a distance
dH, the number of solvent molecules leaving the gap per unit area
of the plates equals dH/v^o, where v^o is the molecular volume of
the solvent. Hence, in this region the free energy per unit area,
Δf_p, is linear in H with slope $-\mu^o/v^o$, which is the osmotic pressure.

The interpretation of Δ becomes clearer when two plates,
originally at very small distance from each other, are separated.
At a certain separation, equal to 2Δ, polymer penetrates into the
gap. In dilute solutions, where the chains behave as individual
coils, Δ is expected to be of the order or r_g, the radius of
gyration. However, at concentrations where the coils overlap,
the osmotic pressure of the solution becomes so high that
narrower gaps can be entered, and Δ becomes smaller than r_g.

These qualitative conclusions are verified by numerical calculations based upon a previously described lattice model which
involves a matrix procedure to account for all possible conformations of the chains (16, 17). (Note: In Ref. 17 a wrong expression
was given for the free energy of interaction. Not the excess Gibbs
surface free energy F^σ should be used for the computation of Δf_p,
but the Gibbs free energy F of the system, leading to $\Delta f_p = \gamma A$,
where γ is the surface tension and A the area per site. For more
details we refer to the errata to Ref. 17, submitted to Adv.
Colloid Interface Sci.)

Some numerical results are given in Figures 2 and 3. Distances in these figures are expressed in units of 1, the lattice step
length. As can be seen in Figure 2, the attraction energy Δf_p is
linear for small H, and to a good approximation this linearity
persists up to $H = 2\Delta$. For $H > 2\Delta$, Δf_p is essentially zero. As
discussed above, the slope of Δf_p versus H equals $-\mu^o/v^o$ or, for
the lattice model, $-\mu^o/1^3$. Hence, the concentration halfway between the plates, as a function of H, may be considered as a step
function, being zero for $H < 2\Delta$ and equal to ϕ_* for $H > 2\Delta$. We
note that the barriers at relatively high values for H which we
reported in Ref. 17 are still present, but they are completely
negligible on the scale used in Figure 2, and are so small that
they will have no effect on the particle interaction for colloidal
particles in the usual size range. Feigin and Napper (10, 11) calculated from their model much higher barriers, and considered them
to be responsible for the (kinetic) restabilisation.

We may now write the interaction energy between two plates
as:

$$H \leqslant 2\Delta \qquad \Delta f_p(H) = -(\mu^o/v^o)(H - 2\Delta)$$

$$H \geqslant 2\Delta \qquad \Delta f_p(H) = 0 \tag{1}$$

The solvent chemical potential is taken to be that given by the
Flory-Huggins expression (18):

$$\mu^o/kT = \phi_*(1 - 1/x) + \ln(1 - \phi_*) + \chi\phi_*^2 \tag{2}$$

Here k and T have their usual meaning, x is the ratio between the
molecular volumes of a polymer chain and a solvent molecule and
χ is the polymer-solvent interaction parameter.
For $H = 0$, Equation 1 reduces to

$$\Delta f_p(0) = 2\mu^o\Delta/v^o \tag{3}$$

With increasing ϕ_*, $-\mu^o$ increases, whilst Δ is constant at low ϕ_*
(and of the order of r_g) but decreases at higher ϕ_*. The variation
of Δf_p with ϕ_* depends therefore on the variation in the product
$\mu^o\Delta$.

Numerical results for the dependency of Δ on ϕ_* are given in

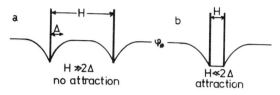

Figure 1. Illustration of depletion effects for two plates in a solution of nonadsorbing polymer of volume fraction ϕ_*. Δ is the depletion thickness.

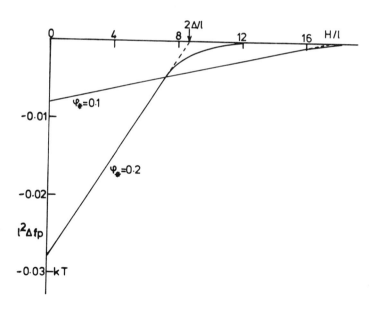

Figure 2. Attraction energy per surface site due to depletion as a function of the plate separation, for two polymer concentrations. The distance is expressed in lattice units (step length 1). $r = 1000$, $\chi = 0.5$, hexagonal lattice.

Figure 3 for four chain lengths, expressed as the number of segments per chain, r. As expected, in dilute solutions Δ is independent of ϕ_*. In this dilute regime, Δ is approximately proportional to the square root of the chain length; for not too short
chains $\Delta/1 = 0.56 \ (\sqrt{r} - 2)$, which is of the order of $r_g/1$. Note
that for a random flight chain $r_g/1 = \sqrt{r/6} = 0.41 \ \sqrt{r}$, and a
lattice chain is expected to be slightly more expanded.

If the chains in solution begin to overlap, Δ decreases.
A rough measure for the overlap concentration ϕ_{ov} is that volume
fraction of polymer at which close-packed spheres with radius r_g
just touch. Then $\phi_{ov} = 0.74 \ r1^3/(4\pi r_g^3/3)$. Taking $r_g \simeq \Delta(\phi_* \to 0) \simeq$
0.56 $1\sqrt{r}$, we find that $\phi_{ov} \simeq 1.03/\sqrt{r}$. This value of ϕ_{ov} is indicated in Figure 3 by the arrows. Indeed the decrease of Δ starts
if ϕ_* becomes comparable with ϕ_{ov}. At higher concentrations, Δ
becomes increasingly independent of chain length, until in pure
bulk polymer ($\phi_* = 1$) $\Delta = 0$, as expected.

We have been able to derive an approximate analytical expression for Δ as a function of ϕ_* which describes the curves shown
in Figure 3 quite accurately over nearly the whole concentration
range, from dilute solutions up to $\phi_* \simeq 0.6$. The derivation is
based upon the greatest eigenvalue of the matrix which, in the
case of nonadsorbing long chains at low concentrations between
the plates, is easily computed (19). We will report the derivation elsewhere and give here only the result, which in the present
context may be considered as an empirical expression:

$$\sin^2 \frac{\pi/2}{2\Delta/1+1} = \frac{2}{r} - \ln(1 - \phi_*) - 2\chi\phi_* \qquad (4)$$

Equation 4 applies for solvency conditions which are not too far
removed from theta-solvents ($\chi = 0.5$). The term $2/r$ is approximate
and applies only in the limit of large r. For smaller r this term
is slightly higher. Using a fitting procedure, the set of curves
in Figure 3, for $\phi_* < 0.6$, could be reproduced to within 1% for Δ
if the first term of the right hand side of Equation 4 is actually
taken to be $(1.95/r)(1 + 2.84/\sqrt{r})$. For application purposes we
will use the simpler form given in Equation 4.

In the limits $\Delta \gg 1$ and $\phi_* \ll 1$, and for $\chi = \frac{1}{2}$, Equation 4
takes the form

$$\frac{\Delta}{1} = \frac{\pi}{4\sqrt{2}} \left[\frac{1}{r} + \frac{1}{4}\phi_*^2 \right]^{-\frac{1}{2}} \simeq \frac{\pi}{4\sqrt{2}} (\phi_{ov}^2 + \phi_*^2/4)^{-\frac{1}{2}} \qquad (5)$$

For $\phi_* \ll \phi_{ov}$, $\Delta = (\pi/4\sqrt{2})1\sqrt{r} = 0.56 \ 1\sqrt{r}$, which is close to r_g,
as discussed above. On the other hand, if $\phi_* \gg \phi_{ov}$, $\Delta/1$ becomes
independent of r because the r^{-1}-term in Equations 5 and 4 is negligible.

Interaction between two hard spheres

A commonly used approximation for transforming the interaction energy between plates (Δf_p) into that between two spheres (Δf_s) is that due to Deryagin (20):

$$\Delta f_s(H) = \pi a \int_0^H \Delta f_p(H) dH \qquad (6)$$

where a is the radius of the spheres. For the moment, we are only interested in $\Delta f_s(0)$ because we want to compare the free energy of a pair of particles at large distance to that of particles in a floc, where they are in close contact. Substituting Equation 1 into Equation 6:

$$\Delta f_s(0) = \frac{2\pi a}{v^o} \mu^o \Delta^2 \qquad (7)$$

The Deryagin approximation is only valid if $\Delta \ll a$. This condition is not always met in experiments with small particles and high molecular weight polymer. If $\Delta f_p(H)$ is obtained using a step function, as in Equation 1, a correction factor may be derived from geometric considerations (Figure 4). When two particles come into close contact, the depletion volume is reduced, as indicated by the hatched region in Figure 4, by an amount $V_{ov} = 2\pi a \Delta^2 (1 + 2\Delta/3a)$. Hence, when two spheres approach each other from large H to H = 0, the number of solvent molecules transferred to the solution equals V_{ov}/v^o, contributing a net decrease in the free energy, given by

$$\Delta f_s(0) = \frac{2\pi a}{v^o} \mu^o \Delta^2 (1 + \frac{2}{3}\frac{\Delta}{a}) \qquad (8)$$

Equation 8 was also applied by Sperry (12), although the underlying assumptions are different in his model. There is also a close analogy between Equation 8 and the pair potential used by De Hek and Vrij. Indeed, Equation 4 of Ref. 6 reduces to our Equation 8 for H = 0, provided that 2Δ is interpreted as the hard sphere diameter of the polymer molecule. Hence, in dilute solutions (where $\Delta \simeq r_g$) the two approaches are very similar. However, in our model Δ is a function of the polymer concentration. Because most experimental depletion studies are carried out at values for ϕ_* that are comparable in magnitude to ϕ_{ov}, our model is more general.

Phase separation of hard spheres

According to Equation 8, two spheres in a solution of nonadsorbing polymer attract each other. The magnitude of the attraction depends on μ^o (or the osmotic pressure) and on Δ, both factors being a function of ϕ_*. At low ϕ_*, Δ is constant and μ^o is proportional to the polymer concentration, so that $-\Delta f_s$ increases linearly with ϕ_*. In more concentrated solutions, $-\mu^o$ increases more strongly with ϕ_* due to higher order terms in ϕ_*, and Δ decreases. Since for spheres Δf_s is proportional to Δ^2, the decrease in Δ as a function of ϕ_* is more important than for plates.

The crucial question is: at what value of ϕ_* is the attraction high enough to induce phase separation? De Hek and Vrij (6) assume that the critical flocculation concentration is equivalent to the phase separation condition defined by the spinodal point. From the pair potential between two hard spheres in a polymer solution they calculate the second virial coefficient B_2 for the particles, and derive from the spinodal condition that if $B_2 = 1/2\phi_d$ (where ϕ_d is the volume fraction of particles in the dispersion) phase separation occurs. For a system in thermodynamic equilibrium, two phases coexist if the chemical potential of the hard spheres is the same in the dispersion and in the floc phase (i.e., the binodal condition).

We consider the change in free energy if one hard-sphere particle is transferred from the dispersion to the floc phase. We can distinguish two contributions to this free energy of transfer. One is the contribution due to depletion, designated as Δf_d, which is negative and, for small Δ/a, proportional to $\Delta f_s(0)$ as given above for a pair of particles; the proportionality constant is a function of the geometry of the floc and the ratio Δ/a and will be considered in more detail below. The other contribution is positive and originates from the difference Δs_s in configurational entropy of a particle in a floc as compared to that in the dispersion (2, 3). Clearly, Δs_s is negative. Phase separation conditions may therefore be defined through the relation

$$\Delta f_d - T\Delta s_s = 0 \tag{9}$$

In this analysis, we will disregard other interparticle forces, such as Van der Waals attraction and electrostatic repulsion, although, in principle, such contributions could be included.

As stated above, Δf_d is related to the contact pair potential $\Delta f_s(0)$. In a floc, each particle is in close contact with z other particles. If Δ/a is small, the z lens-shaped overlap volumes (see Figure 4) surrounding each particle do not overlap with each other, and Δf_d equals $z\Delta f_s(0)/2$ where $\Delta f_s(0)$ is given by Equation 8. For higher values of Δ/a, the lenses overlap partly, and $\Delta f_d < z\Delta f_s(0)/2$. Above a certain value of Δ/a (which depends on the packing of the particles in the floc), there is no polymer left within the interstices of the floc and all the solvent in the floc is within a distance Δ from the surface of at least one particle. Then the volume of solvent which is transferred towards the solution when a particle is added to the floc is readily calculated. In the dispersion, the depletion volume per particle is $(4\pi/3) \{(a + \Delta)^3 - a^3\}$. In the floc, the volume of solvent per particle is $(4\pi/3)a^3\phi_f/(1 - \phi_f)$, where ϕ_f is the volume fraction of particles in the floc phase. The difference between these two volumes is the amount of solvent which contributes to Δf_d. On the

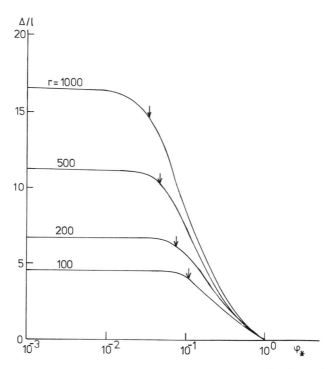

Figure 3.   Depletion thickness Δ for four chain lengths as a function of polymer concentration. The arrows indicate the solution concentration where the polymer coils begin to overlap. $\chi = 0.5$, hexagonal lattice.

Figure 4. Overlap of depletion zones. The hatched region corresponds to the volume of solvent that is transferred when two particles of radius a and depletion thickness Δ come into close contact.

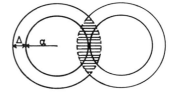

basis of these geometric arguments, we can write

$$\Delta f_d = (z\pi a/v^o) \; \mu^o \Delta^2 \; g(\Delta/a) \tag{10}$$

where g is a geometric factor depending on Δ/a. For a pair of
particles $g = (2/z)(1 + 2\Delta/3a)$. For a floc, an expression for g
can be written down for two ranges of Δ/a:

$$\Delta/a < 0.41 \qquad g(\Delta/a) = 1 + 2\Delta/3a \tag{11a}$$

$$\Delta/a > 0.73 \qquad g(\Delta/a) = \frac{4}{3z}(\frac{a}{\Delta})^2 \{(1 + \frac{\Delta}{a})^3 - \frac{1}{\phi_f}\} \tag{11b}$$

The limits ($\sqrt{2}-1$, $\sqrt{3}-1$) for Δ/a as given in Equation 11 apply
only to a floc in which the particles are arranged in a simple
cubic lattice. For different packings, the limits would be
different, e.g. $\sqrt{2}-1$, $\sqrt{8/3}-1$ for a face-centered cubic lattice
($z = 8$), and $\sqrt{4/3}-1$, $\sqrt{3/2}-1$ for a hexagonal lattice ($z = 12$).
    For the range $0.41 < \Delta/a < 0.73$, g cannot be readily derived.
Fortunately, a simple interpolation is possible, as can be seen
in Figure 5, where g, as given by Equation 11, is plotted as a
function of Δ/a, for $z = 6$ and $\phi_f = 0.52$. It is clear that we
obtain a reasonable approximation for g if we extend the range of
Equation 11a to 0.55, and assume g to be constant above that
value:

$$\Delta/a < 0.55 \qquad g(\Delta/a) = 1 + 2\Delta/3a \tag{12a}$$

$$0.55 < \Delta/a \lesssim 2 \qquad g(\Delta/a) \simeq 1.37 \tag{12b}$$

Obviously, Equation 12b has to be modified somewhat for different
floc packings. However, in this approximate treatment, we only
wish to investigate trends, and for that purpose a simple cubic
arrangement suffices.
    The next problem is to find an expression for Δs_s. This
entropy difference is a function of the particle volume fractions
in the dispersion (ϕ_d) and in the floc (ϕ_f). As a first approximation, we assume that Δs_s is independent of the concentration
and chain length of free polymer. This assumption is not necessarily true: the floc structure, and thus ϕ_f, may depend on the
latter parameters because also the solvent chemical potential in
the solution (affected by the presence of polymer) should be the
same as that in the floc phase (determined by the high particle
concentration). However, we assume that these effects will be
small, and we take ϕ_f as a constant.
    Vincent et al.(3) used a simplified configurational entropy
term $\Delta s_s = -k \ln(\phi_f/\phi_d)$. For a dilute dispersion, the $\ln \phi_d$ term
is probably correct, but for the floc phase, with ϕ_f of the order
of 0.5, a term $\ln \phi_f$ certainly can overestimate the entropy in the
floc, because hard spheres with finite volume have at high concentration much less translational freedom than (volumeless) point

particles. Then more elaborate models, such as those of Percus-
Yevick (21) and/or Carnahan-Starling (22), giving a higher value
for $-\Delta s_s$, should be applied. For the purpose of this paper, however, we shall not consider these more elaborate models, and will
simply assume that Δs_s may be written as

$$-\Delta s_s = C_f + k \ln(\phi_f/\phi_d) \tag{13}$$

where C_f is positive and is constant for a given polymer/particle
system at any ϕ_* and ϕ_d, being a function of ϕ_f only.

In order to illustrate the main features of the model, a plot
of Δf_d vs ϕ_* for two chain lengths is shown in Figure 6. In this
case, Equation 10 was applied with g = 1, neglecting the correction as given in Equation 11. For $\Delta/1$ the numerical values given
in Figure 2 were used, and $z\pi a/1$ was taken to be 500, representa-
tive of a particle diameter of the order of 100 nm.

At low ϕ_* the attraction increases more or less linearly
with ϕ_*, but $-\Delta f_d$ passes through a maximum around $\phi_* = 0.6$ and
decreases again at still higher ϕ_*. This behaviour can be understood from the concentration dependence of μ^o and Δ. The linearity of Δf_d at low ϕ_* persists somewhat longer than that in $-\mu^o$
because of (partial) compensation of the upward trend in $-\mu^o$ and
the downward trend in Δ. For higher concentrations, the decrease
in Δ^2 is stronger than the increase in $-\mu^o$, causing $-\Delta f_d$ to become smaller again at very high ϕ_*.

The behaviour of Δf_d (or Δf_s) for $\phi_* \to 1$ (bulk polymer)
deserves some special attention. From the numerical data, Δf_p
for plates reaches a nonzero limit. Such a limit is easily understood from a physical point of view: even if the thickness of the
depletion layer is zero in bulk polymer, it is unfavourable for
polymer chains to enter the gap between the two plates due to
conformational entropy restrictions. Obviously, the same effect
occurs for spherical particles: two particles in bulk polymer
still attract each other. In our step function approximation,
where Δf_s in supposed to be proportional to $\mu^o \Delta^2$, Δf_s approaches
zero for extremely low solvent concentrations because the decrease
in Δ^2 is stronger than the increase in $-\mu^o$. However, the step
function breaks down for $\phi_* \to 1$, the 'tail' in Figure 2 becoming
non-neglibible for very high polymer concentrations. Therefore,
the data for Δf_d very close to $\phi_* = 1$, as given in Figure 6, are
not reliable.

The chain length dependence of Δf_d is small at very low ϕ_*
since under those conditions $-\mu^o \sim r^{-1}$ and $\Delta^2 \sim r$. At higher ϕ_*,
the attraction is stronger for longer chains due to the nonideal
terms in μ^o (even in a Θ-solvent), at still higher concentrations
of polymer the effect of chain length on Δf_p is again weaker be-
casue Δ decreases with increasing ϕ_*, this decrease starting at
lower ϕ_* for longer chains. However, an additional chain length
dependence is introduced through the correction term $1 + 2\Delta/3a$
(not included in Figure 6). In very concentrated solutions both
μ^o and Δ (and, thus, Δf_d) are independent of r.

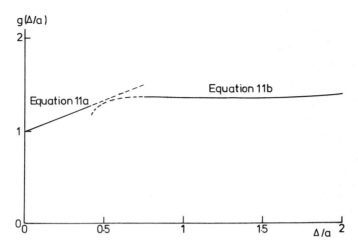

Figure 5. Plot of the geometric factor $g(\Delta/a)$ as given by Equation 11, for a simple cubic lattice ($z = 6$, $\phi_f = 0.52$). In the range for Δ/a where Equations 11a and 11b apply, solid curves are drawn.

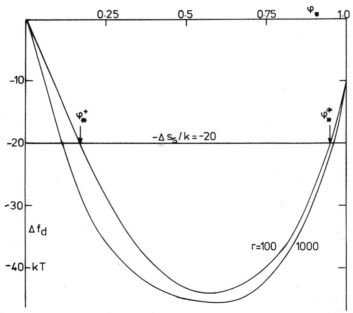

Figure 6. Comparison between the attraction energy per particle Δf_d and the entropy loss per particle $(-\Delta s_s)$ when a particle is transferred from the dispersion towards the floc phase. The dispersion is stable if $\phi_* < \phi_*^+$ or $\phi_* > \phi_*^\ddagger$, flocculation will occur for $\phi_*^+ < \phi_* < \phi_*^\ddagger$. In this figure, $g(\Delta/a)$ was taken to be 1 and $z\pi a/l$ to be 500.

In order to understand the implications of our model for dispersion stability, we have to compare Δf_d with Δs_s, according to Equation 9. In Figure 5 a horizontal line is drawn correspon- ding to $-\Delta s_s/k = 20$. If only the term $\ln(\phi_f/\phi_d)$ in Equation 13 would contribute to Δs_s, this value would correspond to ϕ_d of the order of 10^{-8}, but for a concentrated floc phase ($\phi_f \sim 0.5$) c_f/k is presumably several units, so that $-\Delta s/k = 20$ is probably repre- sentative for ϕ_d in the range $\sim 10^{-4}$.

Now we can readily deduce the stability/instability condi- tions from Figure 6. For $\phi_* < \phi_*^+$ the attraction is too weak to overcome the particle entropy loss and the dispersion is stable. In the range $\phi_*^+ < \phi_* < \phi_*^\ddagger$ the dispersion is unstable, and for $\phi_* > \phi_*^\ddagger$ the depletion effect is again too small to induce floccu- lation. The flocculation limit ϕ_*^+ depends on the chain length, the restabilisation concentration $\phi_*^\ddagger$ only slightly. The instabili- ty region becomes wider (lower ϕ_*^+, higher $\phi_*^\ddagger$) with increasing particle radius (because $\Delta f_d \sim a$) and increasing particle concen- tration (decreasing $-\Delta s_s$). For very small particles or extremely low ϕ_d, $-\Delta s_s$ is so high that the horizontal line in Figure 5 shifts beyond the minimum in Δf_d, and the dispersion is thermody- namically stable over the whole polymer concentration range. Such behaviour has been observed experimentally (3).

An important conclusion of this discussion is the fact that at very high ϕ_* thermodynamic stability is re-established. Resta- bilisation is not a kinetic effect, as suggested by Feigin and Napper (10, 11), but is a consequence of lower free energy of the dispersion as compared to the floc. This conclusion is supported by experimental evidence for soft spheres (3, 5, 23). We should add, however, that for hard spheres $\phi_*^\ddagger$ is so high that experimen- tal verification is difficult for most polymer-solvent systems due to the high viscosity of the solution.

Comparison with experiment

The only experimental data available to date for a system of hard spheres in a polymer solution are those of De Hek and Vrij (6). We shall restrict considerations to the data obtained under Θ-conditons, for silica and polystyrene (PS) in cyclohexane (at 34.5°C). For our interpretation of these data, we use Equation 9 as the stability criterion and Equations 10 and 12 for Δf_d. The quantities μ^o and Δ are given by Equations 2 and 4, respectively. We use Δs_s as an adjustable parameter for which an estimate will be obtained from the experimental data; its magnitude should be consistent with Equation 13.

Before we can apply our model, we have to assign values to the parameters x in Equation 2 and r and 1 in Equation 4. The quantity x is simply defined as $\rho_o M/\rho_p M_o$, where ρ_o and ρ_p are the densities of cyclohexane and PS, respectively, and M_o and M their respective moleculair weights. The choice for r and 1 is less straightforward because it implies a comparison of the properties of a real chain and a lattice chain, a point which invariably arises when theoretical results from a lattice theory are compared with experimental data. We apply the condition, also used above, that $\Delta(\phi_* \to 0) \simeq r_g \simeq 0.56 \; 1\sqrt{r}$. Then the term $2/r$ in Equation 4 can be replaced by $0.63 \; 1^2/r_g^2$, and the only choice to be made is that for 1. Fortunately, the actual choice for this parameter is not very important, since from Equation 4, giving a relation between $\Delta/1$ and $r_g/1$, a value of Δ/r_g is found that is independent of 1 in the limit of high M and low ϕ_*, and the experimental conditions are close to this limit. We chose $1 = 1.5$ nm, since this value gives the most constant parameter C (see Equation 15, below). However, the actual value for 1 does not affect the results strongly.

For the purpose of interpreting the data we write Equation 9, after substitution of Equation 10, in the form

$$(-\mu^o/kT)\Delta^2 g(\Delta/a) = C \tag{14}$$

where C is given by

$$C = \frac{-\Delta s_s}{k} \frac{v^o}{\pi z a} \tag{15}$$

For a given particle concentration and particle radius, C should be a constant. In Table I we compile the results for three sets of data for hard spheres. We use the same notation as in Ref. 4. The particle radii are 21 nm for S6 and 46 nm for SB1, respectively; the particle concentrations are 1% or 5% (w/v).

Table I. Comparison of experimental data of De Hek and Vrij (6) with the present model

	r_g/nm	ϕ_*^+(expt.)	$-10^6\mu^o/kT$	Δ/nm	$10^3 C/nm^2$	ϕ_*^+(calc.)
S6, 1%	2.7	0.082	1352	1.82	4.71	0.086
(a=21 nm)	5.7	0.048	190	4.79	5.03	0.048
	10.8	0.035	45.5	9.68	5.58	0.0325
	11.85	0.031	32.9	10.72	5.06	0.0303
	41.3	0.017	2.68	37.06	5.01	0.0170
SB1, 1%	2.7	0.042	618	1.83	2.13	0.0395
(a=46 nm)	5.7	0.025	84.4	4.85	2.13	0.0237
	8.6	0.0199	30.5	7.72	2.01	0.0200
	11.85	0.0165	13.6	10.92	1.88	0.0173
	24	0.0126	2.92	22.7	2.00	0.0126
	41.3	0.0115	1.20	38.7	2.49	0.0101
SB1, 5%	2.7	0.038	555	1.99	1.92	0.032
(a=46 nm)	5.7	0.0217	72.1	4.99	1.82	0.0193
	8.6	0.0168	24.95	7.85	1.66	0.0163
	11.85	0.014	11.17	11.05	1.55	0.0144
	24	0.0099	2.09	22.8	1.45	0.0107
	41.3	0.0082	0.679	39.2	1.45	0.0087

The first two columns of Table I are taken from Ref. 4, μ^o was
calculated from Equation 2, Δ from Equation 4 and C from Equation
14, using Equation 12 for $g(\Delta/a)$. In each series, C turns out to
be approximately constant, and for the 1% dispersions does not
deviate by more than a few per cent from the average value. This
is gratifying since μ^o varies over 3 decades and r_g by a factor
of 15. Only for the 5% dispersion does there seem to be a slight,
but systematic downward trend in the values for C. This decrease
is probably related to the assumption that Δs_s is independent of
the presence of the polymer. If such a dependency does exist,
the effects would show up more strongly for lower values of $-\Delta s_s$,
i.e., for higher dispersion concentrations.

The (rounded) averages for C in the three series of measure-
ments are 5×10^{-3}, 2×10^{-3} and 1.6×10^{-3} nm^2, respectively.
These values can be compared with Equation 15. First of all, it
may be noted that the value of C is indeed inversely proportional
to a, in excellent agreement with Equation 15. The absolute value
of C is related to the value of $\Delta s_s/z$. Estimating z to be 6, we
obtain from Equation 15, with $v^o = 0.18$ nm^3, for the two 1% systems
a value for $-\Delta s_s/k$ around 11. Assuming ϕ_f to be ~ 0.5, the term
$\ln \phi_f/\phi_d$ in Equation 13 is about 4, suggesting that the constant
C_f/k is around 7. Without placing too much emphasis on the
precise value of Δs_s and C_f, we may conclude that their order of
magnitude is quite reasonable. Using these numbers to assess the
effect of particle concentration (SB1, 1% vs SB1, 5%) we obtain
from Equation 15 that the ratio between the two C-values should
be 0.82. From Table I we find approximately 0.80, showing again
very good agreement.

Taking the average values for the constant C as given above,
we calculated the value of ϕ_*^+ from (the implicit) Equation 14.
The results are given in the last column of Table I, and in
Figure 7 (full curves). This figure shows also the experimental
points (second column of Table I). The overall agreement is
excellent. Apparently, our model describes the molecular weight
dependency of ϕ_*^+ quite well.

The dashed curve in Figure 7 was obtained by substituting
in Equation 14 r_g for Δ, using $C = 2.10^{-3}$ nm^2. This substitution
would bring our model closer to that of De Hek and Vrij, who
regarded the polymer coils as hard spheres of radius $\sim r_g$. For
high molecular weights, the agreement between the dashed curve
and the experimental points is reasonable (and could be improved
by choosing a different C), but for short chains large deviations
occur. Hence, taking Δ and not r_g does improve the agreement
between theory and experiment considerably. This is also clear
from the Δ-values listed in Table I, Δ being lower than r_g for
short chains but approaching r_g for longer ones.

We conclude that our model describes the dependence of the
phase separation conditions on polymer molecular weight, particle
radius and particle concentration at least semi-quantitatively.

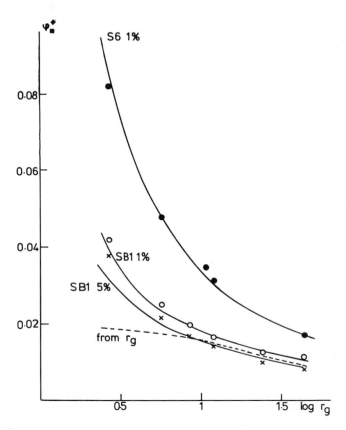

Figure 7. Comparison between the experimental phase separation conditions (points) for silicas S6 and SB1 (6) with our theoretical model (full curves). The dashed curve gives the theoretical dependency if in Equation 14 Δ is replaced by r_g.

Conclusions

We have shown that the simple concept of depletion in combination with binodal phase separation conditoon can account (semi)quantitatively for experimental observations on the stability of dispersions of hard spheres in the presence of nonadsorbing polymer. An important feature of the model is that the depletion thickness is a function of the polymer concentration, being equal to the radius of gyration in dilute solutions and decreasing when the polymer chains in the solution begin to overlap. An analytical expression is available for the dependency of the depletion thickness on polymer concentration. Even if the particle concentration is high and, consequently, phase separation occurs at low polymer concentration, the (small) difference between radius of gyration and depletion thickness has important consequences, especially for low molecular weight polymer. For smaller particle concentrations and higher phase separation concentrations, this difference becomes even more pronounced. Experimental work with systems of this type is in progress.

Our model predicts destabilization of colloidal dispersions at low polymer concentration and restabilisation in (very) concentrated polymer solutions. This restabilisation is not a kinetic effect, but is governed by equilibrium thermodynamics, the dispersed phase being the situation of lowest free energy at high polymer concentration. Restabilisation is a consequence of the fact that the depletion thickness is, in concentrated polymer solutions, (much) lower than the radius of gyration, leading to a weaker attraction.

One may wonder to what extent our predictions for hard spheres apply to a system of soft particles in a polymer solution. A definite answer to this question cannot be given at the moment since numerical data for the depletion of free polymer chains in the neighbourhood of a surface with terminally attached chains are not yet available. Some qualitative features for such a system have been discussed using scaling arguments (24). We may expect that the depleted amount of polymer is, at least in some cases, less than near a hard surface, giving rise to weaker attraction. Both the destabilization concentration (ϕ_*^+) and the restabilisation concentration ($\phi_*^{\ddagger}$) could be much lower. Experimental observations support this qualitative conclusion (1-5). For a more quantitative elaboration, numerical data should be available for an analysis similar to that discussed in the present paper.

Legend of symbols

a	particle radius
C	constant, defined in Equation 15
C_f	constant, defined in Equation 13
g	geometric factor, see Equations 11 and 12

H   separation between two particles
k   Boltzmann's constant
l   lattice step length
r   number of segments per polymer chain
T   temperature
v^o solvent molecular volume
x   ratio between molecular volumes of polymer and solvent
z   co-ordination number of particles in the floc
Δf_p free energy of attraction per unit area, due to depletion, between two plates
Δf_s free energy of attraction, due to depletion, between two spheres
Δf_d free energy difference per particle, due to depletion, between the floc and the dispersion
Δs_s configurational entropy difference per particle between the floc and the dispersion
Δ depletion thickness
μ^o solvent chemical potential in a polymer solution minus that in pure solvent
ϕ_* polymer volume fraction in the bulk solution
$\phi_*^{\dagger}$ polymer volume fraction at which a dispersion is destabilized
$\phi_*^{\ddagger}$ polymer volume fraction at which a dispersion is restabilized
ϕ_{ov} polymer volume fraction at which the coils in solution begin to overlap
ϕ_d particle volume fraction in the dispersion
ϕ_f particle volume fraction in the floc
χ polymer-solvent interaction parameter

Literature Cited

1. Li-In-On, F.K.R.; Vincent, B.; Waite, F.A. Am. Chem. Soc. Symp.Ser. 1975, 9, 165.
2. Cowell, C.; Li-In-On, F.K.R.; Vincent, B. J. Chem. Soc. Faraday Trans. I 1978, 74, 337.
3. Vincent, B.; Luckham, P.F.; Waite, F.A. J. Colloid Interface Sci. 1980, 73, 508.
4. Clarke, J.; Vincent, B. J. Chem. Soc. Faraday Trans. I 1981, 77, 1831.
5. Clarke, J.; Vincent, B. J. Colloid Interface Sci. 1981, 82, 208.
6. De Hek, H.; Vrij, A. J. Colloid Interface Sci. 1981, 84, 409.
7. Pathmamanoharan, C.; De Hek, H.; Vrij, A. Colloid Polymer Sci. 1981, 259, 769.
8. Sperry, P.R.; Hopfenberg, H.B.; Thomas, N.L. J. Colloid Interface Sci. 1981, 82, 62.
9. Joanny, J.F.; Leibler, L.; De Gennes, P.G. J. Polym. Sci. Polym. Phys. Ed. 1979, 17, 1073.
10. Feigin, R.I.; Napper, D.H. J. Colloid Interface Sci. 1980, 74, 561.

11. Feigin, R.I.; Napper, D.H. J. Colloid Interface Sci. 1981, 75, 525.
12. Sperry, P.R. J. Colloid Interface Sci. 1981, 87, 375.
13. Asakura, S.; Oosawa, F. J. Chem. Phys. 1954, 22, 1255; J. Polym.Sci. 1958, 33, 183.
14. Scheutjens, J.M.H.M.; Fleer, G.J. J. Phys. Chem. 1979, 83, 1619.
15. Scheutjens, J.M.H.M.; Fleer, G.J. J. Phys. Chem. 1980, 84, 178.
16. Fleer, G.J.; Scheutjens, J.M.H.M. Adv. Colloid Interface Sci. 1982, 16, 341.
17. Scheutjens, J.M.H.M.; Fleer, G.J. Adv. Colloid Interface Sci. 1982, 16, 361.
18. Flory, P.J. "Principles of Polymer Chemistry"; Cornell Univ. Press: Ithaca, N.Y., 1953.
19. DiMarzio, E.A.; Rubin, R.J. J. Chem. Phys. 1971, 55, 4318.
20. Deryagin, B. Koll. Z. 1934, 69, 155.
21. Percus, J.K.; Yerick, G.J. Phys. Rev. 1958, 110, 1.
22. Carnahan, N.F.; Starling, K.E. J. Chem. Phys. 1969, 51, 635.
23. Clarke, J. Ph.D. Thesis, University of Bristol, 1980.
24. De Gennes, P.G. Macromolecules 1980, 13, 1069.

RECEIVED October 7, 1983

NONAQUEOUS SYSTEMS

Nonaqueous Polymer Dispersions

Anchoring of Diblock Copolymers of Polystyrene and Poly(dimethyl siloxane) on Polymer Particles

J. V. DAWKINS, G. TAYLOR,[1] and G. GHAEM-MAGHAMI—Department of Chemistry, Loughborough University of Technology, Loughborough, Leicestershire LE11 3TU, England

J. S. HIGGINS—Department of Chemical Engineering and Chemical Technology, Imperial College, London SW7 2BY, England

Dispersion polymerizations of monomers in aliphatic hydrocarbons were performed in the presence of well-defined diblock copolymers of polystyrene (PS) and poly(dimethyl siloxane) (PDMS). The polymer dispersions were characterized by electron microscopy, silicon analysis, viscometry, and small angle neutron scattering, in order to study the packing and conformation of both the PS and PDMS blocks at the particle-liquid interface. Estimates of the thickness of the stabilizing surface layer suggested that the PDMS blocks have somewhat extended chain conformations. Scattering intensity data for polystyrene dispersions indicated that PS blocks anchor within particles by mixing with polystyrene chains. Scattering intensities for poly-(methyl methacrylate) dispersions were much higher, suggesting segregation of the PS blocks into domains. Effective anchoring arises because the PS blocks which are incompatible with chains in the particle core become trapped within a hard polymer matrix. For some soft particles effective anchoring may require covalent grafting of the incompatible PS blocks to the core polymer.

The interfacial properties of chain-like molecules in many polymeric and colloidal systems are dependent on the conformation of the chains adsorbed at the interface (1). Chains adsorbed at the solid-liquid interface may be produced by anchoring diblock copolymers to particles in a polymer dispersion. Such dispersions are conveniently prepared by polymerizing in the presence of a preformed AB diblock copolymer a monomer dissolved in a diluent which is a precipitant for the polymer. The A block which is

[1] Current address: Unilever Research, Port Sunlight, Wirral, Merseyside, England.

insoluble in the diluent anchors on or in the precipitating
particles, whereas the B block which is compatible with the diluent
extends away from the particle-liquid interface into the diluent.
The surface layer of B blocks protects the particles from flocculation by a mechanism known as steric stabilization (1,2).

The dimensions of the stabilizing B blocks are of interest
not only to steric stabilization in particular but also to the
general problem of adsorbed chains at solid-liquid interfaces. A
near-monodisperse diblock copolymer would be expected to give a
constant layer thickness of B blocks around a particle. Stable
dispersions of polystyrene (PS) and poly(methyl methacrylate)
(PMMA) in aliphatic hydrocarbons have been prepared by polymerizing
the monomers in the presence of diblock copolymers of polystyrene
and poly(dimethyl siloxane) (3,4). These block copolymers
have well-defined block lengths and a narrow chain length distribution, stabilizing polymer particles with a surface layer of
PDMS chains. In this paper an interpretation is proposed for the
packing and conformation of the PDMS chains at the particle-liquid
interface from data for the surface coverage of the particles by
the PDMS chains and from results for the hydrodynamic thickness
of the PDMS surface layer.

Much work on the preparation of nonaqueous polymer dispersions
has involved the radical polymerization of acrylic monomers in
the presence of copolymers having the A block the same as the
acrylic polymer in the particle core (2). The preparation of
polymer dispersions other than polystyrene in the presence of a
PS-PDMS diblock copolymer is of interest because effective
anchoring of the copolymer may be influenced by the degree of
compatibility between the PS anchor block and the polymer molecules in the particle core. The present paper describes the
interpretation of experimental studies performed with the aim of
determining the mode of anchoring of PS blocks to polystyrene,
poly(methyl methacrylate), and poly(vinyl acetate) (PVA) particles.

Experimental

Dispersion Polymerization. Diblock copolymers were prepared
using anionic polymerization techniques by the addition of
hexamethylcyclotrisiloxane to "living" polystyryllithium. Polymerizations were performed under conditions of rigorous purity
using an inert gas blanket technique or a high vacuum procedure
as described elsewhere (4,5). Block copolymers prepared over a
range of molecular weights and compositions were characterized
by gel permeation chromatography (GPC), osmometry and silicon
analysis. These techniques yielded the copolymer composition,
the number average molecular weight $\bar{M}_n$(PS) of the polystyrene
block, the number average molecular weight $\bar{M}_n$(PDMS) of the poly-
(dimethyl siloxane) block, and the copolymer polydispersity
defined as the ratio of the weight average and number average
molecular weights $\bar{M}_w/\bar{M}_n$ (typically <1.25). Block copolymers

containing protonated polystyrene blocks PS(H), and deuterated polystyrene blocks PS(D) by preparing "living" polystyryllithium from perdeuterostyrene, were synthesised.

Polymer dispersions in aliphatic hydrocarbons were prepared by polymerizing monomer with a concentration in the range 10-20 weight per cent in the presence of PS-PDMS diblock copolymer having a concentration of about 5 weight per cent. Anionic dispersion polymerization with n-butyl lithium as initiator at 298 K was employed for styrene (3), and radical dispersion polymerization with azobisisobutyronitrile as initiator in the temperature range 323-343 K was used for methyl methacrylate and vinyl acetate. Seeding techniques were frequently used in the dispersion polymerizations. Dispersions were washed by repeated centrifuge/ diluent exchange cycles to remove unadsorbed stabilizer and unconverted monomer, which also served to exchange a diluent for a different one.

Dispersion Properties. Particle diameters were estimated from transmission electron micrographs. The surface coverage of a particle defined as the area occupied or stabilized by a given PDMS chain was estimated from silicon analysis on dry particles and the particle diameter D. Dispersion stability was assessed visually with the dispersion contained in a cylindrical glass cell with a light beam arranged so that light scattered by the dispersion at about 45° from the transmitted beam could conveniently be observed by the human eye (6). The relative viscosity η_r of a dispersion was determined with an Ostwald-Fenske capillary viscometer at 298 K. The viscometer was treated with a solution of chlorotrimethylsilane to prevent adhesion of particles to the walls. The volume fraction of the polymer particle cores ϕ_0 was calculated from the total polymer content of the dispersion, the PDMS content and the density of the core. Dried PMMA and PVA dispersions were subjected to Soxhlet extraction, with boiling acetonitrile for at least 5 days. Infrared spectra (IR) were obtained from KBr discs with a Perkin-Elmer 177 grating spectrometer.

Small-angle neutron scattering (SANS) experiments on dispersions containing PS(D) were carried out using the D17 spectrometer at ILL Grenoble. The experimental conditions have been reported elsewhere (7). All normalization was made using the incoherent scattering from a water sample under identical experimental conditions. Contrast in a neutron scattering experiment arises from differences in the net scattering probabilities of neutrons from different nuclear species, the important parameter being the scattering length. Because of the large difference in scattering lengths of hydrogen and deuterium, there is contrast between PS(D) blocks and the surrounding molecules, so that a scattering pattern for the PS(D) blocks may be observed. Each dispersion was prepared with a mixture of two block copolymers, one containing PS(H) blocks and the other having PS(D) blocks. The

scattering pattern from the PS(D) blocks in a dispersion was
obtained by subtracting the scattering from an identical dispersion
with no deuteration. The isotropic scattering observed on the
multidetector is grouped according to radial distance r from the
beam centre to give a radial distribution of scattered intensities
I(r). The angle of scatter θ is then given by r/L where L is the
sample to detector distance. The scattering wave vector K is
given by

$$K = (4\pi/\lambda)\sin(\theta/2) = 2\pi r/\lambda L \qquad (1)$$

where λ is the wavelength of the neutron beam. From I(r) the
normalized scattered intensity I(K) was obtained using water
scattering data.

Results and Discussion

PS Particles. Viscosity data for the dispersions (3) were plotted
according to Equation 2

$$\phi_o/\ln \eta_r = (1/k_1 f) - (k\phi_o/k_1) \qquad (2)$$

in which k_1 is the Einstein coefficient for solid spheres, f is a
factor representing an increase in the Einstein coefficient
because of the adsorbed surface layer of PDMS and k is a crowding
factor. From the reciprocal of the intercept of this plot,
Goodwin (8) proposed that the thickness of the stabilizing surface
layer δ may be calculated with Equation 3

$$k_1 f = k_1 [1 + (2\delta/D)]^3 \qquad (3)$$

in which k_1 was confirmed to be close to 2.5 for spherical particles free from aggregation (3). Values of δ as a function of
$\overline{M}_n$(PDMS) are shown in Figure 1. Calculations of the molecular
weight dependence of the end-to-end distance for an extended chain
conformation were performed. For a PDMS chain it was assumed that
this conformation was a helix with six repeating units per turn,
giving a value of 0.138 nm for the length of a repeating unit pro-
jected along the chain axis (9). The results for the hydrodynamic
thickness in Figure 1 indicate that the PDMS chains in the surface
layer of PS particles are in somewhat extended chain conformations.
     In Figure 2 the scattering function I(K) is plotted against
the wave vector K for PS dispersions containing PS(D) blocks in
n-heptane. These data may be analysed by the Zimm treatment (7)
according to Equation 4

$$\chi c/I(K) = (1/\overline{M}_w)[1 + (K^2 <s^2>_z/3)] + 2A_2 c \qquad (4)$$

where c is the concentration of PS(D), χ is a constant containing
the contrast factor and instrumental parameters, $<s^2>_z$ is the z

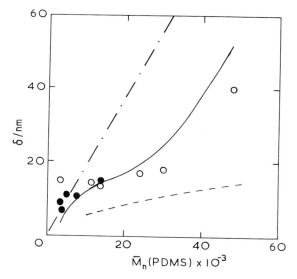

Figure 1.   Dependence of surface layer thickness on $\bar{M}_n$(PDMS) :(●)δ for PS particles; (O)δ for PMMA particles; (——) thickness h from surface coverage data for PMMA particles; (—— · ——) extended chain length model; (---) twice root-mean-square radius of gyration for random coil model.

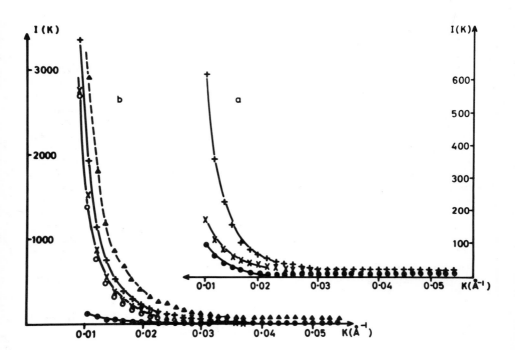

Figure 2. Scattering intensity from PS(D) blocks in PS
particles (a) and PMMA particles (b) : (+, x, ▲, o) different
PS(D)/PS(H) ratios between 1/2 and 1/12 in the particles;
(●) undeuterated particles (reproduced from Higgins, J.S.,
Dawkins, J.V., and Taylor, G. Polymer 1980, 21, 627 by
permission of the publishers Butterworth and Co. (Publishers)
Ltd. ©).

average mean-square radius of gyration, and A_2 is the second
virial coefficient. A plot of $c/I(K)$ against K^2 according to
Equation 4 is shown in Figure 3. At low K there is a region of
sharply varying signal arising from scattering from the spherical
particles (7), but above $K^2 \sim 10^{-3} \text{Å}^{-2}$ a linear region of K^2 is
observed with intensity approximately proportional to concentration
of PS(D) blocks. From this region (using Equation 4 and assuming
$A_2 = 0$) it is possible to obtain values of $<s^2>_z$ and $\bar{M}_w$ from the
slope and intercept respectively. The values of $(<s^2>_z)^{\frac{1}{2}}$ were
found to be 55 Å and 60 Å respectively for PS(D) blocks in PS
particles prepared with PS(D)/PS(H) in the ratios 1:6 and 1:3.
The block copolymer containing PS(D) had $\bar{M}_n(PS) = 23400$, and the
same free PS chain in bulk polystyrene would have $(<s^2>_z)^{\frac{1}{2}} = 43$ Å
(7). The results indicate that the size of a PS(D) block when
anchored at the PS particle-liquid interface is extended beyond
the random coil dimensions. Examination of Equation 4 shows that,
whilst the evaluation of $<s^2>_z$ is independent of normalization
and a precise knowledge of contrast factors, the determination of
$\bar{M}_w$ does depend on these parameters. Furthermore, although the
ratio PS(D)/PS(H) is known at the start of the dispersion polymerization, the incorporation of blocks into particles may occur
in a different ratio owing to the difference in $\bar{M}_n(PS)$ for PS(D)
and PS(H) thus changing the solubility and anchoring characteristics. Since this ratio for a particle may be uncertain to
within a factor of 2 or 3, the determination of $\bar{M}_w$ from the intercepts in Figure 3 is subject to this uncertainty. It is only
possible to say that the $\bar{M}_w$ values of 72000 and 63000 from Figure
3 are of a similar magnitude to $\bar{M}_n = 23400$ obtained for the PS(D)
block by GPC. From these estimates of $<s^2>_z$ and $\bar{M}_w$, we may
tentatively suggest that the PS(D) blocks are molecularly dispersed
in PS particles.

PMMA Particles. Viscosity data plotted according to Equation 2
have been reported previously (9). Values of δ calculated with
Equation 3 are shown as a function of $\bar{M}_n(PDMS)$ in Figure 1. The
results indicate that the hydrodynamic thickness of the adsorbed
PDMS surface layer is similar on both PMMA and PS particles. The
surface layer thickness is always larger than twice the root-mean-
square radius of gyration for a free PDMS chain in solution. The
radius of gyration was calculated with the Flory-Fox equation and
solution viscosity data of PDMS (9). For $\bar{M}_n(PDMS) < 10000$ the
experimental surface layer thickness is closer to the extended
chain length than to twice the radius of gyration. For $\bar{M}_n(PDMS) >$
10000 it appears that the PDMS blocks have a size intermediate
between the two limiting models.

The existence of an extended chain conformation is also
suggested from a consideration of the surface coverage data.
Results for the surface area occupied by each PDMS chain (9)
indicate that total coverage of the particles may be assumed,
that the area occupied by a given PDMS chain is similar on both

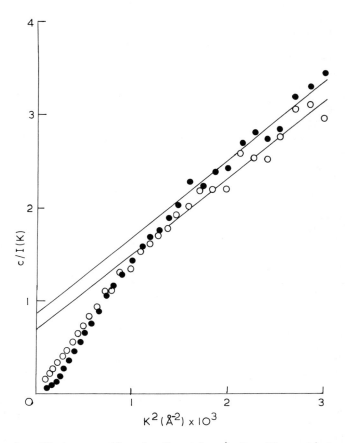

Figure 3. Plot according to Equation 4 for PS particles containing PS(D) blocks with undeuterated particle signal subtracted : (●) PS(D)/PS(H) = 1:3; (○) PS(D)/PS(H) = 1:6 (reproduced from Higgins, J.S., Dawkins, J.V., and Taylor, G. Polymer 1980, 21, 627 by permission of the publishers Butterworth and Co. (Publishers) Ltd. ©).

PS and PMMA particles, that the area occupied is independent of the length of the PS anchor block, and that the area occupied increases as $\overline{M}_n$(PDMS) rises. Consequently, a PDMS chain may be regarded as being terminally anchored at the particle surface with no significant extension of the PS anchor block into the dispersion medium. It is then possible to calculate the separation distance d between neighbouring PDMS chains at the surface of a particle, assuming each chain is terminally adsorbed in the centre of a regular hexagon. It was observed that this distance d was similar to the root-mean-square radius of gyration of the PDMS chain (9) which provides a possible reason why values of δ suggest an extended chain conformation. If adjacent PDMS chains do not interact because of excluded volume effects, i.e. no overlap of neighbouring chains, the volume of each chain can be represented by a prolate ellipsoid having minor axis d. The major axis h was then calculated assuming that the volume of the chain represented as a prolate ellipsoid was equal to the volume of the same chain represented as a random coil. It is evident in Figure 1 that the experimental estimates of the hydrodynamic thickness δ are in reasonable agreement with the thickness h calculated from surface coverage data assuming a prolate ellipsoid model.

In Figure 2 the scattering function I(K) is plotted against the wave vector K for PMMA dispersions containing PS(D) blocks in n-heptane. The intensity scattered from the PMMA particles relative to the background of undeuterated particles is an order of magnitude higher than that from the PS particles with corresponding concentrations of PS(D) blocks. This suggests that there are larger scattering objects in the PMMA dispersions and hence aggregates of PS(D) blocks. In Figure 4, we present a plot of c/I(K) against K^2 according to Equation 4. There is no linear region from which a value of $<s^2>_z$ can be obtained. The scattered intensity may be compared with curves calculated from model systems (7). Curves representing either thin discs or spheres give a reasonable fit to the experimental dependence of I(K) on K. We may conclude that the PS(D) blocks cluster into domains in PMMA particles.

Flocculation studies (6) indicated that the mechanism of steric stabilization operates for the PMMA dispersions. The stability of PMMA dispersions was examined further by redispersion of the particles in cyclohexane at 333 K. Above 307 K, cyclohexane is a good solvent for PS and PDMS, and if the PS-PDMS block copolymer was not firmly anchored, desorption of stabilizer by dissolution should occur at 333 K followed by flocculation of the PMMA dispersion. However, little change in dispersion stability was observed over a period of 60 h. Consequently, we may conclude that the PS blocks are firmly anchored within the hard PMMA matrix. However, the indication from neutron scattering of aggregates of PS(D) blocks in PMMA particles may be explained by the observation that two different polymers are often not very compatible on mixing (10) so that the PS(D) blocks are tending to

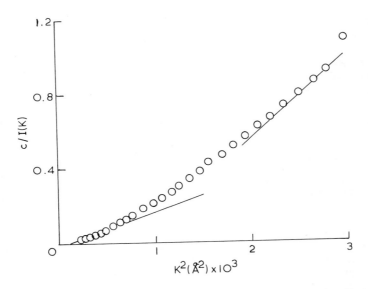

Figure 4. Plot according to Equation 4 for PMMA particles
containing PS(D) blocks with undeuterated particle signal
subtracted (reproduced from Higgins, J.S., Dawkins, J.V.,
and Taylor, G. Polymer 1980, 21, 627 by permission of the
publishers Butterworth and Co. (Publishers) Ltd. ©).

minimise contacts with PMMA chains. Therefore, it might be argued
that the strong anchoring of PS-PDMS to PMMA particles could arise
during dispersion polymerization from a grafting reaction between
the PMMA radicals and the block copolymer. This possibility was
investigated by removing PMMA homopolymer by extraction from a
washed and dried sample of a PMMA dispersed phase. Dispersions
having $\bar{M}_n$(PMMA) in the range $10^5 - 10^6$ were studied. The residue
was washed, dried and characterized by GPC and IR. The GPC
results for the original block copolymer and the block copolymer
residue were identical. For block copolymers having $\bar{M}_n$(PS) in the
range 15000 to 50000, IR spectra on the residues did not display
a peak for ester groups, suggesting that block copolymer had not
been grafted onto particles. In the absence of covalent
grafting of block copolymer to the particles, these results
suggest that for polymer particles having a glass transition
temperature above the dispersion polymerization temperature the
PS-PDMS block copolymer becomes trapped within a hard polymer
matrix despite the polymer incompatibility effect and stabilizes
polymer particles after removal of excess block copolymer by
redispersion. Since the results in Figure 2 indicate that the
PS blocks are not compatible with PMMA, it is possible at temperatures above the glass transition temperature of PMMA that the PS
blocks diffuse through the soft PMMA matrix to the particle
surface. If the PS block is soluble in the n-alkane diluent at
elevated temperatures, then flocculation of the dispersion may
occur above the glass transition temperature of the core polymer.

<u>PVA Particles</u>. Dispersions were prepared in order to examine
stabilization for a core polymer having a glass transition
temperature below the dispersion polymerization temperature. PVA
particles prepared with a block copolymer having $\bar{M}_n$(PS) $\sim$ 10000
showed a tendency to flocculate at ambient temperature during redispersion cycles to remove excess block copolymer, particularly
if the dispersion polymerization had not proceeded to 100% con-
version of monomer. It is well documented that on mixing solutions
of polystyrene and poly(vinyl acetate) homopolymers phase separa-
tion tends to occur (<u>10</u>,<u>11</u>), and solubility studies (<u>12</u>) of PS in
n-heptane suggest that PS blocks with $\bar{M}_n$(PS) $\sim$ 10000 will be close
to dissolution when dispersion polymerizations are performed at
343 K. Consequently, we may postulate that for soft polymer
particles the block copolymer is rejected from the particle
because of an incompatibility effect and is adsorbed at the
particle surface. If the block copolymer desorbs from the
particle surface, then particle agglomeration will occur unless
rapid adsorption of other copolymer molecules occurs from a
reservoir of excess block copolymer.

With a careful redispersion technique stable dispersions free
of excess block copolymer are produced for PVA particles with
the anchoring PS block having $\bar{M}_n$(PS) > 30000. This suggests that
more effective anchoring occurs when the solubility of the block

copolymer in the dispersion medium is reduced. In view of the incompatibility effect of PS in the soft PVA matrix and the possible diffusion of the PS blocks to the particle-liquid inter-face where desorption of the block copolymer may occur, effective anchoring of the PDMS chains may require covalent grafting of the copolymer to the particles by reaction between PVA radicals and PS-PDMS during dispersion polymerization. Literature values for chain transfer constants for the reaction between PVA radicals and PS suggest that the grafting reaction is more likely than the chain transfer reaction between PVA radicals and PVA homopolymer which produces branched PVA at high conversions of monomer (13). In order to confirm the existence of covalent grafting of PS-PDMS to the particles, block copolymer from a washed and dried sample of a PVA dispersed phase has been isolated by removing the core polymer by extraction. This residue was washed, dried, and characterized by IR and GPC. The IR spectrum in Figure 5 clearly demonstrates an intense absorption at about 1735 cm^{-1}, indicating the presence of ester groups in the copolymer residue, and an absorption at 700 cm^{-1} characteristic of phenyl groups in the block copolymer. GPC also showed that the molecular weight distribution of this residue was broader than that of the original block copolymer. It is concluded that for particles containing soft core polymers effective anchoring of PS-PDMS block copolymer is aided by covalent grafting.

Acknowledgments

This work was supported by the Science and Engineering Research Council and by an S.E.R.C. Case award in collaboration with Dow Corning.

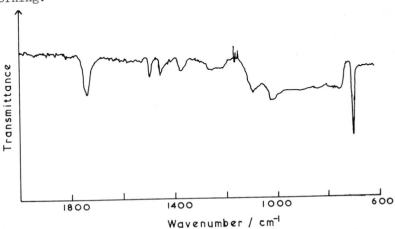

Figure 5. Infrared spectrum of block copolymer residue after Soxhlet extraction of PVA core polymer with aceto-nitrile.

Literature Cited

1. Vincent, B. Adv.Colloid Interface Sci., 1974, 4, 193.
2. Barrett, K.E.J., Ed. "Dispersion Polymerization in Organic Media"; Wiley: New York, 1975.
3. Dawkins, J.V.; Taylor, G. In "Polymer Colloids II"; Fitch, R.M., Ed.; Plenum: New York, 1980; p.447.
4. Dawkins, J.V.; Taylor, G. Polymer 1979, 20, 599.
5. Dawkins, J.V.; Taylor, G. Makromol.Chem, 1979, 180, 1737.
6. Dawkins, J.V.; Taylor, G. Colloid Polym.Sci., 1980, 258, 79.
7. Higgins, J.S.; Dawkins, J.V.; Taylor, G., Polymer 1980, 21, 627.
8. Goodwin, J.W. in "Colloid Science"; Everett, D.H., Ed.; Specialist Periodical Report, The Chemical Society: London, 1975; Vol.1, Chapter 7.
9. Dawkins, J.V.; Taylor, G., J.C.S. Faraday I 1980, 76, 1263.
10. Dobry, A.; Boyer-Kawenoki, F., J.Polym.Sci., 1947, 2, 90.
11. Kern, R.J.; Slocombe, R.J., J.Polym.Sci., 1955, 15, 183.
12. Dawkins, J.V.; Taylor, G., Eur.Polym.J., 1979, 15, 453.
13. Brandrup, J.; Immergut, E.H. Eds. "Polymer Handbook"; Wiley-Interscience: New York, 1976.

RECEIVED October 7, 1983

Preparation and Stability of Polymer-Grafted Silica Dispersions

J. EDWARDS, S. LENON,[1] A. F. TOUSSAINT, and B. VINCENT

School of Chemistry, University of Bristol, Cantock's Close, Bristol BS8 1TS, England

Stable, non-aqueous dispersions of monodisperse, spherical silica particles, over the size range 50 to 600 nm diameter and which carry terminally-grafted polymer layers (polystyrene or polydimethyl-siloxane), have been prepared by methods which avoid any "dry" stage for the silica particles. The polymer chains are of narrow molecular weight distribution, having been prepared by anionic poly-merisation routes. The amount of grafted polymer has been established using elemental microanalysis and in some cases thermogravimetric analysis.

The stability of these dispersions has been investigated. A strong dependence of critical flocculation conditions (temperature or volume fraction of added non-solvent) on particle concen-tration was found. Moreover, there seems to be little or no correlation between the critical flocculation conditions and the corresponding theta-conditions for the stabilising polymer chains, as proposed by Napper. Although a detailed explanation is difficult to give a tentative explanation for this unexpected behaviour is suggested in terms of the weak flocculation theory of Vincent et al.

In studying the stability of colloidal dispersions it is of con-siderable advantage if the particles concerned are monodisperse and spherical. For aqueous, charge-stabilised systems polymer latices have proved invaluable in this regard. With non-aqueous systems, steric stabilisation is usually required. In this case it

[1] Current address: I.C.I. Paints Division plc, Slough, Berkshire, SL2 5DS, England.

0097–6156/84/0240–0281$06.00/0

is also necessary that the stabilising polymer sheath should be
well-characterised. Moreover, polymer latices may be inadequate
if swelling occurs. Methods have been developed in this
laboratory for producing both aqueous (1) and non-aqueous (2)
dispersions of monodisperse, spherical silica particles, over a
wide range of particle diameters (20 nm to 1 μm), to which monodisperse polymer chains (prepared by anionic polymerisation
techniques) have been terminally grafted, at a controlled level of
coverage. In this previous work poly(ethylene oxide)(1) and
polystyrene (2) were the two polymers used. In the latter case
the method of preparation involved the direct reaction of "living"
polystyrene anions with surface-modified silica particles (e.g.
chlorinated or thermally dehydroxylated), dispersed in a suitable
solvent. One disadvantage of this route, however, is that the
surface modification step involves a "dry" stage for the particles.
This can lead to difficulties in achieving total redispersion of the
particles in the solvent used for the subsequent polymer grafting
reaction. Even after sonification small aggregates may persist,
particularly when the primary particles are small (< say 100 nm).
Such aggregates can be difficult to remove, e.g. by filtration.
Clearly, a method which circumvents this dry stage is desirable.
In this paper we describe methods in which polystyrene (PS) and
polydimethylsiloxane (PDMS) have been successfully grafted to
silica particles, avoiding the dry stage.

In the case of PS the polymer is prepared anionically and
then reacted with a large excess of trichlorosilane, thus leaving
the polymer chains, in principle, with two terminal chloro-groups.
These are then reacted with methanol to give terminal methoxy
groups. The silica particles are prepared as an ethanolic dispersion and then transferred to dimethylformamide (DMF). The
dispersions in DMF are very stable to aggregation, presumably
through charge stabilisation (the dielectric constant of DMF is 37)
and / or DMF solvation sheaths around the particles. The methoxy-
terminated polystyrene is added to the silica/DMF dispersion and
the mixture heated under reflux. By varying the time and conditions of the reaction the coverage may be controlled. By using
a centrifugation/redispersion cycling technique, stable dispersions
in a wide variety of liquids, which are good solvents for polystyrene, could be achieved.

For the PDMS-grafted systems a somewhat different method was
used since PDMS is not soluble in DMF. An anionic polymerisation
method was again used to produce "living" PDMS chains, but in this
case these were reacted with acetic acid to give hydroxyl-
terminated chains. The silica particle dispersions in ethanol
were stable, and remained stable on adding n-heptane to give a
1:1 (by volume) solvent mixture in which PDMS is still soluble.
The hydroxyl-terminated polymer was then added to the dispersion
and the mixture allowed to stand for 24 hr to achieve adsorption
equilibrium. Further n-heptane was then added to give a 4:1 (by
volume) n-heptane:ethanol solvent composition, and the sample

heated under reflux for 24 hr.   It was then rotary-evaporated to remove most of the solvent and the particles redispersed in n-heptane.

For both the SiO_2-g-PS and the SiO_2-g-PDMS systems the surface coverage of the polymer was determined by elemental micro-analysis.   In the former case this was supplemented by thermo-gravimetric analysis.

The stability of the various dispersions was assessed and compared by determining the critical flocculation conditions (temperature or volume fraction of added non-solvent for the grafted polymer), as a function of particle concentration.

Materials

Monomers.   tetraethylsilicate (TES) and styrene were BDH AnalaR grade and hexamethylcyclotrisiloxane (HMCTS) was supplied by Aldrich.   The styrene was distilled under reduced pressure from calcium hydrides prior to use and HMCTS sublimed under vacuum directly into the reaction vessel.

Reagents.   n-butyl lithium (Koch-Light) was supplied as a solution in n-hexane (1.55 mol dm^{-3}) and transferred to the reaction vessel via a suba-seal cap using a syringe.   Chlorotrimethylsilane and trichloromethylsilane (Aldrich) were distilled under reduced pressure.   Ammonia (BDH) was supplied as an "0.880" solution in water.

Solvents.   water was doubly-distilled from an all-Pyrex apparatus.   All the other solvents were supplied by BDH and mostly used as supplied, except that tetrahydrofuran (THF) was first distilled from lithium aluminium hydride and then from a sodium/naphthalene mixture (the green coloration of the latter being indicative of the absence of water).

Analytical Techniques

Transmission electron microscopy (T.E.M.).   electron micrographs of the silica particles were produced using an Hitachi HU11B apparatus.   Particle size distributions were obtained from these using a Carl Zeiss particle size analyser.

Photon correlation spectroscopy (P.C.S.).   this was used as an alternative method of determining particle diameters from derived diffusion coefficients.   The instrumentation consisted of a Coherent Kr ion laser (CR 2000K), plus a Malvern Instruments PCS 100 set up, linked to a Malvern Instruments multibit correlator (K7025);   data was analysed using an on-line 'Apple II' mini computer.

Gel permeation chromatography (G.P.C.).   the molecular weight distributions, M_n and M_w were obtained using a Waters instrument with o-chlorobenzene as the solvent.

Nuclear magnetic resonance (N.M.R.). a Jeol PS-100 instrument was used to produce ^{1}H N.M.R. spectra of the modified PS samples (see below). $CDCl_3$ was used as the solvent.

Elemental microanalysis (E.M.A.). quantitative analyses for C, H and N were obtained for the silica/grafted polymer samples using a Perkin Elmer 240 elemental analyser. Grafted amounts (g polymer/ g silica) were calculated from the C+H percentages, based on the residue (assumed to be only silica). A small correction was found to be necessary in the case of the SiO_2-g-PS systems since a small percentage of N was usually found; this was assumed to be due to trapped DMF. The grafted amount, Γ (mg m^{-2}), was then calculated, assuming the specific surface area to be the geometric area obtained from the T.E.M. particle size analysis. For this purpose the density of the silica particles was taken to be 1.85 g cm^{-3} (3).

Thermal gravimetric analysis (T.G.A.). measurement of the weight loss, as a function of temperature, of some of the SiO_2-g-PS samples was carried out using a Stanton Redcroft TG 750 instrument at a heating rate of 5° min^{-1} under a nitrogen atmosphere, and at a gas flow rate of 20 cm^3 min^{-1}.

Preparation of Silica Particles

The method used here was essentially that described by Stöber et al. (4) which involves the room-temperature hydrolysis of tetra-ethylsilicate in ethanol containing varying amounts of ammonia and water, the latter two components control the final particle morphology and size. The method has been modified slightly by Bridger (2,5) and by van Helden and Vrij (3).
    Details of the concentrations of the reactants used and the average particle diameters produced are given in table I.

Table I.   Silica Dispersions

No.	Concentration/(mol dm^{-3})			Average diameter/nm		
	TES	H_2O	NH_3	TEM	PCS(H_2O)	PCS(DMF)
S6	0.30	3.8	1.9	308 ±24	-	-
S7	0.34	2.3	2.2	105 ±15	106 ±10	110 ±10
S10	0.22	0.5	1.5	198 ±17	210 ±10	220 ±20
S11	0.28	9.6	4.0	598 ±13	-	-
S12	0.22	0.5	1.5	172 ±16	190 ±10	205 ±10
S14	0.20	1.4	0.7	55 ±11	-	-
S15	0.19	0.45	1.3	260 ±10	-	-

It may be seen that, within experimental error, the diameters
determined by TEM and PCS agree. Moreover, where studied, the
PCS diameters are very similar for the silica dispersions in water
and DMF, suggesting that the particles do exist as singlets in
both solvents.

Polymer Preparations/Modifications

Polystyrene was prepared by the anionic polymerisation of styrene
in toluene plus THF mixtures (4:1 volume ratio) using n-butyl
lithium as initiator. After removing a sample for analysis at
this stage, the remainder of the living polystyrene was reacted
with a five molar excess of trichloromethylsilane for 15 min and
then excess methanol introduced. The methoxy-terminated polystyrene
was freeze-dried from dioxan. The method described here
essentially follows the route proposed by Laible and Hamann (6).
     Polydimethylsiloxane was prepared by the anionic poly-
merisation of hexamethylcyclotrisiloxane, in a solvent mixture of
cyclohexane and THF (4:1 volume ratio), using n-butyllithium as
the initiator. After a reaction period of 48 hr termination was
effected by adding a small quantity of acetic acid.
     The number average molecular weight ($\bar{M}_n$) and polydispersity
index ($\bar{M}_w/\bar{M}_n$) are given in Table II for the various PS and PDMS
samples prepared.

Table II.		Polymers			
		Before Modification		After Modification	
Type	No.	$\bar{M}_n$	$\bar{M}_w/\bar{M}_n$	$\bar{M}_n$	$\bar{M}_w/\bar{M}_n$
PS	11	3,700	1.09	4,400	1.08
PS	13	25,600	1.29	30,500	1.32
PS	16	13,800	1.14	14,300	1.19
PS	18	7,400	1.25	–	–
PS	19	34,400	1.19	–	–
PDMS	3	72,440	1.57	–	–
PDMS	5	6,7C0	1.34	–	–

The "before" and "after" modification data in Table II refer to
the polystyrene samples prior to, and subsequent to, reaction with
trichloromethylsilane, respectively. It can be seen that "after"
$\bar{M}_n$ values are somewhat higher than the "before" ones (although the
polydispersity index does not change significantly). This suggests
that, either some polymer–polymer coupling has occurred through
two (or three) polymer chains reacting with a single trichlorosilane molecule, or that a short, oligomeric siloxane chain has

been terminally added to each polystyrene chain, i.e. leading to structures of the form,

$$Bu \left(CH_2 - \underset{\underset{x}{\underset{|}{\bigcirc}}}{CH} \right) \left(\underset{\underset{OMe}{|}}{\overset{\overset{OMe}{|}}{Si}} - CH_2 \right)_{y-1} \underset{\underset{OMe}{|}}{\overset{\overset{OMe}{|}}{Si}} - Me \qquad\qquad I$$

In order to investigate this further ^{1}H NMR spectra were obtained for the modified polymers and a comparison made between the intensities of the peaks for the aromatic ring protons in the main PS chain and the OMe protons in the siloxane moeity. Thus, for example, for PS 16 the difference in $\bar{M}_n$ values would suggest y = 5 (see structure I). This would imply a theoretical ratio aromatic protons:OMe protons, R = 25, if structures such as I do exist, whereas R = 113 if there is only one OMe group per PS chain (i.e. y = 1), or even greater values of R if polymer-polymer coupling occurs. The NMR spectrum for the unpurified polymer led to an R value of 13.8, but this increased to 16.8 after distilling off low molecular weight impurities at 66°C. The implication is that short oligometric siloxane chains are terminally added to the polystyrene, i.e. structures such as I are produced by this reaction route rather than any significant amount of polymer polymer coupling. This may well be advantageous in grafting to silica particles since the presence of more than one OMe group at the end of the polymer chain increases the number of reactive centres for grafting.

    Similar features were not, of course, observed in the case of the OH-termined PDMS chains, since in this case the living polymer was simply "killed" by adding acetic acid in the conventional manner.

Grafting of Polystyrene to Silica

The SiO_2-g-PS systems were prepared by adding the methoxy-terminated PS to the silica dispersion in DMF. The mass ratio PS:SiO_2 used in each case is recorded in Table III. The dispersion was then heated at 120°C, under nitrogen, for varying periods up to 45 hr. A plot of grafted amount (Γ) versus time for one of the samples (S7/PS13) is shown in figure 1. At the end of the reaction period several centrifugation/redispersed cycles in the solvent required were carried out: this removed any free polystyrene.

    In one case, S12/PS13b (Table III), an attempt was made to see if further PS could be grafted by making the solvent environment less polar. In this case some of the SiO_2-g-PS particles were redispersed in toluene and further methoxy-terminated PS added. The grafted reaction was continued for a further period of 24 hr. This sample is referred to as number S12/PS13c in table III.

    In the dispersions prepared in the above manner the SiO_2-g-PS

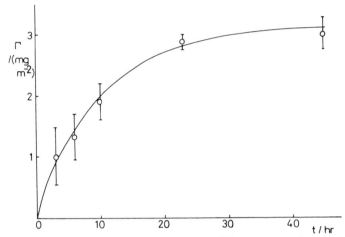

Figure 1.   Amount of PS grafted (Γ) versus time (t) for SiO_2-g-PS sample S7/PS13.

particles retain most of their surface hydroxyl groups (i.e. except at those small fraction of surface sites where a PS chain has grafted). In the earlier grafting procedure proposed by Bridger et al. (2), the underlying silica surface was hydrophobic. In order to make a comparison with these earlier systems one of the samples, S12/PS13b, was reacted with chlorotrimethylsilane, plus an organic base, N,N-diisobutyl-3-amino-2,4-dimethylpentane, to react with the HCl liberated (6), in toluene at 50°C overnight. Subsequent microanalysis (for C+H) indicated that a large fraction of the remaining surface -OH groups had been converted to surface $-OSi(CH_3)_3$ groups by this method. This sample will be referred to as S12/PS13b*.

Also, for the sake of comparison, one SiO_2-g-PS sample (S11/PS19) was prepared following the Bridger et al.(2) route. In this case some of the S11 silica was freeze-dried and degassed at 10^{-5} Torr and 150°C and then reacted with trichloromethylsilane in the vapour phase; this replaced the surface hydroxyl groups by chloro groups. The particles were then redispersed (with the aid of ultrasonics) in a 4:1 volume ratio toluene: THF solvent mixture. "Living" polystyrene (PS19), in a similar solvent mixture was then introduced and the grafting reaction allowed to proceed for 24 hr at room temperature.

Finally, in order to make a comparison of the amount of polymer that could be physisorbed, as distinct from terminally-grafted, one sample (S12/PS19, Table III) was prepared in which "dead" PS19 was added to a dispersion of silica S12 in DMF, using essentially similar conditions and quantities as in the preparation of sample S12/PS13a by the grafting route.

Table III				SiO_2-g-PS systems			
No.	Wt. ratio PS:SiO$_2$	reaction time/hr	diam. /nm	$\bar{M}_n$	$\Gamma^{(1)}$ /(mg m^{-2})	$\sigma^{(2)}$ /nm^2	$\sigma/\pi<s^2>$
S6/PS18	23:1	24	308	7,400	-	-	-
S7/PS15	4:1	20	105	13,800	1.2	18	0.51
S7/PS13	4:1	45	105	25,600	3.4	13	0.18
S14/PS13	4:1	24	55	30,000			
S12/ PS13 a (3)	4:1	19			3.6	12	0.17
S12/ PS13 b (3)	3:2	24	172	25,600	1.6	26	0.38
S12/ PS13 c (3)	5:1	15			7.3	5.8	0.08
S12/PS19 (4)	4:1	24	172	34,400	2.1	28	0.28
S11/PS19 (5)	10:1	24	598	34,400	4.6	13	0.14

(1) PS grafted amount; (2) area per grafted molecule; (3) prepared by further grafting onto sample S12/PS13b (see text); (4) polymer physisorbed rather than grafted; (5) prepared by the Bridger route (2)(see text).

In table III, the grafted amounts (Γ) and the areas per grafted polymer chain (σ) are given. Also listed are the values of the ratio of the area of a grafted chain to the area subtended by an equivalent solution random coil, $\sigma/\pi<s^2>$ where $<s^2>^{1/2}$ is the radius of gyration of that molecular weight polystyrene in toluene (7). In all cases this ratio is less than unity, in some cases considerably so. This would imply that the chains are largely in an extended conformation normal to the interface, i.e. primarily in tails, but it is possible that there are some loops and trains also. Unfortunately, it was not possible to determine the effective polymer layer thickness, with any degree of accuracy, for these samples. Attempts at using P.C.S. were made, but the errors involved in determining particle size by this method were found to be rather large (5-10%, table I). For example, for sample S12/PS13a the diameter of the SiO_2-g-PS particles in toluene was estimated to be 300 ±20 nm; comparing this with the P.C.S. diameter of the bare S12 particles gives a polymer sheath thickness, δ, of 50 ±15 nm. This in turn is to be compared with values of $\sim$9 nm for $2<s^2>^{1/2}$, and a fully extended chain length of $\sim$62 nm, for PS $\bar{M}_n$ 25,000. However, this would lend support, albeit tentative, for an extended conformation normal to the interface. Assuming a value for δ of 50 nm and for Γ of 3.6 mg m^{-2} leads to an average segment volume fraction in the sheath of $\sim$0.047; this compares favourably with the segment volume fraction in a PS random coil having $\bar{M}_n$ 25,600 of $\sim$0.035 in bulk solution in a good solvent.

A comparison of samples S12/PS13a and S12/PS13c with sample S12/PS13b shows that increasing the initial PS:SiO_2 mass ratio increases the final grafted amount in DMF, and also that more efficient grafting is obtained, if the solvent is changed from DMF to toluene at some intermediate stage in the grafting process. This probably has to do with the fact that DMF strongly hydrogen bonds to the surface -OH groups, which could inhibit the reaction with the methoxy-terminated PS chains.

In comparing the values of $\sigma/\pi<s^2>$ for, say, S12/PS13c (new grafting route) and S11/PS19 (earlier Bridger route) it may be concluded that for the same solvent medium (toluene), the present route is somewhat more efficient, but that if DMF is used exclusively in the present route (as is the general case) then they are of comparable efficiency. However, the most important advantage of the present route is the avoidance of a "dry stage" for the silica particles in the reaction scheme, and hence the risk of irreversible aggregation.

In an earlier study in this laboratory (8) it had been shown that PS does not adsorb onto hydrophobised (methylated) silica from DMF. It is clear from the present results, however, (sample S12/PS19, table III) that PS does adsorb onto silica particles which retain their surface hydroxyl groups, despite the strong hydrogen bonding between DMF and these groups referred to above. However, this adsorption is weak and reversible, since the PS

chains could be desorbed by repeated centrifugation/redispersion
in fresh solvent cycles; this is not the case for the grafted
samples, however.

The Γ values quoted in table III were obtained from elemental
microanalysis determinations. In order to check the reliability
of these values, thermogravimetric (TGA) studies were carried out
on several of the SiO_2-g-PS samples. The weight (w) of the sample
is followed as a function of temperature and hence α, the
fractional weight loss, determined, where α is given by

$$\alpha = \left[w(T) - w_o\right] / \left[w_f - w_o\right] \qquad (1)$$

Here $w(T)$ is the value of w at temperature T, w_o the initial value
and w_f the final (high temperature) value. A typical plot of α
versus T is shown in figure 2 for a sample of S12/P13a in DMF that
has been "dried" by pumping under vacuum at ambient temperature.
The initial weight loss up to $\sim320^oC$ may be ascribed to the
removal of physisorbed (H-bonded) or "trapped" DMF (normal B.Pt.
152^oC). The second region of substantial weight loss (i.e. between
~400 and 600^oC) is due to thermal degradation of the grafted PS
chains (9). From the value of Γ at 400^oC the mass of PS/unit mass
of silica may be calculated, and hence Γ. For S12/PS13a the TGA
method gave a value for Γ of 3.1 mg m^{-2}; this compares well with
the value for Γ of 3.6 mg m^{-2} obtained from this sample by
elemental analysis (table III).

Grafting of Polydimethylsiloxane to Silica

The system S15/PDMS3 was prepared by addition of PDMS3 to a dispersion of S15 in a mixture of heptane and ethanol (1:1 volume
ratio). After 24 hr the dispersion was mixed with a three-fold
excess of heptane, and then evaporated, leaving the silica
particles in a PDMS melt. This was then heated to 150^oC under
nitrogen for about 5 hr and redispersed in heptane. This dispersion was the centrifuged and redispersed three times in heptane
to remove any excess polymers. The preparation of S15/PDMS5 was
similar, except that it was heated in refluxing heptane for 24 hr,
instead of the polymer melt. Details of both samples are given in
table IV.

In general, the Γ values for PDMS are very much higher than
the corresponding values for PS of similar molecular weight (e.g.
compare S6/PS18, table III and S15/PDMS5, table IV). This would
imply an even more extended conformation. It is possible that the
greater flexibility chains compared to PS chains would allow this.

Dispersion Stability

Two methods were used to detect the onset of flocculation in the
dispersions: direct visual observation and turbidity/wavelength

Table IV		SiO$_2$-g-PDMS systems			
No.	/nm	$\bar{M}_n$	$\Gamma^{(1)}$ /(mg m^{-2})	$\sigma^{(2)}$ /(nm)^2	$\sigma/\pi<s^2>$
S15/PDMS3	260	72,440	14.3	8.4	.052
S15/PDMS5	260	6,700	9.8	1.14	.066

(1) grafted amount;   (2) area per grafted molecule; $<s^2>^{\frac{1}{2}}$ values assumed to be the same as those for PS in toluene (8)

scans (10). The latter technique was used for silica dispersions in the particle volume fraction (ϕ) range $\sim10^{-5}$ to $\sim10^{-3}$. To this end a Pye Unicam u.v./visible spectrophotometer linked to an AR25 pen recorder was used; the wavelength range used was generally 400-600 nm. Visual assessment was also used, particularly for $\phi > 10^{-3}$. Although this method is somewhat subjective, reproducibility was reasonable ($\sim1\%$) and similar results were obtained by both methods where a direct comparison was made.

For both kinds of polymer-grafted particles, flocculation was induced either by changing the temperature or by adding a non-solvent for the stabilising polymer. In this way critical flocculation temperature (c.f.T) and critical flocculation vol. fractions of non-solvent (c.f.v.) values were obtained, in general as a function of ϕ.

With regard to the SiO$_2$-g-PDMS dispersions, these could be readily redispersed in both methyl ethyl ketone (θ-temp. = 20°C) and bromocyclohexane (θ-temp. = 30°C) to give stable dispersions at room temperature (~20°C). Indeed, the dispersions in bromo-cyclohexane had to be cooled considerably below the θ-temperature before any flocculation was observed. This may be seen in figure 3 where plots of c.f.T. versus ϕ are given for the two SiO$_2$-g-PDMS systems studied (table IV). The lower the c.f.T. the more intrinsically stable the dispersion, but both dispersions are stable under much worse-than-θ conditions. It would seem that the particles with the lower molecular weight grafted PDMS chains are more stable. In both cases the c.f.T. is strongly ϕ-dependent, which would indicate that flocculation is occurring into a shallow minimum in the interparticle interaction energy - separation curve. Vincent et al. (10-12) have shown that particle concentration dependence of the critical flocculation condition results from a balance of energy and entropy terms in the (reversible) floccula-tion process. The question arises: what is the origin of the shallow minimum in this case? Clearly, it is a balance between the steric interaction associated with the perturbation of the grafted polymer layers on two approaching particles, and the

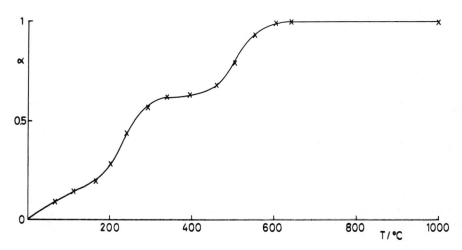

Figure 2.   Thermal gravimetric analysis of SiO_2-g-PS sample
S12/PS13a: α versus temperature (T)

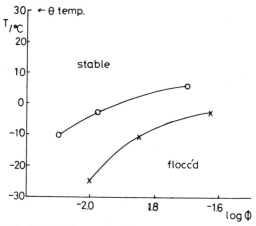

Figure 3.   Critical flocculation temperature (T) versus log
(particle volume fraction ϕ) for the two SiO_2-g-PDMS
dispersions in bromocyclohexane: O, S15/PDMS5;   ×, S15/
PDMS3.

composite van der Waals interactions between the polymer-coated particles across the solvent medium. The fact that the dispersions are stable under worse-than-θ conditions would imply that little-or-no interpenetration of the polymer sheaths occurs as discussed below.

Dobbie et al. (13) showed that stability under worse-than-θ conditions also arose in the case of an aqueous latex system in which an amphipathic block copolymer was adsorbed onto the latex particles at low coverage, such that the stabilising moeities (in this case the polethylene oxide chains) were present in a loop and train conformation, rather than as extended tails. Interpenetration of loops is clearly more difficult than tails. A similar situation could be expected if the tails were present at a very high coverage; once again significant interpenetration would be very difficult. As discussed earlier in this paper, it does seem, from the microanalysis results on the SiO_2-g-PDMS systems (table IV), that the PDMS tails are indeed present at very high coverages. If little interpenetration occurs then the number of potential segment/segment contacts from chains on the two particles is greatly diminished, reducing the contribution from the mixing term. Hence, one has to go to very much worse-than-θ conditions before this (attractive) interaction (in combination with the van der Waals term) builds up to such a level that the depth of the energy minimum becomes significant for flocculation to be observed. The exact contribution from the van der Waals term is, unfortunately, difficult to assess.

The results with the SiO_2-g-PS dispersions are even more complex and difficult to interpret. For example, all the dispersions were stable in toluene at room temperature (good solvent), but whereas S12/PS13b flocculated in cyclohexane (θ-temp = 34.5°C) dispersion S12/PS13a was stable at room temperature. As may be seen from table III the latter dispersion has a high coverage of polystyrene chains. Similar features were observed with n-butyl formate (θ-temp. = -9°C) as the dispersion medium. In this case the higher coverage dispersion S12/PS13a showed no signs of flocculation above -25°C (φ = 1.3 x 10^{-2}). Thus stability under worse-than-θ conditions again results with these very high coverage particles. It had been shown previously (14) that SiO_2-g-PS dispersions produced by the Bridger method, flocculated close to θ-conditions in n-butyl formate.

A somewhat different picture emerged, however, when the SiO_2-g-PS dispersions in toluene were flocculated by adding a non-solvent (n-hexane) at a fixed temperature (24 ±1°C). The results are summarized in fig.4, where the critical solvent composition (volume fraction) is plotted as a function of particle volume fraction. The θ-composition is ∿0.45 volume fraction toluene, as interpolated from data in the literature (15). Therefore, in this case the dispersions produced by the new grafting procedure (S12/ PS13 series) flocculated under better than θ-conditions, the higher-coverage samples being seemingly less stable than the

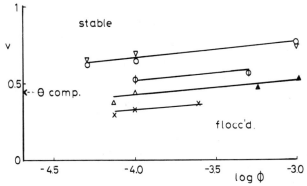

Figure 4. Critical flocculation solvent composition:
toluene + n-hexane (v = volume fraction of toluene), versus
log (particle volume fraction, ϕ) for various SiO_2-g-PS
systems at 24 $\pm 1^{\circ}$C: ∇, S12/PS13c; O, S12/PS13a;
▲, S12/PS13b; Δ, S12/PS13b* (hydrophobed); ϕ, S14/PS13;
×, S11/PS19 (Bridger route).

lower-coverage ones. It is also evident from fig.4 that the
sample prepared by the Bridger route (S11/PS19) requires much
higher concentrations of non-solvent to induce flocculation.
However, a direct comparison is complicated by the different
particle size and polymer molecular weight involved in this sample.
It may be seen from fig.4 that post-hydrophobisation of the
surfaces of the SiO_2-g-PS particles (compare S12/PS13b* with
S12/PS13b) makes little or no difference to their critical
flocculation behaviour. This is not unexpected, since the grafted
PS tails will, effectively, mask any contribution from the surface
groups.
Although detailed interpretation of the results reported here
is difficult, a number of conclusions emerge. Firstly, for the
dispersions produced by the new high-coverage grafting procedures
described in this paper, there is no apparent correlation between
the critical conditions for flocculation and θ-conditions for the
stabilising polymer moeities, as has been found by Napper (16) in
many of his studies on sterically-stabilised dispersions. Secondly,
there is a distinct difference in the stability behaviour of the
dispersions to flocculation induced by a change of temperature to
that produced by added non-solvent. The strong particle-concen-
tration dependence of the critical flocculation conditions (not
found by Napper (16)), implies that flocculation occurs into a
shallow interaction energy minimum. The balance between the
various interactions involved (steric and van der Waals) is a
subtle one in these systems, but it would seem that the mixing
contribution to the steric interaction is significantly reduced at
very high coverages by the grafted polymer chains.

Literature Cited

1. Bridger, K.; Vincent, B. European Polymer J. 1980, 16, 1017.
2. Bridger, K.; Fairhurst, D.; Vincent, B. J. Colloid Interface
    Sci. 1979, 68, 190.
3. Van Helden, A.K.; Jansen, J.W.; Vrij, A. J. Colloid Interface
    Sci. 1981, 81, 354.
4. Stober, W.; Fink, A.; Bohn, E. J. Colloid Interface Sci.
    1968, 26, 62.
5. Bridger, K. Ph.D. Thesis, Bristol, 1979.
6. Laible, R.; Hamann, K. Adv. Colloid Interface Sci. 1980, 13, 65.
7. Rossi, C.; Bianchi, U.; Bianchi, E. Makromol. Chemie 1960,
    41, 31.
8. Lesniewicz, A. M.Sc. Thesis, Bristol, 1981.
9. Malhotta, S.L.; Hesse, J.; Blanchard, L.P. Polymer, 1975, 16,
    81.
10. Long, J.A.; Osmond, D.W.J.; Vincent, B. J. Colloid Interface
    Sci. 1973, 42, 545.
11. Vincent, B.; Luckham, P.F.; Waite, F.A.W. J. Colloid Interface
    Sci. 1980, 78, 508.
12. Cowell, C.; Vincent, B. J.Colloid Interface Sci. 1982, 87, 518.

13. Dobbie, J.W.; Evans, R.; Gibson, D.V.; Smitham, J.B.; Napper, D.H. J. Colloid Interface Sci. 1973, 45, 557.
14. Clarke, J.; Vincent, B. J. Colloid Interface Sci. 1981, 82 208.
15. Bradrup, J.; Immergut, E.H. (ed.) "Polymer Handbook" (Wiley-Interscience) 1975, IV, 157.
16. Napper, D.H. J. Colloid Interface Sci. 1977, 58, 390.

RECEIVED October 7, 1983

Adsorption of, and Steric Stabilization of Silica Particles by, Styrene/Methyl Methacrylate Copolymers in Solvent/Nonsolvent Mixtures

I. F. GUTHRIE[1] and G. J. HOWARD[2]

Department of Polymer and Fiber Science, University of Manchester Institute of Science and Technology, Manchester M60 1QD, England

The adsorption of block and random copolymers of styrene and methyl methacrylate on to silica from their solutions in carbon tetrachloride/n-heptane, and the resulting dispersion stability, has been investigated. Theta-conditions for the homopolymers and analogous critical non-solvent volume fractions for random copolymers were determined by cloud-point titration. The adsorption of block copolymers varied steadily with the non-solvent content, whilst that of the random copolymers became progressively more dependent on solvent quality only as theta-conditions and phase separation were approached.

Colloid stability conferred by random copolymers decreased as solvent quality worsened and became increasingly solvent dependent around theta-conditions. However, dispersions maintain some stability at the theta-point but destabilize close to the appropriate phase separation condition. With block polymers of more than 20% styrene decrease of solvent quality initially worsens dispersion stability, but thereafter the stability improves. This may be due to a better anchoring of block copolymers adsorbed from a micellar solution.

The steric stabilization of dispersed particles by both grafted chains and by physically adsorbed polymers has been much studied in recent years. In the present paper we extend earlier work on

[1]Current address: A.B.M. Chemicals Ltd., Bristol Road, Gloucester GL2 6BX, England.
[2]Current position: Visiting scientist, Marshall Laboratory, E.I. duPont de Nemours, Philadelphia, PA 19146.

the adsorption and stabilization behavior of styrene/methyl methacrylate copolymers (1-3) to mixed solvent/non-solvent solutions.

Experimental

The precipitated silica (J. Crosfield & Sons) was heated <u>in vacuo</u> at 120° for 24h. before use. Two grades of surface areas 186 and 227 m^2 g^{-1} (BET,N_2), were used during this project. Random copolymers, poly(methyl methacrylates) and polystyrene PS I were prepared by radical polymerization; block polymers and the other polystyrenes were made by anionic polymerization with either sodium naphthalene or sodium α methylstyrene tetramer as initiator. The polymer compositions and molecular weights are given in Table I.

Carbon tetrachloride (Analar) was used as received; n-heptane (IP spec.) was redistilled, the middle fraction at 98.0 ± 0.5° being collected. When mixed solvents were used, the polymer was first dissolved in the calculated volume of CCl_4 and the required amount of C_7H_{16} then added.

Cloud-point titrations were made visually under blue illumination with a black background. A small volume of polymer solution in CCl_4 of a concentration such as to give a final value between 3×10^{-2} and 3×10^{-4} g cm^{-3} at the cloud-point was taken and C_7H_{16} added slowly until the system just became turbid. Having noted the end-point, a further increment of CCl_4 was added to redissolve the polymer and non-solvent titration repeated. By starting with several initial polymer concentrations, a set, usually of 10 to 20 end-points, of non-solvent volume fractions (ν_{ns}) and corresponding polymer contents was obtained.

As the cloud-points became difficult to observe accurately at high dilutions, the lowest practical end-point concentration was about 3×10^{-4} g cm^{-3}.

For adsorption measurements a known mass (usually 0.500g) of silica 186 was contacted with 20 cm^3 of polymer solution and the system gently agitated at 25° for 20h., after which the supernatant was separated by centrifugation and the solute concentration determined gravimetrically.

The relative adsorptions of the two liquids (CCl_4 and C_7H_{16}) was found by measuring refractive indices of the initial and final mixtures after contact with the higher area silica. They are found to be almost identical and apparent adsorptions (Table II) are low.

The colloidal stability of silica suspensions in the present work was assessed by sediment volumes and from the optical coagulation rate constant. In the first method, 50 mg of silica was dispersed in 5 cm^3 polymer solution (concentration 10^{-2} g cm^{-3}) in a narrow tube and the sediment height found at equilibrium. Coagulation rates of the same systems were found by plotting reciprocal optical densities (500nm, 1cm cell) against time. When unstable dispersions were handled, the coagulation was followed in

Table I.   Characterization of Polymer Samples.

CODE	f_s	$10^3 M_n$	$10^3 M_v$	n_s	n_m	n_{rs}	n_{rm}
PS III	1.00	174		1671	0		
PS II	1.00		64	614	0		
PS I	1.00		10	96	0		
PMM II	0.00	290		0	2897		
PMM I	0.00		8.7	0	87		
RC 08	0.08	148		118	1356	1.01	11.6
RC 09	0.09	832		745	7535	1.01	10.2
RC 51	0.51	430		2146	2062	1.52	1.46
RC 86	0.86	62		515	84	6.38	1.04
RC 94	0.94	220		1990	127	16.00	1.02
BC 10	0.10	88		88	788		
BC 19	0.19	190		358	1525		
BC 42	0.42	133		549	758		
BC 90	0.90		7.9	69	8		
BC 97	0.97	46		429	13		

f_s = mol fraction styrene in polymer
n_s = average number styrene units
n_m = average number methacrylate units
n_{rs} = average run length of styrene units
n_{rm} = average run length of methacrylate units

for homopolymers, $n_{rs} = n_s$ and $n_{rm} = n_m$; for block polymers, $n_{rs} = n_s$ and $n_{rm} = 0.5 n_m$

Table II.   Relative Adsorption (mg/g) of Solvent
and Non-solvent.

INITIAL (ν_{ns})	FINAL (ν_{ns})	ADSORPTION OF C_7H_{16}
0.00410	0.00355	+3.9
0.01010	0.00980	+1.7
0.02015	0.02040	-4.4
0.04030	0.04160	-7.9
0.04980	0.04650	+1.3
0.99535	0.99505	+2.0

the spectrophotometer by continuous recording of the optical density on a Servoscribe recorder. The reproducibility of the coagulation rate measurements was not good, which was attributed to a
tendency for silica particles to adhere to the walls of the measuring cell.
    Attempts to measure a critical flocculation volume of non-
solvent by titration with non-solvent as used by Napper (4) were
not successful. A sharp transition between a relatively stable
dispersion and a sudden loss of all colloidal stability was never
observed and no unambiguous end-points could be detected.

Results

The theta (θ) conditions for the homopolymers and the random copolymers were determined in binary mixtures of CCl_4 and C_7H_{16} at
25°. The cloud-point titration technique of Elias (5) as modified
by Cornet and van Ballegooijen (6) was employed. The volume fraction of non-solvent at the cloud-point was plotted against the
polymer concentration on a semilogarithmic basis and extrapolation
to $c_2 = 1$ made by least squares analysis of the straight line
plot. Use of concentration rather than polymer volume fraction,
as is required theoretically (6,7), produces little error of the
extrapolated value since the polymers have densities close to
unity.
    The values of $(\nu_{ns})_{crit}$ for the homopolymers and random co-
polymers are regarded as θ-conditions, although caution has to be
exercised (8) as the system is a ternary one of polymer/solvent/
non-solvent. Our results show the critical non-solvent volume
fraction to increase non-linearly with the proportion of styrene
in the random copolymer (Figure 1). The θ-conditions for the random copolymers are at slightly worse solvent quality to that expected from the simple compositional average of the parent homopolymers. Similar observations have been made in other systems
(9-11). Although the higher M.W. samples have similar slopes to
their cloud-point/concentration curves, the lower polymers show
steeper gradients. According to Napper (7), the technique is most
suitable in the M.W. range 10^5 to 10^7. The discrepancy in the
$(\nu_{ns})_{crit}$ for the two polystyrenes may be traced to their molecular weights; the preferred θ-value is taken to be that of the high
M.W. sample. Values of $(\nu_{ns})_{crit}$ are collected in Table III.
Although the negative value for poly(methyl methacrylate) cannot
be realised in practice, the value is to be expected from a polymer dissolved in a solvent below the θ-temperature. This is reported to be 27° (12) in CCl_4, whilst the cloud-point titrations
were made at 25°.
    Cloud-point measurements were also made with the block poly-
mers even though the theta concept has little meaning in this
case. With the block copolymers the cloud-point is less easily
seen as the change is to a low turbidity only. Unlike the random
copolymers and the homopolymers, where gross phase separation

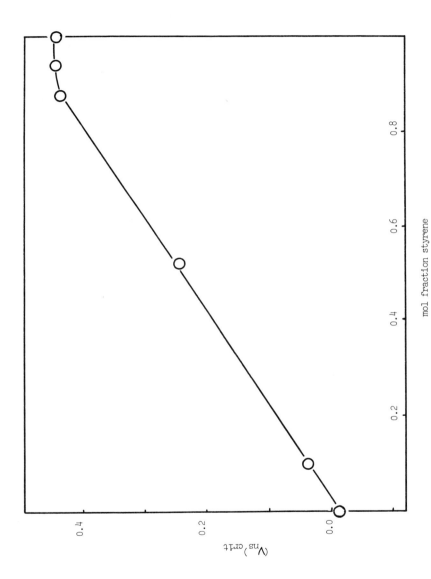

Figure 1.   Random copolymers of styrene and methyl methacrylate. $(\nu_{ns})_{crit}$ of CCl_4/C_7H_{16} mixtures as function of styrene content.

occurred immediately beyond the end-point, the block polymers showed a wide range of solvent/non-solvent compositions after the
'end-point' in which the liquid was cloudy but colloidally stable. This observation is interpreted as a micro-phase separation
to form micelles, a general feature with block copolymers in selective solvents; the 'insoluble' blocks are protected from macroscopic precipitation by the selectively solvated 'soluble' sequences (13-15). In most cases, only when the non-solvent content was close to that critical for polystyrene did block copolymers show macro-phase separation. Table III thus includes cloud-
point data at finite concentrations as well as $(v_{ns})_{crit}$.

		Table III.	Cloud-point Titrations	
code	$(v_{ns})_{crit}$	$(v_{ns})^1$	(v_{ns}) stability limit	
PS III	0.442	0.482	)	
PS I	0.415	0.517	)	
			)	
PMM II	−0.016	0.018^2	)	unstable beyond
PMM I	−0.014	0.128	)	cloud-point
			)	
RC 08	0.036	0.065	)	
RC 51	0.242	0.272	)	
RC 86	0.435	0.470	)	
RC 94	0.444	0.477	)	
BC 10	0.006	0.049	> 0.059	
BC 19	−0.009	0.053	> 0.392	
BC 42	−0.014	0.071	> 0.400	
BC 90	0.011	0.158	> 0.196	
BC 97	−0.160	$0.2--0.3^3$	> 0.449	

^{1}at 10^{-2} g cm^{-3}
^{2}not completely soluble
^{3}end-point difficult to detect

Previous studies of styrene/methyl methacrylate copolymers and homopolymers had shown that adsorption equilibrium is normally attained in an hour or two at 25° (1,3) except in the case of graft
copolymers (3). In the present instance, block copolymer BC 42
adsorbed from CCl_4 reaches equilibrium in 2h.; however, when the
same polymer is adsorbed from a mixed CCl_4/C_7H_{16} solvent $(v_{ns}) =$
0.40, where the solution is micellar, the process is slower, re-
quiring some 20h. for completion. Adsorption isotherms were of
the high affinity type and an example is shown as Figure 2. The
concentration for micelle formation is marked on the curve and no
discontinuity in this region of the isotherm is seen.
    In general, the relation between polymer adsorption at the

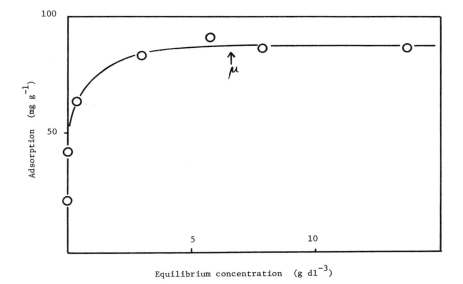

Figure 2. Adsorption isotherm of BC 42 in CCl_4/C_7H_{16} at $(\nu_{ns}) = 0.08$. Arrow marks micelle formation.

isotherm plateau and polymer composition is as we have found in the past (1,2,16). Poly(methyl methacrylate) is better adsorbed than polystyrene, and the copolymers, whether random or block, are adsorbed at least as well as the better adsorbed homopolymer. The results from CCl_4 solution are given as Table IV; some of the variability, as with BC 90, may be attributed to molecular size effects.

Table IV.   Plateau Adsorption (mg g^{-1}) on Silica[1] from CCl_4

code	adsorption	code	adsorption	code	adsorption
PS III	41	RC 08	72	BC 10	62
PS II	35	RC 09	60	BC 19	69
PS I	34	RC 51	48	BC 42	74
		RC 86	71	BC 90	55
PMM I	60	RC 94	72	BC 97	93

[1]surface area 186 m^2g^{-1}

The adsorption behavior from solvent/non-solvent mixtures is summarized in Figures 3 and 4. Methyl methacrylate homopolymer and the random copolymer of low styrene content have limited solubility ranges; here the adsorption steadily increases through the θ-condition as phase separation is approached. Polystyrene, on the other hand, maintains a fairly constant level of adsorption until the solvency of the medium is substantially worsened, when the amount adsorbed increases at an increasing rate through the θ-point and becomes very high close to the limit of measurement near phase separation. The high styrene random copolymers have the same shaped curve as polystyrene; only RC 86 is drawn in Figure 3 as the data points for RC 94 are nearly the same. The random copolymer of intermediate composition shows adsorption behavior midway between the extremes. The block copolymers have a steadily increasing adsorption as non-solvent is added to the system at all polymer compositions and with no apparent discontinuity in the micellar region. Polymer BC 90 is an exception; its adsorption is low and remains unchanged as the solvency is worsened. However, this sample is a low M.W. polymer, and is essentially a polystyrene chain end-capped with four methyl methacrylate units. Although it shows a poorly defined micellar behavior, it may be expected to adsorb in a similar manner to polystyrene.

The sediment volume of silica in CCl_4 solutions of poly (methyl methacrylate) was approximately 9 cc^4g^{-1} but variable results were found in solutions of polystyrene, depending on the molecular wt. of the polymer. Lower M.W. samples are poor stabilizers and the dispersions are so unstable that optical coagulation rates could not be measured with confidence. Figure 5 shows the general trend in CCl_4. All polymers, whatever their composition, are superior to the pure solvent.

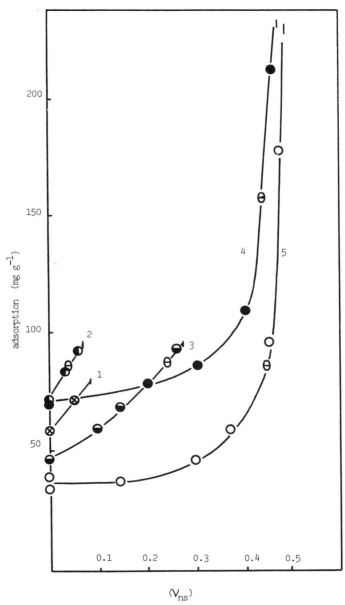

Figure 3.   Plateau adsorption from solvent/non-solvent
mixtures.   curve 1, PMM I; 2, RC 08; 3, RC 51; 4, RC 86;
5, PS III.   θ marks the theta-point.   Vertical lines are
(v_{ns}) for phase separation at c = 10^{-2} g cm^{-3}.

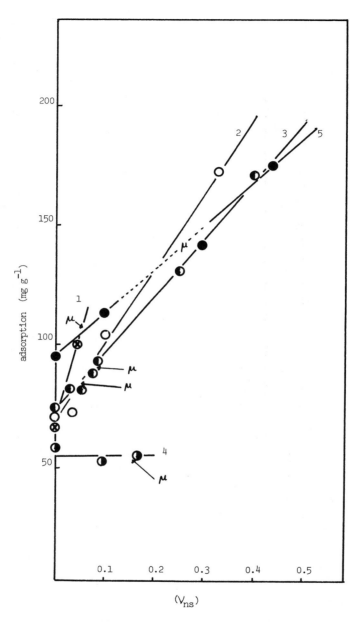

Figure 4. Plateau adsorption from solvent/non-solvent
mixtures. curve 1, BC 10; 2, BC 19; 3, BC 42; 4, BC 90;
5, BC 97. μ marks micelle formation at c = 10^{-2} g cm^{-3}.

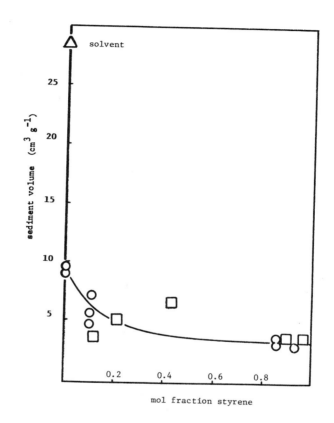

Figure 5.   Sediment volume of silica 186 in CCl_4 solutions of polymers of various styrene contents.   Squares, block polymers; circles, random copolymers or homopolymers.

In the absence of polymer the sediment volume of silica depends on the non-solvent fraction of the medium as shown in Figure
6. The sediment volume assessment of steric stabilization behavior of the copolymers is illustrated in Figures 7a to 7c. At low
styrene contents, both the random and block copolymers show a
steady increase in sediment volume as the non-solvent content is
raised up to the phase separation value. With polystyrene and
random copolymers of high styrene content, the sediment volume
stays largely constant with alteration in the non-solvent fraction
until the theta-point is approached and then continues to become
larger as the limit of solubility is reached. In Figure 7b only
the data points of RC 86 are shown, RC 94 giving almost identical
values.

Block copolymers at high styrene contents behave similarly,
with no break around the micellar region. Two of the block copolymers are shown separately in Figure 7c. The low M.W. BC 90
moves from an apparently adequate stabilization in CCl_4 to a new
level of modest protection at higher C_7H_{16} volume fractions. The
block polymer of 42% styrene gives a hint of a discontinuity at
the non-solvent content for micelle formation, but thereafter
stabilizes the silica until the conditions approach those for
phase separation.

As judged by the optical coagulation rate, the compositional
dependence of silica stabilization in CCl_4 (Figure 8) is much the
same as is shown by sediment volumes. Changing the non-solvent
fraction in polymer solutions may produce very large changes in
the coagulation of the silica dispersions, and Figure 9 shows an
example of this. Poly(methyl methacrylate) and the low styrene
random copolymer rapidly become poor stabilizers as the heptane
content is increased towards the phase separation value as seen in
Figure 10. This figure also shows that polystyrene and the high
styrene copolymers gradually worsen as stabilizers through the
theta-point and become poor close to the solvent composition for
polymer precipitation. Again, as with the sediment volume measurements, RC 51 occupies an intermediate position.

The block polymer of 10% styrene content behaves like the
corresponding random copolymer as the non-solvent is added. However, the other block polymers exhibit a more complex pattern.
Thus, Figure 11a shows that both the 19% and the 97% polymers give
worse stabilization up to the micellar region but then improve.
Polymer BC 42 was studied in more detail around the micellar
region and Figure 11b suggests that a break in coagulation rates
occurs.

Discussion

Colloid stability assessments of silica dispersions in CCl_4 by
sediment volume and coagulation rate are in general concordance
and confirm the pattern previously reported by Barron and Howard

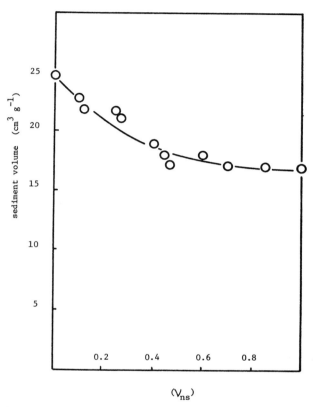

Figure 6.   Sediment volume of silica 227 in polymer-free CCl_4/C_7H_{16} mixtures.

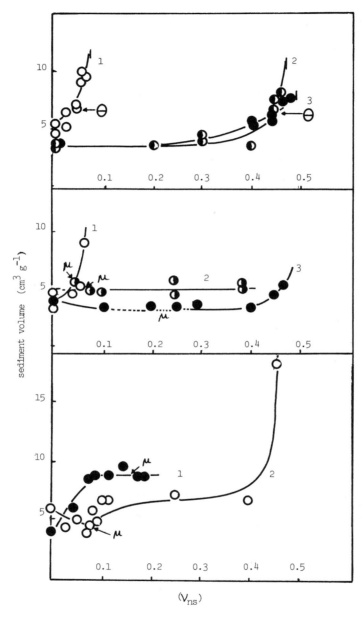

Figure 7. Sediment volumes of silica 186 in solutions of
polymers at various non-solvent contents. Plateau adsorption.
(a) curve 1, RC 08; 2, RC 86; 3, PS III. (b) curve 1, BC 10;
2, BC 19; 3, BC 97. (c) curve 1, BC 90; 2, BC 42. Sediment
volume in pure CCl_4 is 28.5 cm^3/g and at (ν_{ns}) = 0.5 is approx.
18 cm^3/g.

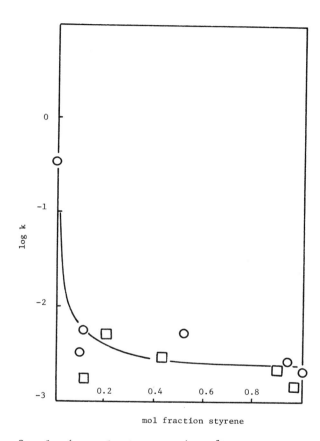

Figure 8.   log(coagulation rate/min^{-1}) of silica 186 in
CCl$_4$ solutions of polymers with various styrene contents.
Squares, block polymers; circles, random copolymers or
homopolymers.

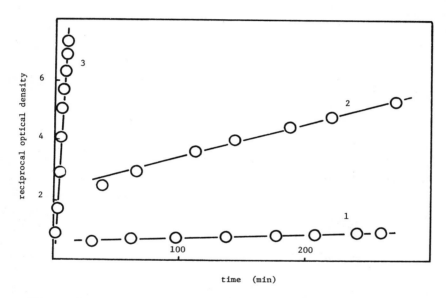

Figure 9. Reciprocal optical density as function of time for silica 186 dispersions in solutions of RC 86. curve 1, $(\nu_{ns}) = 0.00$, $k = 1.05 \times 10^{-3}$; 2, $(\nu_{ns}) = 0.20$, $k = 1.07 \times 10^{-2}$; 2, $(\nu_{ns}) = 0.45$, $k = 1.29$.

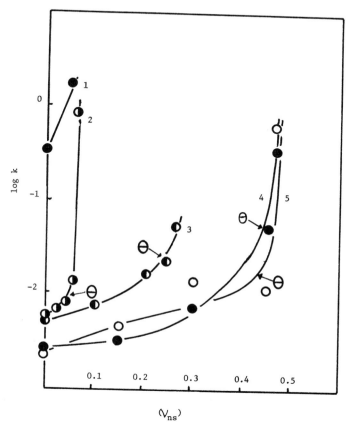

Figure 10. log(coagulation rate/min^{-1}) of silica 186 in solutions of polymers at various non-solvent contents. Plateau adsorption.   curve 1, PMM I; 2, RC 08; 3, RC 51; 4, RC 94; 5, PS III.

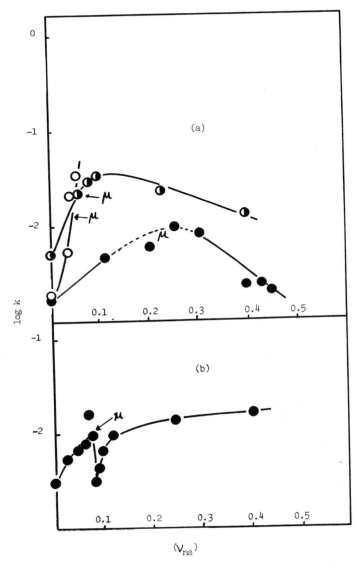

Figure 11. log(coagulation rate/min⁻¹) of silica 186 in
solutions of polymers at various non-solvent contents.
(a) curve 1, BC 10; 2, BC 19; 3, BC 97.
(b) BC 42.

(3). Poly(methyl methacrylate) provides a level of stabilization
even though the solution in CCl_4 is below the θ-temperature. All
the copolymers, both random and block, are better stabilizers than
PMM, the methacrylate units acting as anchors, with stabilizing
sequences of styrene loops, of block copolymers, or mixed loops
and tails, of random copolymers, at better than θ-conditions.
Higher M.W. polystyrenes give silica dispersions too unstable to
measure by our optical method: the sediment volumes are between
those of poly(methyl methacrylate) solutions and pure solvent.
When solutions of random copolymers in solvent/non-solvent mixtures were used, the silica sediment volumes are found to remain
at the level found for CCl_4 solutions until the solvent composition gets close to the θ-point. However, the sediment volume in
the polymer-free solvent/non-solvent mixtures decreases with (ν_{ns})
so that a progressive lessening in stability is indicated, as is
confirmed by the optical coagulation rate data. The weakly stabilizing polystyrene also shows the same pattern. The silica dispersions remain stable beyond the $(\nu_{ns})_{crit}$ value, identified here
as the θ-condition, and lose their stability completely only at
the phase separation condition appropriate for the concentration
of polymer in the system. Thus the steric stabilization progressively decreases through the θ-region even though the amount of
polymer adsorbed increases markedly. The block polymer of low
styrene content is quite similar to the corresponding random copolymer but the other block polymers, although generally similar
to the random copolymers in sediment volume behavior, show some
interesting differences in their destabilization rate constants.
In the micellar region the trend to decreasing colloid stability
is arrested and a partial improvement, in line with the enhanced
level of polymer adsorption, is noted until the conditions for
gross phase separation are reached. Only the intermediate block
copolymer BC 42 shows indications of discontinuities in behavior
at the solvent composition for micelle formation. The results
presented here do not show the sharp transition from stability to
instability found experimentally (4,8,17) by Napper and generally
expected on theoretical grounds. However, there are important
differences in experimental methodology that must be emphasised.
In common with some other authors (18-20), Napper removed excess
stabilizer from the dispersion medium so as to give the dispersed
particles full surface coverage, leaving negligible amounts of
free polymer in solution. As the solvency was worsened, no more
polymer could be adsorbed, so that critical flocculation conditions do not necessarily correspond to surface saturation. In
the present work, which may refer more closely with some practical
applications, the stabilizer is kept at the plateau adsorption
level but at the expense of complicating the system by the presence of free polymer. Clarke and Vincent (21) have reported on
the effect of free polystyrene on the stability of silica with
terminally-attached sytrene chains, but the very considerable differences to our studies make an assessment of the possible role
played by unadsorbed polymer unproductive.

316 POLYMER ADSORPTION AND DISPERSION STABILITY

Literature Cited

1. Herd, J. M.; Hopkins, A. J.; Howard, G. J. J. Polymer Sci. 1971, C34, 211.
2. Hopkins, A. J.; Howard, G. J. J. Polymer Sci. 1971, A-2 9, 841.
3. Barron, M. J.; Howard, G. J. J. Polymer Sci., Polymer Chem. 1974, 12, 1269.
4. Napper, D. H. Trans. Faraday Soc. 1968, 64, 1701.
5. Elias, H. G. Makromol. Chem. 1961, 50, 1.
6. Cornet, C. F.; van Ballegooijen, H. Polymer 1966, 7, 263.
7. Napper, D. H. Polymer 1969, 10, 181.
8. Dondos, A.; Benoit, H. J. Polymer Sci. 1969, B7, 335.
9. Dondos, A. J. Polymer Sci. 1971, B9, 871.
10. Kotliar, A. M. J. Polymer Sci. 1961, 55, 71.
11. Kotaka, T.; Ohnuma, H.; Inagaki, H. Polymer 1969, 10, 517.
12. Fox, T. G. Polymer 1962, 3, 111.
13. Tuzar, Z.; Kratochvil, M. Makromol. Chem. 1972, 160, 301.
14. Krause, S. J. Physical Chem. 1962, 68, 1948.
15. Selb, J.; Gallot, Y. J. Polymer Sci. 1975, B13, 615.
16. Howard, G. J.; McGrath, M. J. J. Polymer Sci., Polymer Chem., 1977, 15, 1721.
17. Evans, R.; Napper, D. H. J. Colloid & Interface Sci. 1975, 52, 260.
18. Walbridge, D. J.; Waters, J. A. Discussions Faraday Soc. 1966, 42, 294.
19. Croucher, M. D.; Hair, M. L. J. Colloid & Interface Sci. 1981, 81, 257.
20. Cowell, C.;Li-In-On, R.; Vincent, B. J. Chemical Soc. Faraday I 1978, 74, 337.
21. Clarke, J.; Vincent, B. J. Colloid & Interface Sci. 1981, 82, 208.

RECEIVED November 22, 1983

Stability of Sterically Stabilized Nonaqueous Dispersions at Elevated Temperatures and Pressures

M. D. CROUCHER and K. P. LOK

Xerox Research Centre of Canada, 2480 Dunwin Drive, Mississauga, Ontario
L5L 1J9, Canada

The effect of an applied pressure on the UCFT has been
investigated for polymer particles that are sterically
stabilized by polyisobutylene and dispersed in 2-
methyl-butane. It was observed that the UCFT was
shifted to a higher temperature as the hydrostatic
pressure applied to the system increased. There
was also a qualitative correlation between the UCFT
as a function of applied pressure and the θ conditions
of PIB + 2-methylbutane in (P,T) space. These results
can be rationalized by considering the effect of pressure on the free volume dissimilarity contribution to
the free energy of close approach of interacting particles. Application of corresponding states concepts
to the theory of steric stabilization enables a
qualitative prediction of the observed stability
behaviour as a function of temperature and pressure.

During the past decade, considerable effort has been expended
in establishing the limits of colloidal stability of sterically
stabilized dispersions. The stability has been monitored by
changing the solvent quality of the dispersion medium relative
to that of the stabilizing polymer. This change can be brought
about by the addition of non-solvent for the steric stabilizer
or by changing the temperature of the system. The incipient
instability caused by these changes is a reversible phenomenon
and spontaneous redispersion occurs if the solvency of the disperse medium is improved with respect to that of the stabilizing
macromolecular moiety.

It is now well established that the critical flocculation
conditions for dispersions with a low particle concentration
can be correlated with the θ conditions of the steric stabilizing moiety in free solution (1). This correlation is only
found in systems where desorption of the stabilizer does not
occur and where the thickness of the steric barrier is sufficient to completely screen the attractive van der Waals

0097–6156/84/0240–0317$06.00/0

interactions between the particles. Although the stability
criteria for sterically stabilized particles in both aqueous
and nonaqueous media are the same, their phase behaviour show
important differences. For instance, it has been shown (2)
that, in principle, all sterically stabilized nonaqueous dispersions exhibit two flocculation temperatures which are known
as the upper critical flocculation temperature (UCFT) and the
lower critical flocculation temperature (LCFT). There is a
qualitative correlation between the UCFT and the θ temperature
associated with the lower critical solution temperature (θ_L)
while the LCFT correlates with the θ temperature associated with
the upper critical solution temperature (θ_u). In non-polar polymer
solutions, it is found that $\theta_L > \theta_u$ while for most aqueous solutions $\theta_u > \theta_L$. The mechanisms of phase separation in aqueous
systems are quite different in nature from those observed in
nonaqueous polymer soltuions. This will also hold true for the
origin of flocculation in aqueous and nonaqueous sterically
stabilized dispersions.

The analogous phase behaviour between non-polar polymer
solutions and nonaqueous polymer dispersions has allowed the
incipient flocculation behaviour of sterically stabilized dispersions to be rationalized using the concepts inherent in
modern polymer solution thermodynamics (3). This analysis indicates that it is the combinational entropy of the steric
stabilizer in the dispersion medium that stabilizes the particles against flocculation while the contact energy and free
volume dissimiliarity between the steric stabilizer and the dispersion medium promote flocculation of the dispersion. In principle, flocculation at the LCFT is caused by the contact energy
dissimilarity term while flocculation at the UCFT is caused by
the free volume dissimilarity contribution to the free energy
of the interacting particles.

Besides temperature and addition of non-solvent, pressure
can also be expected to affect the solvency of the dispersion
medium for the solvated steric stabilizer. A previous analysis
(3) of the effect of an applied pressure indicated that the UCFT
should increase as the applied pressure increases, while the
LCFT should be relatively insensitive to applied pressure. The
purpose of this communication is to examine the UCFT of a non-
aqueous dispersion as a function of applied pressure. For dispersions of polymer particles stabilized by polyisobutylene (PIB)
and dispersed in 2-methylbutane, it was observed that the UCFT
moves to higher temperatures with increasing applied pressure.
These results can qualitatively be rationalized by considering
the effect of pressure on the free volume dissimilarity contribution to the free energy of close approach of the interacting
particles.

EXPERIMENTAL SECTION

Materials. The solvent 2-methylbutane (Wiley Organics) was greater than 99% pure and was used as received. The Isopar G (Exxon) is a pure high boiling mixture of aliphatic hydrocarbons and was used without further purification. The monomers, methyl methacrylate (Matheson, Coleman and Bell) and vinyl acetate (Matheson, Coleman and Bell) were distilled to remove inhibitor and kept over 4 A molecular sieves before being used. Two samples of PIB (Polysciences) were used as the steric stabilizers. The high molecular weight sample was found to have $M_n \simeq 2 \times 10^5$ while the lower molecular sample had $M_n \simeq 4 \times 10^4$. These values were obtained from GPC curves which had been calibrated using polystyrene standards and are therefore only relative values.

Dispersion Polymerization. This was carried out in two stages. Firstly, the amphipathic stabilizers poly(isobutylene-g-methyl methacrylate) and poly(isobutylene-g-vinyl acetate) were prepared by dissolving PIB (10 g) in Isopar G (200mL) and adding either vinyl acetate or methyl methacrylate (2 g) and benzoyl peroxide to this solution at 353 K. The polymerization was allowed to proceed overnight under constant stirring after which a clear solution was obtained. To these respective graft copolymer solutions at 353 K were added further vinyl acetate or methyl methacrylate (40 g) and benzoyl peroxide (0.7 g). The mixture became opalescent within 45 minutes and the reaction allowed to proceed for a further 12 hours, after which the particles were centrifuged, excess solvent decanted off and the particles redispersed in fresh 2-methylbutane. This cleaning procedure was carried out until no more free polymer was precipitated by the addition of a non-solvent to the decanted disperse medium.

The poly(vinyl acetate) particles stabilized by PIB were found, using a Coulter Nanosizer, to have a diameter of ~0.3μm while the poly(methyl methacrylate) particles were ~0.4μm diameter.

Flocculation Measurements. These high pressure flocculation measurements were carried out using equipment that was originally desiged by Bardin (4) and Zeman (5). The high pressure equipment used is shown schematically in Figure 1(a). All fittings, valves and tubing (High Pressure Equipment and Autoclave Engineers Company) were made of stainless steel. The pressure is applied with a manual pump (Model 37-6-30) through high pressure tubes with an inside diameter of 0.083 inches. The pressure transmitting fluid used was Dow Corning 200 siloxane fluid. A set of high pressure valves enables the introduction of pressure fluid from the reservoir without interfering with the pressure maintained inside the pressure vessel or the gauge. The pressure was measured using a 0-3000 bar factory calibrated Heise solid front gauge.

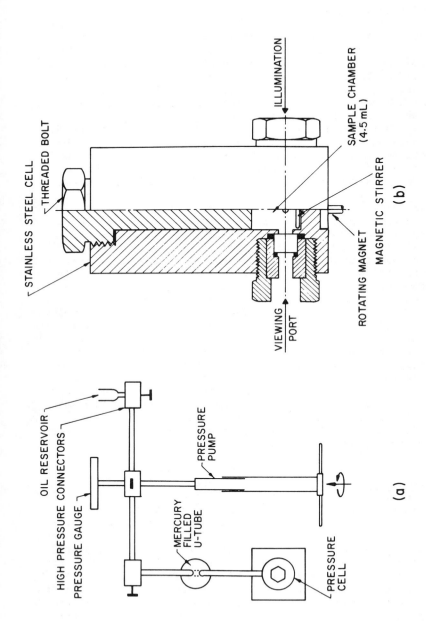

Figure 1 (a) Shows a schematic diagram of the apparatus used for the high pressure measurements. (b) Shows a schematic diagram of the pressure bomb.

The flocculation measurements were carried out in a stainless
steel optical cell which had glass windows (0.5 inches diameter)
sealed with Teflon O-rings. A schematic diagram of the cell is
shown in Figure 1(b). The total volume of the cell is 4.5mL and
the dispersion could be kept agitated with a small magnetic
stirrer. The pressure generator was connected to the pressure
cell via a mercury filled steel U-tube. The cell was heated
using a heating tape and controlled using a Variac. The volume
of metal in the cell relative to that of the solution was such
that uniform temperatures were attained in the cell and a constant temperature bath was unnecessary. A chromel-alumel thermocouple in direct contact with the dispersion was used to measure
the temperature.

It was observed that both the poly (vinyl acetate)(PVAc) and
poly(methyl methacrylate) (PMMA) latexes stabilized by PIB and

All the measurements reported in this paper were carried out
at a particle concentration of $\leqslant 1$ weight %. Only one concentration was investigated since it has been observed previously ($\underline{6}$)
that there is little variation in the UCFT as a function of
particle concentration in the dilute concentration regime. The
dispersion being investigated was added to the pressure bomb
which was sealed and ~200 bars pressure applied to the system.
The latex was then equilibrated at a specific temperature while
being continuously agitated. The pressure was then slowly released until flocculation of the latex was observed at which
point the light illuminating the opposite side of the cell was
clearly visible. In the same instance application of pressure
and agitation of the dispersion usually caused the flocculated
latex to redisperse. The flocculation pressures reported are
for readily apparent flocculation as observed through a travel-
ing microscope and may not represent the onset of flocculation.
Since the pressure gauge was calibrated in 2 bar graduated steps
and flocculation appeared to take place over a range of pressures
the UCFP values reported are probably only accurate to $\underline{5+}$ bars.
Phase equilibria measurements on PIB in 2-methylbutane were also
carried out in the same cell, the solution containing ~4% by
weight PIB.

RESULTS AND DISCUSSION

General Comments. The (P, T) cloud curve for the PIB of M_n~2 x10^5
dissolved in 2-methylbutane agreed,within experimental error,
with other values reported in the literature ($\underline{6},\underline{7}$). The slope
of the curve differed from other results but this could have
been caused by the molecular weight distribution exhibited by
the sample used in this study. The cloud point curve for an
infinite molecular weight polymer, i.e. θ conditions, was established from our measurements and from literature data and is shown
plotted in Figure 2. It can be seen that θ_L increase as a function of applied pressure with a slope $(dT/dP)_c$ of 0.56.

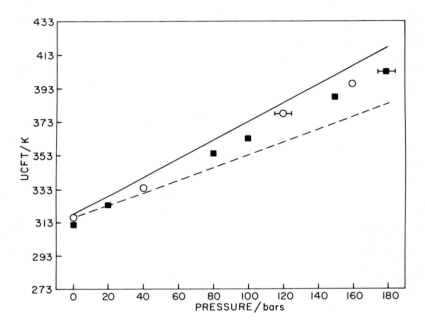

Figure 2   The upper critical flocculation temperature is shown
plotted against the applied pressure. ∎ refers to the PMMA
latex while, o refers to the PVAc latex.   The solid line
represents θ conditions for a solution of PIB + 2-methylbutane
while the dashed line represents the theoretically calculated
UCFT as a function of pressure.

dispersed in 2-methylbutane flocculated on heating. The PMMA latex flocculated at 312 K while the PVAc latex flocculated at 316 K. The θ temperature for PIB for 2-methylbutane has been reported at 318 K (8). The result again confirms the observation that the θ temperature associated with the upper critical solution temperature of the macromolecular steric stabilizer dissolved in the dispersion medium normally represents the upper limit for the stability of nonaqueous dispersions.

When pressure is applied to the latex, the UCFT is seen to move to higher temperatures as indicated in Figure 2. It was found that the PMMA latex stabilized by PIB of $M_n \sim 2 \times 10^5$ could be fitted to the same curve as the PVAc latex stabilized by PIB of $M_n \sim 4 \times 10^4$. A linear regression analysis of the UCFT as a function of applied pressure gave:

$$T_{UCFT} = 0.504P + 315.2 \qquad (1)$$

where P is the pressure in bars and T_{UCFT} is given in degrees K. Figure 2 also indicates that the latexes consistently flocculate under worse than θ conditions. The slope of UCFT data, $(dT/dP)_{UCFT}$ = 0.50, which is smaller than the slope of the critical solution behaviour, indicating that the correlation with θ conditions becomes worse as the pressure increases. More importantly, however, the trend observed in the UCFT as a function of applied pressure parallels the behaviour of the PIB solution. Given the uncertainties involved in calculating θ conditions and the subjective nature of the flocculation measurements, we prefer not to ascribe any special significance to the differences between the θ and the UCFT data. Figure 2 also indicates that the nature of the core polymer and the molecular weight of the stabilizer have little effect on the (P, T) flocculation conditions of the latex indicating that the van der Waals forces between the particles are well screened.

It was suggested in a previous publication (9) that flocculation at the UCFT can be ascribed to the free volume dissimilarity between the polymer stabilizing the particle and the low molecular weight dispersion medium. Incorporating this idea in a quantitative way into the theory of steric stabilization allowed for a qualitative interpretation of the experimental data. This idea is further extended to include the effect of pressure on the critical flocculation conditions.

Theory of Steric Stabilization. A detailed description of the competing theories can be obtained from other publications (1-3) and only an outline will be given here. Almost all the acceptable theoretical descriptions have their origins in the Flory-Krigbaum theory (10) for a dilute polymer solution which has been adapted to the case of sterically stabilized particles.

The simplest expression for the free energy of interpenetration of two particles, ($\underline{1}$), $\Delta G_1{}^M$, is:

$$\Delta G_1{}^M = 2\pi N\omega^2 a\left(v_2{}^2 \over V_1\right)(1/2 - \chi)kTS \qquad (2)$$

where ω is the weight of stabilizing moiety per unit surface area and v_2 the partial specific column. V_1 is the molar volume of the disperse medium, a is the radius of the particles and N is Avogadro's number. The parameter χ characterizes the interaction between the stabilizer and the dispersion medium while the S parameter describes the distance dependence of the free energy of interaction.

The S parameter is a function of the segment density distribution of the stabilizing chains. The conformation, and hence the segment density distribution function of polymers at interfaces, has been the subject of intensive experimental and theoretical work and is a subject of much debate ($\underline{1}$). Since we are only interested in qualitative and not quantitative predictions, we choose the simplest distribution function, namely the constant segment density function, which leads to an S function of the form ($\underline{11}$):

$$S = 2\left(1 - {d_o \over 2L}\right)^2 \qquad (3)$$

where d_o is the minimum distance of separation of the chains which must lie between $L \leqslant d_o \leqslant 2L$.

If a sterically stabilized dispersion is to be stable, then the free energy of mixing in the interpenetration regime ($\Delta G_1{}^M$) must be positive. Equation 2 indicates that $\Delta G_1{}^M$ is positive when $\chi < 1/2$ and negative when $\chi > 1/2$. Thus the transition from stability to instability is predicted to occur under slightly worse than θ conditions (at the θ point $\chi = 1/2$). Therefore, the stability of the dispersion is controlled by the antipathy between the stabilizing polymer and the dispersion medium. In a previous analysis ($\underline{3}$) of the LCFT and UCFT data using corresponding states theory, it was argued that flocculation at the LCFT is caused mainly by the contact energy dissimilarity between the stabilizing moiety and the dispersion medium, while flocculation at the UCFT is caused by the free volume dissimilarity between the stabilizer and the dispersion medium. Both of these contributions to $\Delta G_1{}^M$ are embodied in the χ parameter and this is discussed in quantitative terms in the following section.

Corresponding States Expressions. In corresponding states theory ($\underline{12}$) the basic parameters characterizing a liquid are the reduced temperature $(\tilde{T})$, volume $(\tilde{V})$ and pressure $(\tilde{P})$ defined by:

$$\tilde{T} = \frac{T}{T^*}; \qquad \tilde{P} = \frac{P}{P^*} \qquad \text{and} \qquad \tilde{V} = \frac{V}{V^*} \tag{4}$$

where the starred quantities are reduction parameters which are obtained from equation of state data. In the Flory model $\tilde{P}$, $\tilde{V}$ and $\tilde{T}$ are linked by an equation of state of the form (13):

$$\frac{\tilde{P}\tilde{V}}{\tilde{T}} = \frac{\tilde{V}^{1/3}}{\tilde{V}^{1/3}-1} - \frac{1}{\tilde{V}\tilde{T}} \tag{5}$$

from which $\tilde{V}$ can be obtained at any temperature and pressure. The expression for the $\chi(P,T)$ parameter obtained from the Prigogine-Patterson-Flory type theories (12-14) is:

$$\chi(P,T) = \frac{U_1}{RT}\nu^2 + \frac{C_{P,1}}{2R}\left[\tau + \frac{\beta_1 P_1}{\alpha_1 T_1}\pi\right]^2 \tag{6}$$

where U_1 is the molar configurational energy, $C_{P,1}$ is the molar configurational heat capacity, α_1 and β_1 are the thermal expansion coefficient and isothermal compressibility of the solvent at a pressure P, respectively. The free volume dissimilarity between the stabilizing polymer and the dispersion medium enters through the τ parameter which is defined as:

$$\tau = 1 - \frac{T_1^*}{T_2^*} \tag{7}$$

The ν parameter in Equation 6 expresses the contact energy dissimilarity between the stabilizer and the dispersion medium while π describes the differences in P^* between the components, viz:

$$\pi = \frac{P_1^*}{P_2^*} - 1 \tag{8}$$

The expressions for U_1 and $C_{P,1}$ in Equation 6 are of the van der Waals type, thus:

$$U_1 = -P_1^* V_1^* \tilde{V}_1^{-1} \tag{9}$$

and

$$C_{P,1} = \frac{P_1^* V_1^*}{T_1^*} \quad \tilde{C}_{P,1} = cR\, \tilde{C}_{p,1} \quad (10)$$

where $3c$ is the number of external degrees of freedom of the polymeric moiety. The reduced heat capacity is described by:

$$\tilde{C}_{P,1}^{-1} = (1 - 2/3\, \tilde{v}_1^{-1/3}) - \frac{2(1-\tilde{v}_1^{-1/3})}{1 + \tilde{P}_1 \tilde{v}_1^2} \quad (11)$$

and

$$\frac{\beta_1 P_1}{\alpha_1 T_1} = \frac{\tilde{P}_1 \tilde{v}_1^2}{1 + \tilde{P}_1 \tilde{v}_1^2} \quad (12)$$

The reduction parameters required for application of the theory can be calculated from equation of state quantities using the equations of Flory (13) or by using values reported in the literature.

Comparison of Theory and Experiment. The expression for the free energy of interpenetration of sterically stabilized particles may be obtained by combining Equations 2, 3 and 6. Using these expressions ΔG_1^M can be calculated as a function of both temperature and pressure. In a previous publication (9) we were able to correlate theory and experiment for particles stabilized by PIB and dispersed in aliphatic hydrocarbons by considering only the combinational and free volume terms in ΔG_1^M, i.e., we put $v_2 = 0$ in Equation 6. ΔG_1^M can then be written as:

$$\Delta G_1^M = \Delta G_1^M(\text{comb}) + \Delta G_1^M(\text{free vol}) \quad (13)$$

The combinational contribution to ΔG_1^M for PMMA particles stabilized by PIB in 2-methylbutane is shown plotted as a function of temperature in Figure 3(a). The values of the parameters used in Equations 2 and 3 were $\omega = 8 \times 10^{-8}$ g cm^{-2}, $a = 300$ nm, $v_2 = 1.09$ cm^{3}g^{-1} and $V_1 = 116.4$ cm^3 mole^{-1}. The thickness of the steric barrier, L, was taken to be 25 nm and the particle separation, d_0, was fixed at 30 nm. It can be seen from Figure 3(a) that ΔG_1^M (comb) is a positive quantity that becomes more positive as the temperature increases, indicating that in the absence of other contributions to ΔG_1^M, the particle would become more stable with increasing temperature. In the above calculation, we have assumed that the S function, Equation 3, remains invariant with temperature, which is incorrect.

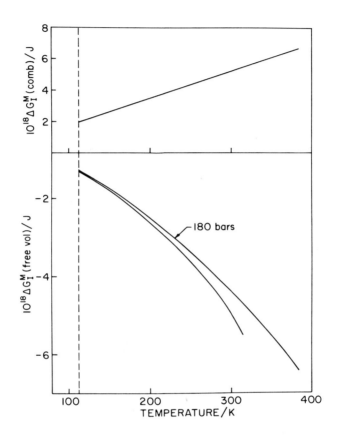

Figure 3 (a) Shows the combinational contribution of ΔG_1^M plotted as a function of temperature while, (b) Shows the free volume dissimilarity contribution to ΔG_1^M plotted as a function of temperature for atmospheric and 180 bars pressure.

However, the change is thought to be small and we feel justified
in ignoring it. Similarly, the S function is pressure dependent,
but since the change is also expected to be small, we consider
$\Delta G_1^M(\text{comb})$ to be essentially independent of pressure.

The $\Delta G_1^M(\text{free vol})$ contribution to ΔG_1^M is shown plotted in
Figure 3(b) at both atmospheric pressure and for an applied
pressure of 180 bars. These curves were calculated using
$\nu = \pi = 0$ in Equation 6. Assuming that $\chi = 1/2$ at the UCFT
from Equations 10, 11 (with $\tilde{P} = 0$) and 6, we have that:

$$C\tau^2 = 4/3 \ \tilde{V}_1^{-1/3} - 1 \qquad\qquad (14)$$

Since the UCFT at $P = 0$ is, from Equation 1, 313.8 K and T_1^*
for 2-methylbutane is 4085 K(9), then V_1 can be calculated from
Equation 5. Using $\tilde{V}$ in Equation 13 gives a value for $C\tau^2$ of
0.189 which was used in all the calculations. Figure 3(b) shows
that $\Delta G_1^M(\text{free vol})$ is a negative quantity which becomes more
negative as the temperature increases. Application of a hydrostatic pressure to the dispersion makes $\Delta G_1^M(\text{free vol})$ less negative which means that the quality of the dispersion medium for
the steric stabilizer has improved. Addition of the free volume
and combinational terms gives the total ΔG_1^M which is shown
plotted in Figure 4. The figure indicates that ΔG_1^M is a parabolic function of temperature. The system does not exhibit a
LCFT because the dispersion medium becomes glassy before this
occurs. Flocculation is only observed when $\Delta G_1^M < 0$ which occurs
when $|\Delta G_1^M(\text{free vol})| > |\Delta G_1^M(\text{comb})|$. Since the free volume term
becomes smaller with increasing applied pressure, the system
has to be raised to a higher temperature before the critical
conditions for flocculation occur. An applied pressure therefore increases the temperature range of colloidal stability of
nonaqueous dispersions.

From the family of $\Delta G_1^M(P, T)$ curves the projection on the
(P, T) plane of the critical lines corresponding to the UCFT
for these latexes can be calculated and this is shown plotted
in Figure 4. It can be seen that the UCFT curve is linear over
the pressure range studied. The slope of the theoretical projection is 0.38 which is smaller than the experimental data line.
Agreement between theory and experiment could be improved by re-
laxing the condition that $\nu = \pi = 0$ in Equation 6 and/or by allowing χ to be an adjustable parameter. However, since the
main features of the experimental data can be qualitatively predicted by theory, this option is not pursued here. It is apparent from the data presented that the free volume dissimilarity
between the steric stabilizer and the dispersion medium plays an
important role in the colloidal stabilization of sterically
stabilized nonaqueous dispersions.

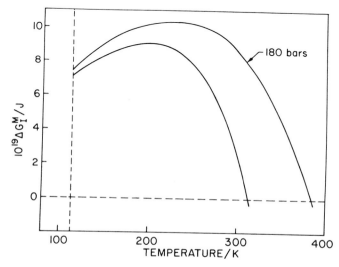

Figure 4   The total free energy of interpenetration of two particles is shown plotted as a function of temperature for atmospheric and 180 bars pressure.

Acknowledgments

We are extremely grateful to Professor D. Patterson for allowing us the use of his laboratory facilities.

Literature Cited

1. D.H. Napper, J. Colloid Interface Sci., 58, 390 (1977); and
   D.H. Napper, Colloidal Dispersions, Royal Society of Chemistry Special Publication, No. 43, Ed. by J.W. Goodwin,
   Ch.5 (1982).
2. M.D. Croucher and M.L. Hair, Macromolecules, 11, 874 (1978).
3. M.D. Croucher and M.L. Hair, J. Phys. Chem., 83, 1712 (1979).
4. J.M. Bardin, Ph.D. Thesis, McGill University, (1972).
5. L. Zeman, Ph.D. Thesis, McGill University (1972).
6. L. Zeman, J. Biros, G. Delmas and D. Patterson, J. Phys.
   Chem., 76, 1206 (1972).
7. G. Allen and C.H. Baker, Polymer, 6, 181 (1965).
8. D. Gaeckle and D. Patterson, Macromolecules, 5, 136 (1972).
9. M.D. Croucher and M.L. Hair, J. Colloid Interface Sci., 81,
   257 (1981).
10. P.J. Flory and W.R. Krigbaum, J. Chem. Phys., 18, 1086 (1950).
11. R. Evans, J.B. Smitham and D.H. Napper, Colloid Polymer Sci.,
    255, 161 (1977).
12. D. Patterson and G. Delmas, Discuss. Faraday Soc., 49, 98
    (1970).
13. P.J. Flory, Discuss. Faraday Soc., 49, 7 (1970).
14. D. Patterson and G. Delmas, Trans. Faraday Soc., 65, 708
    (1969).

RECEIVED October 7, 1983

Steric and Electrostatic Contributions to the Colloidal Properties of Nonaqueous Dispersions

F. M. FOWKES and R. J. PUGH[1]

Department of Chemistry, Lehigh University, Bethlehem, PA 18015

Dispersions of carbon black in dodecane and kerosene have been prepared with a basic poly-isobutene succinamide, the most extensively used commercial non-aqueous dispersant. The basic anchoring groups adsorb strongly onto the acidic surface sites of the carbon black, and with 1 w% or more of dispersant (based on the carbon black) the 50 Å - long polyisobutene chains extend out into the solution to provide a steric barrier 100 Å thick between particles, as evidenced by a million-fold decrease in electrical conductivity and a twenty-fold decrease in viscosity, but with no degree whatsoever of deflocculation. Only at much higher dispersant levels is deflocculation observed. When the concentration of unadsorbed dispersant in the oil phase exceeds 0.1%, the conductivity increases as counterions form, large negative zeta-potentials develop (-140 to -300 mV), the stability ratios climb towards infinity and the dispersions become completely deflocculated.

Dispersions of finely divided solids in non-aqueous media have been important for paints, inks, reinforced polymers and lubricating oils, but with the development of liquid toner systems and "ultra-structure" processing of ceramics as fine powders dispersed in organic media, the understanding and optimization of such systems is more important than ever.

[1]Current address: Ytkemiska Institutet Box 5607, Institute for Surface Chemistry, Stockholm, Sweden S-114 86.

0097–6156/84/0240–0331$07.00/0

Theories of Colloidal Stability in Non-Aqueous Media

Electrostatics in Non-Aqueous Media. A popular misconception in studies of non-aqueous dispersions concerns electrostatic effects. Because these are more difficult to measure than in aqueous media, there has been a general tendency to ignore them completely. However, the few investigators who have measured zeta-potentials or electrodeposition with these systems have become convinced of their importance. With the advent of modern commercial instrumentation for zeta-potentials in non-aqueous media it is to hoped that these effects will be measured rather than ignored.

Thirty years ago van der Minne and Hermanie showed that carbon black in benzene developed appreciable zeta potentials and colloidal stability in the presence of calcium soaps (which gave positive zeta-potentials) or quaternary ammonium picrates (which gave negative zeta-potentials); their mixtures gave low zeta-potentials and colloidal instability.(1,2) Twenty years ago the senior author and co-workers showed that the mechanism of electrostatic charging in non-aqueous is the reverse of that in aqueous media. (3) In aqueous solutions surfactants ionize and then the surface-active ions adsorb onto surfaces to give electrostatically charged surfaces. However in organic media basic dispersants adsorb as neutral molecules onto acidic surfaces where proton-transfer from acidic sites charges the adsorbed bases positively. If the concentration of dispersant dissolved in the oil phase is sufficiently high that dynamic adsorption and desorption occurs, some proton-carrying dispersants will desorb into solution, and provide the counterions for the negative charges left on the surface. Figure 1 illustrates this mechanism, which has been demonstrated in some detail by using carbon-14 tagged basic polymeric dispersants (4,5) and tritium-tagged acidic sites on surfaces. In Figure 1 a polymeric dispersant is indicated, for the radiotracer studies were done with high molecular weight polyalkylmethacrylates having vinyl pyridine basic sites. However the mechanism has also been demonstrated with lower molecular weight materials and even with micellar metal soaps and sulfonates. This mechanism results in negatively-charged acidic particles with basic dispersants and positively-charged basic particles with acidic dispersants, a principle that has been demonstrated experimentally a great many times.(4,5)

Steric Stabilization. Steric stabilization was a term first introduced by Heller to explain how adsorbed polyethylene oxide polymers increased the salt concentration required for flocculation of negatively charged aqueous suspensions.(6) Heller's systems were stabilized by both mechanisms, as are most commercial dispersions today, aqueous and non-aqueous. Much of the more recent literature on steric stabilizers has been preoccupied with solubility requirements, for the solubility of polymers is a delicate matter and very sensitive to temperature and solvent

composition. This preoccupation with solubility requirements has
led some investigators to believe that precipitation of stabilizers is the main mechanism of colloidal instability, rather than
the traditional dispersion force attractions between particles.
It should be obvious that a dispersant and solvent system must be
chosen so that the dispersant does not precipitate, but this
limitation has nothing to do with the mechanisms of collodial
stability.

In studies of steric stabilizers too little attention is
generally paid to the dispersion force attractions between particles and the critical separation distance (H_{cr}) needed to keep
particles from flocculating. Adsorbed steric stabilizers can
provide a certain film thickness on each particle but if the separation distance between colliding particles is less than H_{cr} the
particles will flocculate. The calculation of H_{cr} is not
difficult and measurements to prove or disprove such calculations
are not difficult either. For equal-sized spheres of substance 1
with radius or in medium 2, the Hamaker equation for the dispersion
force attractive energy (U_{121}^d) at close approach is (7):

$$U_{121}^d = a\ A_{121}f/12\ H \qquad\qquad (1)$$

where A_{121}, the Hamaker constant, can be related to the dispersion
force contribution to the surface energies γ_1^d and γ_2^d:

$$A_{121} = 1.5 \times 10^{-14}\ cm^2\ \left(\sqrt{\gamma_1^d} - \sqrt{\gamma_2^d} \right)^2 \qquad\qquad (2)$$

Hamaker constants can sometimes be calculated from refractive
index data by the Lifshitz equations (8), but it now appears that
γ^d values are closely related to refractive indices and are a
direct measure of the Lifshitz attractions. In Equation 1 a correction factor f for "retardation" of dispersion forces is shown
which can be determined from Figure 2, a graph of 1/f at various
values of H and a as a function of λ_1, the characteristic wavelength of the most energetic dispersion forces, calculable and
tabulated in the literature (9).

Table I lists some characteristic wave lengths from the work
of Gregory (9). The calculations of f shown in Figure 2 are taken
from the work of Clayfield and Lumb.(10) By using these calculations one can determine the attractive energy per pair of
particles at various separation distances, and determine for any
particular value of A_{121}, λ_1, and radius (a) the critical value
of H that makes $U_{121}^d=-kT$, where k is the Boltzmann constant and
kT is the average vibrational energy of a pair of particles flocculated at separation distance H. If U_{121}^d is greater than $-kT$
the particles will nearly always bounce apart on collision, but
if it is less than $-kT$ the particles tend to flocculate.
Figure 3 is a graph of H_{cr} vs. particle radius (a) for carbon
particles in oil where the Hamaker constant is relatively high
($A_{121}=2.8\times10^{-13}$ergs), for polystyrene particles in water

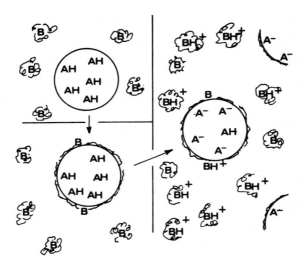

Figure 1. Mechanism of electrostatic charging in oil of
particles with acidic sites (AH) by a polymeric dispersant
with basic sites (B). Reproduced with permission from
Ref. (5).Copyright 1982, American Chemical Society.

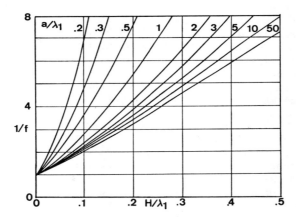

Figure 2. Retardation correction factor (f) for dispersion
force attractions between spherical particles of radius (a)
at separation distance (H), with dispersion force wavelength λ_1. (10)

($A_{121}=5.3\text{x}10^{-14}$ergs), and for oil-in-water emulsions where the Hamaker constant is quite low ($A_{121}=9.3\text{x}10^{-15}$ergs). For the system under study in this paper (carbon in oil, with average radius a= 0.2 μm) it is seen that H_{cr} is 260 Å and that the adsorbed steric barrier molecules must provide films 130 Å in thickness at collision to prevent flocculation. Since the dispersant used in this paper provides 50 Å films and an H at collision of 100 Å it should be no surprise that when zeta-potentials are small the particles flocculate in every collision.

Table I.   Characteristic Wave Lengths of Dispersion Force
Attractions (9)

Substance	λ_1 in Å
water	896
n-octane	882
benzene	1181
quartz	793
polystryene	1145

The calculations in Figure 3 were made on the assumption that the Hamaker constants of the adsorbed dispersant films are the same as the liquid media. This is an excellent assumption for polymers, since this means that the solubility parameter (δ^d) of the dispersant and of the medium must be about the same, which is the basic requirement for solubility of polymers.

In the earlier literature on steric stabilization there was a tendency to ignore the importance of anchoring sites for steric stabilizers. Without strong anchors the adsorbed molecules are easily swept aside in collisions, as has been so well illustrated with polystyrene adsorbed onto carbon blacks in hydrocarbon solutions; in these systems particles flocculate in every collision.(11)

Many investigators of steric stabilization have measured colloidal stability without taking the effort to find out whether the stability actually resulted from electrostatic stabilization. In many published articles it has been concluded that steric stabilization had been attained and further study showed this was not the case. One such example is a recent paper on "steric" stabilization by an additive of the same type used in this work. (12) The published photograph shows the silica particles in oil stabilized at interparticle separations several times the distances provided by the adsorbed films; no electrical measurements had been made, but it they had, this particular dispersant would have provided about -200 mV of zeta-potential and given excellent electrostatic repulsion. The reader should be wary of any claims of steric stabilization unless the electrostatic contribution has been measured.

<u>Combined Electrostatic and Steric Stabilization.</u> The combination
of the two mechanisms is illustrated in <u>Figure 4</u>, taken from
Shaw's textbook, (13) where the repulsion of the steric barrier
during a collision falls off so rapidly as the colliding particles
bounce apart that the dispersion force attractions hold the particles together in the "secondary minimum". This is exactly what
happens in the system investigated in this paper.

     In such systems the requirement of the electrostatic contri-
bution to colloidal stability is quite different than when no
steric barrier is present. In the latter case an energy barrier
of about 30 kT is desirable, with a Debye length $1/\kappa$ of not more
than 1000 Å. This is attainable in non-aqueous systems (5), but
not by most dispersants. However <u>when the steric barrier is</u>
<u>present, the only requirement for the electrostatic repulsion is</u>
<u>to eliminate the secondary minimum</u> and this is easily achieved
with zeta-potentials far below those required to operate entirely
by the electrostatic mechanism.

Dispersant

The dispersant used in these studies is Chevron Chemicals OLOA
1200, a polybutene of about 70 carbon atoms attached to a
succinic acid group which is reacted with diethylene triamine to
provide the basic anchoring group. Film balance studies showed
that the adsorbed films have a film thickness of 50 Å. This dispersant is supplied as a 50 w% solution in a mineral oil. It can
be deoiled by adsorption from toluene onto silica with elution by
acetone. In this paper the w% of dispersant refers to the deoiled
material.

     The basicity of OLOA 1200 has been evidenced by its inter-
action with the oil-soluble acidic indicator dye, Brom Phenol
Magenta E (EK 6810) which is normally yellow but turns blue and
then magenta with increasing bacicity. The acidic form has an
adsorption peak at 390 nm, the basic at 610 nm, and the isobestic
point is at 460 nm. These spectra have be used to determine the
concentration of OLOA 1200 in solution for adsorption isotherms.

Adsorption Isotherms on Carbon Black (14)

The carbon black used in all of these studies was Cabot's Sterling
NS (25 m^2/g), a furnace black which was extracted of solubles
with acetone and hexane and then dried at 60°C. under vacuum.

     Carbon black adsorbed OLOA 1200 very strongly, eventually
picking up 5% of its weight in dispersant. The first 2% adsorbed
almost instantly, but additional increments adsorbed more and more
slowly (see Figure 5). Such time-dependence in adsorption of
large molecules is quite common (15), but is seldom studied. The
adsorption isotherms determined after 48 hours of tumbling at 25°

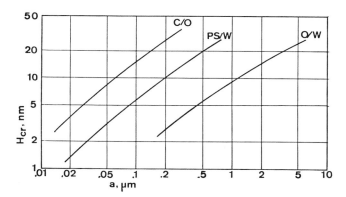

Figure 3. Critical separation distance (H_{cr}) of spherical particles of radius (a) to prevent flocculation at 25°C. Carbon-in-oil dispersions (C/O), polystyrene in water latexes (PS/W), and oil-in-water emulsions (O/W).

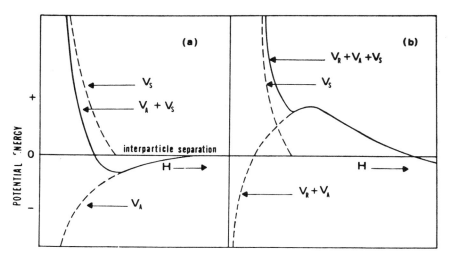

Figure 4. Potential energy diagrams for a pair of particles with: on the left, a steric barrier (V_s) and dispersion force attraction (V_A); and on the right, with electrostatic repulsion (V_R) added. Reproduced with permission from Ref. (13).Copyright 1980, Butterworths.

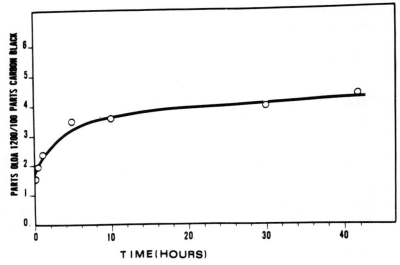

Figure 5. Adsorption of OLOA-1200 dispersant on carbon black versus agitation time at 25°C. Reproduced with permission from Ref. (14).Copyright 1983, Elsevier Science Publishers.

and at 50° (see Figure 6) are probably not equilibrium values, as suggested by the greater adsorption at 50°C. The area per molecule with 5 w% of dispersant adsorbed onto the carbon black is 100$\overset{\circ}{A}^2$.

Calorimetric Heats of Adsorption on Carbon Black(14)

Heats of adsorption were determined with a Microscal Flow Microcalorimeter, using flow rates of one ml. per hour under a gravitional head, and 70 to 80 mg of Sterling NS in the bed. The results of a typical run are shown in Figure 7, which illustrates the rapidity of adsorbing 2.25% OLOA 1200. The area under this peak corresponds to the generation of 6.8 millicalories of heat, a ΔH_{ads} of -4.7 kcal/mole. The results of several such experiments are summarized in Table II.

Table II. Heats of Adsorption of OLOA 1200 on Carbon Black
By Flow Microcalorimetry (40°C.)

a) Aliquots of dispersant injected at 2-3 hour intervals.

Parts OLOA 1200/ 100 parts of injected (no bed change)	Approximate* Surface area per molecule ($\overset{\circ}{A}^2$)	Amount of heat absorbed (millicalories)	Heat of adsorption* (Kcal/mole)
1.5	330	-6.7	-7.0
1.5	167	-5.5	-5.7
1.5	110	-4.7	-4.9

b) Freshly prepared beds of carbon black prepared before each aliquot injected.

0.75	660	-3.6	-7.5
1.5	330	-6.7	-7.0
2.25	220	-6.8	-4.7

*Assuming an average molecular weight of 1200 for the dispersant and a surface area of 25 m²/gm for the carbon black.
In part (a) of Table II is is seen that the first third of a monolayer to adsorb tends to occupy the more strongly acid sites, for each successive increment is less strongly adsorbed. In part (b) the decrease in average heats of adsorption with increasing coverage is quite consistent with the above.

Electrical Conductivity of Carbon Black Dispersions in Dodecane(16)

Sterling NS is a fairly conductive carbon black and dispersions of

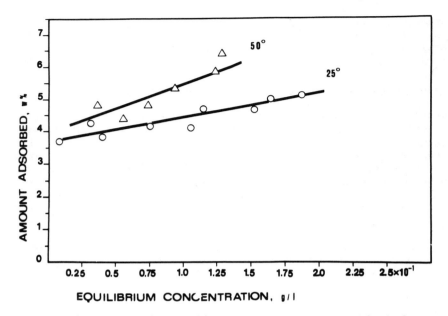

Figure 6. Amount of OLOA-1200 adsorbed on carbon black from odorless kerosene in 48 hours. Reproduced with permission from Ref. (14) Copyright 1983, Elsevier Science Publishers.

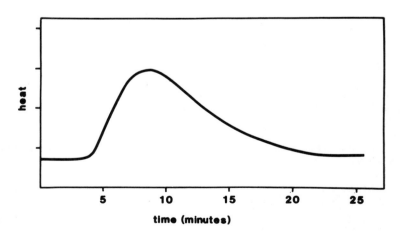

Figure 7. Exotherm for adsorption of OLOA-1200 from odorless kerosene onto carbon black by flow microcalorimetry. Reproduced with permission from Ref (14).Copyright 1983, Elsevier Science Publishers.

10 w% in dodecane have a conductivity of about $5 \times 10^{-4} \mathrm{ohm}^{-1} \mathrm{m}^{-1}$, measured with platinum electrodes in a stirred conductance cell, using a Keithley electrometer. This conductivity results from chains of particle-to-particle contacts which are broken and re-made during stirring, with electron-tunnelling currents between closely adjacent conductive carbon particles (17). With incremental additions of OLOA-1200 to these dispersions the ad-sorbed layers increase the thickness of the insulating gap be-tween carbon particles, and since tunnelling currents decrease exponentially with separation distance (17), the conductance is seen in Figure 8 to decrease exponentially with OLOA-1200 content up to 1 w% and then to decrease more slowly up to 2 w% where the conductance is about one millionth of what is was with no OLOA-1200. The minimum conductivity observed in this system is in-dicative of the 100 Å separation between particles expected with OLOA-1200, for electron-tunnelling currents become negligibly small across insulating gaps of 100 Å thickness.

In Figure 8 the conductance is seen to increase with disper-sant content after reaching a minimum. This is because the content of dispersant left in solution becomes significant in the region above the minimum. For example, the conductance measured after 45 minutes rises after a minimum at 2.5% OLOA-1200; this can compared with Figure 5 which shows that 2% is adsorbed in about 10 minutes and 2.5% is adsorbed in about an hour. On the other hand, the 12-hour conductance reached a minimum at about 4% in Figure 8 and Figure 5 shows that about 4% is adsorbed in 12 hours. Thus the rise of conductance after the minimum is a good measure of the presence of significant concentrations of dispersant in solution, which is a requirement for the develop-ment of electrostatic charging, illustrated in Figure 1. The increase in overall dispersant levels required to provide an excess in solution increases with time because of the slow ki-netics of adsorption in the approach to saturated surface con-centrations, as discussed earlier. The increasing conductivity of the dispersion, once excess dispersant is left in solution, is probably due mostly to the increasing concentration of proton-carrying OLOA-1200 molecules, the positive counter-ions illus-trated in Figure 1. Solutions of OLOA-1200 in dodecane have some conductance, however, and it is fairly linear with concentration, so not all of the increasing conductance can be attributed to counterions.

Zeta-Potentials of Carbon Black Dispersions in Hydrocarbons with OLOA-1200 Dispersant (14-16)

Initial studies were made with the Rank Bros. electrophoresis unit, using the dilute supernatant suspension over a dispersion of 3.33g of carbon black per liter of dodecane equilibrated for 24 hours with the added OLOA-1200. The electrophoretic mobility (μ) of 1-3 μm clumps of particles was observed at a field of 100 volts per centimeter. The zeta-potentials (ζ) were calculated

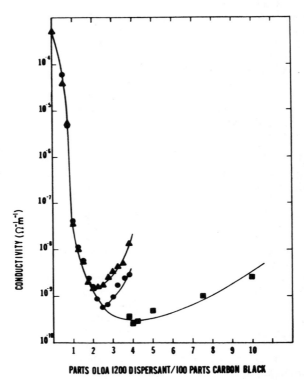

Figure 8. Conductivity of stirred 10% suspensions of carbon black in dodecane with OLOA-1200 dispersant. Triangles- 5 minutes after dispersant added; circles- 45 minutes after addition; and squares- 12 hours after addition. Reproduced with permission from Ref. (16). Copyright 1983, Elsevier Science Publishers.

from the Hückel equation (18) for systems in which the Debye length exceeds the particle radius:

$$\zeta = \frac{3}{2} \frac{\eta \mu}{\varepsilon_r \varepsilon_o} \tag{3}$$

in which η is the viscosity, ε_r is the dielectric constant and ε_o is the permittivity of free space.   Figure 9 shows the magnitude of the negative zeta-potentials in this system, with potentials in excess of 100 mV when the dispersant level exceeded 2 w% of the carbon black.

Later studies, using the Pen Kem 3000, employed sonicated and well-dispersed carbon black in kerosene systems in which all of the particles were sub-micron in size. This instrument uses a Doppler-shift type of measurement and analyses the motion of many particles simultaneously by a Fourier transform of the multiple sensings.   Figure 10 shows a typical histogram of the distribution of the electrophoretic mobilities of carbon blacks in 0.2% solutions of OLOA-1200 in kerosene; in this case the average mobility   was -1.0×10^{-9} and the average zeta potential was -153 mV. Table III lists the average zeta-potentials obtained with dispersions of 10 mg of carbon black sonicated in 100 ml. of kerosene with 0, 0.2, 0.5, and 0.8% OLOA-1200 in solution.

Table III. Average Zeta-Potentials of Carbon Black in Kerosene Dispersions Determined by Pen Kem 3000

%OLOA-1200	Time Constant, sec.	ζ-Potenital, mV	
0	60	+0.1	
0	60	+0.5	
0.2	10	−156	
0.2	10	−124	−144
0.2	60	−153	
0.5	10	−181	
0.5	62	−144	
0.5	255	−137	−177
0.5	600	−247	
0.8	10	−319	
0.8	10	−136	−218
0.8	60	−201	
0.8	60	−213	

The time constant in the above table is the time after the field is applied and before the mobilities are measured.   This time is needed to establish the field and is an RC time constant of ten seconds when the conductivity is 10^{-9} $ohm^{-1}m^{-1}$.   The above solutions had conductivities slightly greater than this value.

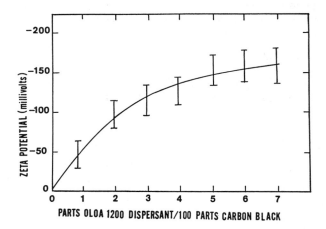

Figure 9. Zeta-potential of carbon black dispersed in dodecane with OLOA-1200 dispersant (23°C.). Sampled from dispersions of 3.33 g of carbon black per liter of dodecane. Reproduced with permission from Ref. (14). Copyright 1983, Elsevier Science Publishers.

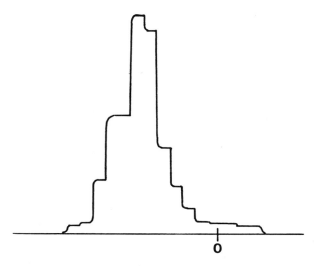

Figure 10. Distribution of zeta-potentials of carbon black in kerosene with 0.1% OLOA-1200. Average zeta-potential was -110mV.

The zeta-potentials of Table III are greater than those in Figure 9 because the concentration of OLOA-1200 in solution was appreciably higher. The results are quite consistent at the same concentration in solution. These findings show that the zeta-potential in organic media is not a function of how much dispersant is adsorbed, but how much dispersant is left in solution. This is in contrast to the steric barriers, which depend on how much is adsorbed and not on how much is left in solution.

The Electrostatic Energy Barriers

The energy of electrostatic repulsion (per pair of particles) which results from zeta-particles is estimated from the Deryagin equation (19):

$$U_{121}^e = 2\pi\varepsilon_r\varepsilon_o \, a\psi_o^2 \, \ln \, (1+e^{-\kappa H}) \tag{4}$$

where $1/\kappa$ is the Debye length and ψ_o is the surface potential, approximated here by the zeta-potential. This equation applies equally well to aqueous or non-aqueous media.

The Debye length $1/\kappa$ tends to be much longer than in aqueous media, but not always (5). For this system we used the equation of Klinkenberg and van der Minne:(20)

$$1/\kappa = \sqrt{\varepsilon_r\varepsilon_o D/2\sigma} \tag{5}$$

where D is the diffusion constant for the charge-carrying species and σ is the conductivity. The value of D can be closely estimated from the Stokes-Einstein equation for spheres

$$D_o = kT/6\pi r\eta \tag{6}$$

corrected with an appropriate value of f/f_o for rods:

$$D = D_o x \, f/f_o \tag{7}$$

For OLOA-1200 we assume a molecular weight of 1200, a density of 0.9, and one electronic charge per molecule (5), and f/f_o =1.2; D=2.7×10^{-10}. The conductivity of a 0.2% solution of OLOA-1200 in kerosene is 1×10^{-8}ohm^{-1}m^{-1}, so the Debye length is 0.5 μm(5000Å). This Debye length is about the same as in the iridescent aqueous polystyrene latexes which have had serum replacement with distilled water. In these iridescent latexes the extensive Debye lengths give electrostatic repulsions that provide a distance between the centers of hexagonally packed particles matching visible light wavelengths so that Bragg reflections occur. These iridescent latexes are stabilized by the electrostatic repulsion at Debye lengths of the same order as occur in the OLOA solutions in kerosene.

In $\underline{\text{Figure 11}}$ the sum of the dispersion force attraction
(U_{121}^{d}) of equation (1) and of the electrostatic repulsion (U_{121}^{e})
of equation (4) are plotted as a function of the separation
distance H between carbon black particles with radius 200 nm, the
average diameter of our carbon black as determined by electron
microscopy of a thoroughly deflocculated sample, and using a λ_1 of
100 nm. Two curves are shown, one for solutions with 0.2 %
OLOA-1200 ($1/\kappa$=500 nm, ζ=-144 mV) and another for solutions with
0.8% OLOA-1200 ($1/\kappa$=250 nm, ζ=-218 mV). The maximum slope, a
measure of the force between particles, is 0.23 kT/nm and
0.9 kT/nm respectively. During the approach of particles in a
collision, the energy loss per 100 nm in climbing the above
slopes would be 23 kT and 90 kT, sufficient to slow and stop the
approach in almost all collisions. The dashed line just above
the peak of electrostatic repulsion represents the 5 nm steric
barrier of adsorbed OLOA-1200 which tends to extend the barrier
much higher.

Flocculation Rates and Stability Ratios (16)

Dispersions of 3.33 g of carbon black per liter of dodecane
(matching the compositions used in determing zeta-potentials in
$\underline{\text{Figure 9}}$) and dispersions of 0.33 g. per liter were investigated
for flocculation rates by turbidity measurements immediately
after sonication. From the slope of absorptivity vs. time the
flocculation half-time was determined. The half-times determined
with no dispersant were used as the rapid flocculation half-time
(t_r) used as the basis for determining the stability ratio (W).
In $\underline{\text{Table IV}}$ t_r is 6 minutes for the dispersions containing
3.33 g/liter and 40 minutes with 0.33 g/liter. Upon adding dispersant the flocculation time increased and the ratio of the
longer flocculation time to t_r is the stability ratio.
    As the OLOA-1200 content of these dispersions increased it
should be remembered that the steric barrier is well-developed at
1% and optimum at about 2% OLOA-1200, as evidenced by the conductivity and viscosity measurements of $\underline{\text{Figures 8 and 13.}}$
However in $\underline{\text{Table IV}}$ we see no increase in W at 1%, and only a
small increase at 2% of dispersant. The value of W increases
rapidly at about the same concentration that the conductivity
increases, the counterion concentration increases and the zeta-
potential increases. At OLOA-1200 levels of 3.5% and higher the
stability ratio exceeds 5×10^4, with half-times in excess of seven
months; these stability ratios developed when zeta-potentials
were -120 mV or more.
    These findings show that the steric barrier provided by the
50 Å adsorbed films was inadequate to deflocculate the dispersion
at all, even though it provided a million times more electrical
resistance and reduced the viscosity very appreciably. On the
other hand, the electrostatic barrier was very effective in
deflocculating the system, but it took more dispersant than

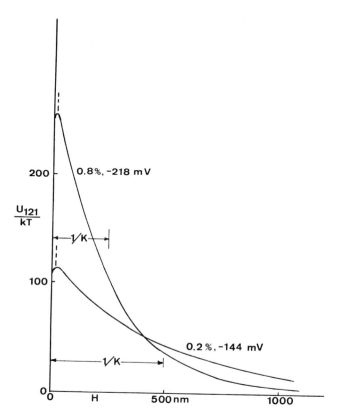

Figure 11. Potential energy diagram for two spherical carbon black particles of radius 0.2 μm with Debye lengths and
zeta potentials determined for 0.2% and 0.8% solutions of
OLOA–1200 in odorless kerosene.

Table IV. Stability of Carbon Black in Dodecane

(A) Concentration 3.33 gl^{-1}

Parts OLOA 1200 per 100 parts carbon black	Flocculation sedimentation time	W (stability ratio)
0	6 min	1
½	6 min	1
1	7 min	1.16
1½	9 min	1.5
2	1.5 h	15
2½	5 h	50
3	24 h	2.4×10^2
3½	>7 months	5 $\times 10^4$
4	>7 months	>5 $\times 10^4$
4½	>7 months	>5 $\times 10^4$
5	>7 months	>5 $\times 10^4$
6	>7 months	>5 $\times 10^4$

(B) Concentration 0.33 gl^{-1}

Parts OLOA 1200 per 100 parts carbon black	Flocculation sedimentation time	W (stability ratio)
0	40 min	1
½	40	1
1	50 min	1.25
1½	90 min	2.25
2	3 h	4.5
2½	24 h	36
3	2.5 days	90
3½	10 days	3.6×10^2
4	>6 months	>6 $\times 10^3$
4½	>6 months	>6 $\times 10^3$
5	>6 months	>6 $\times 10^3$

needed for the steric barrier to provide the excess in solution needed to promote counterion formation. The electrostatic barrier is seen in Figure 11 to be very sensitive to the concentration of OLOA-1200 left in solution, with a slope proportional to that concentration. Concentrations of OLOA-1200 in solution probably need to exceed 0.1% for really effective electrostatic deflocculation. Figure 12 compares the stability ratio to the conductivity (at 12 hours) to illustrate that the steric barrier forms in the 1-2% range of dispersant, but that in this range so much is adsorbed that none is left over to provide counterions in solutions. At about 4% dispersant the conductivity rises as counterions develop, the Debye length decreases and the zeta-potential climbs to provide a rapid increase in the stability ratio W.

Viscosity of Dispersions of Carbon Black in Hydrocarbons (16)

Viscosities of concentrated suspensions of carbon black in a white mineral oil (Fisher "paraffin" oil of 125/135 Saybolt viscosity) were measured with a Brookfield viscometer as a function of OLOA-1200 content. Figure 13 shows the viscosities of dispersions with 30 w%, 35 w% and 70 w% carbon black. In all cases the viscosity fell rapidly as the OLOA-1200 content increased from 0 to 1%, then fell more gradually and levelled off as the OLOA-1200 content approached 2%. In many respects the reduction in viscosity with increasing OLOA-1200 content parallels the conductivity measurements; both phenomena are sensing the build-up of the steric barrier, and this steric barrier weakens, softens, and lubricates the interparticle contacts. As evidenced in foregoing sections, the particles are still flocculated but can be easily stirred and separated mechanically. The onset of electrostatic repulsion at OLOA-1200 contents in excess of 2.5% did not affect viscosities.

Sedimentation Volumes of Carbon Black Dispersions in Kerosene (14)

In the foregoing stability measurements the 1-20 µm agglomerates of carbon black (as received) were broken down to 0.1-1 µm particles for flocculation studies, but for sedimentation studies the agglomerates were left intact and these sedimented rapidly under gravitational forces. The sediment volume tends to be a measure of particle-particle interaction energies. If these forces are strong, colliding particles may stick together tightly on first contact and form a very loose voluminous sediment. If added dispersant reduces the interaction energy sufficiently, particles may slide past one another under gravitational forces and form a tightly-packed sediment.

In the sedimentation studies the dispersions were tumbled in a rolling mill for 25, 50, 75, or 150 hours, allowed to sediment over night and the volumes read. As can be seen in Figure 14 the

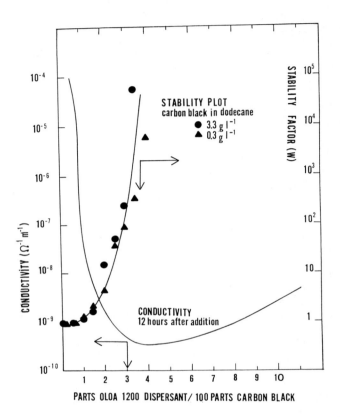

Figure 12. Comparison of the dispersant concentration and
dependence of the stability ratio W the conductivity
of carbon black dispersions in dodecane. Reproduced with
permission from Ref. (16). Copyright 1983, Elsevier Science
Publishers.

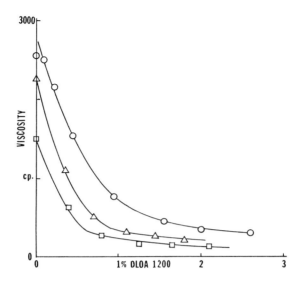

Figure 13.   Effect of OLOA-1200 concentration (parts of OLOA-1200 per 100 parts carbon black) on the Brookfield viscosity (at 30 r.p.m.) of dispersion of carbon black in paraffin oil. Squares – 30 W% carbon black; triangles 35 W%; and circles – 70 W% carbon black.

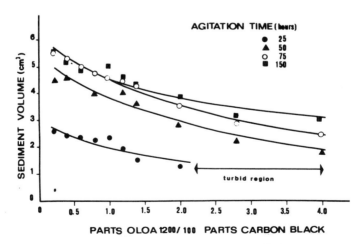

Figure 14.   Sedimentation volume of 10 W% dispersions of carbon black in odorless kerosene as a function of OLOA-1200 content and agitation time.   Sedimentation time was 24 hours.   Reproduced with permission from Ref. (14). Copyright 1983, Elsevier Science Publishers.

sediment volumes increased quite appreciably with increased time
of agitation, possibly because the agglomerates became less dense.
The most important findings are that the sediment volumes decreased with increased dispersant levels, as is also evidenced in
the photographs of Figure 15 Here it is surprising to see that
the densest sediment was found for the dispersion with no dispersant, and the least dense with 0.2% of OLOA-1200, which allows
only a very small fraction of an adsorbed monolayer. The very
voluminous sediments obtained at low dispersant levels were most
easily stirred, while the dense sediments obtained at high dispersant levels were hard and difficult to stir.

Some further light may be shed on carbon floc structure by
the electron micrographs of Figure 16 showing an appreciable
decrease in floc size with increase in dispersant content (for
the suspensions tumbled for 150 hours). One might conclude that
the OLOA-1200 was an efficient "grinding aid"

Conclusions

1.   OLOA-1200, a polybutene succinamide with a basic anchoring
group and a 50 Å extended polybutene chain, provided both steric
and electrostatic stabilization to dispersions of carbon black
in hydrocarbon media.
2.   The steric barrier developed upon adsorption of 1-2% of the
dispersant was evidenced by a million-fold decrease in conductivity, a twenty-fold decrease in viscosity, a two-fold increase in sediment volume, but no deflocculation of any degree.
3.   The electrostatic barrier developed only after enough dispersant adsorbed that a concentration of dissolved dispersant of
about 0.1% or more remained in the oil phase, where counterions
developed as evidenced by increased conductivity, the development
of large negative zeta potentials, steeply rising stability
ratios, and complete deflocculation.

Acknowledgments

The authors wish to express their appreciation and thanks to
Dr. Vittorio de Nora and the Diamond Shamrock Corporation for the
establishment of the Vittorio de Nora-Diamond Shamrock Post-
Doctoral Fellowships at Lehigh University, funds from which
supported this research project.

The Pen Kem 3000 measurements were made by Christina Blom,
a summer student from Stockholm. The 70% carbon black viscosities
were measured by Douglas Seifert, a Lehigh graduate student, and
several contributions to the electrostatic studies were made by
Dr. Trisno Makgawinata, the current de Nora-Diamond Shamrock
Fellow.

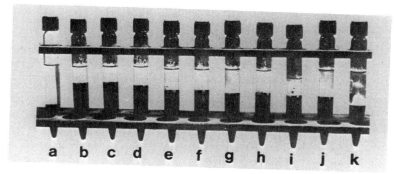

Figure 15. Photograph of sedimentation of carbon black (10 W%) in odorless kerosene as a function of OLOA-1200 content. Agitated 150 hours, sedimented 24 hours. OLOA-1200 contents: (a)-0, (b)-0.2, (c)-0.4, (d)-0.6, (e)-0.8, (f)-1.0, (g)-1.2, (h)-1.4, (i)-2.0, (j)-2.8, and (k)-4.0 parts OLOA-1200 per 100 parts carbon black. Reproduced with permission from Ref. (14) Elsevier Science Publishers.

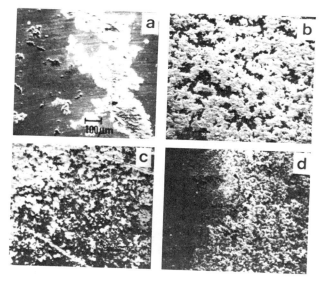

Figure 16. Electron micrographs showing floc structure of carbon black dispersed in odorless kerosene after 150 hours of agitation. Parts OLOA-1200 per 100 parts of carbon black: (a)-0, (b)-0.4, (c)-2.0, (d)-4.0. These are from samples (a), (c), (i) and (k) of Figure 15. Reproduced with permission from Ref. (14). Copyright 1983, Elsevier Science Publishers.

Literature Cited

1. van der Minne, J. L.; Hermanie, P. H. J. J. Colloid Sci. 1952, 7, 600.
2. van der Minne, J. L.; Hermanie, P. H. J. J. Colloid Sci. 1953, 8, 38.
3. Fowkes, F. M.; Disc. Faraday Soc. 1966, 42, 246.
4. Tamaribuchi, K.; Smith, M. L., J. Colloid Interface Sci. 1966, 22, 404.
5. Fowkes, F. M.; Jinnai, H.; Mostafa, M A.; Anderson, F. W.; Moore, R. J., in "Colloids and Surfaces in Reprographic Technology"; Hair, M.; Croucher, M. D., Eds.; ACS SYMPOSIUM SERIES No. 200, American Chemical Society: Washington, D. C., 1982, p 307.
6. Heller, W.; Pugh, T. J. Poly. Sci. 1960, 47, 203-219.
7. Hamaker, H. C., Physica 1937, 4, 1068.
8. Parsegian, V. A., in "Physical Chemistry: Enriching Topics from Colloid and Surface Science", van Olphen & Mysels, Eds.; Theorex, La Jolla, CA., 1975, p 27.
9. Gregory, J., Adv. Colloid Interface Sci. 1970, 2, 396.
10. Clayfield, E. J.; Lumb, E. C.; Mackey, P. H., J. Colloid Interface Sci. 1971, 37, 382.
11. Achorn, P. Ph.D. Thesis, Lehigh University, Bethlehem, PA., 1970.
12. de Hek, H.; Vrij, A., J. Colloid Interface Sci. 1981, 79, 289.
13. Shaw, D. J. "Introduction to Colloid and Surface Chemistry", Butterworths, London, 1966, p 211.
14. Pugh, R. J.; Fowkes, F. M. submitted to Colloids and Surfaces 1983.
15. Fowkes, F. M. J. Phys. Chem. 1962, 66, 385.
16. Pugh, R. J.; Matsunaga, T.; Fowkes, F. M. "Colloids and Surfaces", in press, 1983.
17. Sichel, E. K.; Gittleman, G. I.; Sheng, P. in "Carbon-Black-Polymer Composites. The Physics of Electrically Conducting Composites", Sichel, E. K., Ed., Dekker, 1982, p 51-77.
18. Hückel, E. Phys. Z. 1924, 25, p 204.
19. Deryagin, B. V.; Landau, L. D. Acta Physicochim URSS, 1941 14, 633.
20. Klinkenburg, A.; van der Minne, J. L. "Electrostatics in the Petroleum Industry", Elsevier, 1958, p 40.

RECEIVED October 19, 1983

FLOCCULATION
AND FLOW PHENOMENA

Flocculation of Precipitated and Pyrogenic Silica Hydrosols by Polyethylene Glycols

Influence of Mixing Procedure, pH, and Electrolyte Concentration

E. KILLMANN, N. GUTLING, and TH. WILD

Institut für Technische Chemie der Technischen Universität München, Lehrstuhl für Makromolekulare Stoffe, Lichtenbergstrasse 4, D 8046 Garching, Federal Republic of Germany

The flocculation of Silica Hydrosols is reproducible by the adsorption of Polyethylene glycols provided the mixing conditions are controlled. With a Laser-photo sedimentometer one obtains parameters which enable characterization of the turbidity and of the hindered sedimentation in the flocculated suspension. By continuous addition of the polymer solution to the silica suspension the influences of the time of addition, stirring time, stirring intensity, polymer coverage, concentration of silica, pH and ionic strength on the flocculation state can be quantified. In contrast to pyrogenic silica precipitated silica is only flocculable by decreasing the pH below pH = 3.5 or by addition of salt above 10^{-2} mol/l. The flocculation of pyrogenic silica is markedly dependent on the mixing conditions at high pH and without salt. At high salt concentrations and pH < 3.5 the flocculation of precipitated and pyrogenic silicas becomes independent of mixing conditions.

Polymer adsorption as a means of influencing and controlling the stability of colloidal dispersons is becoming increasingly important. The identification and elucidation of the fundamental processes of adsorption and flocculation by polymers in the model system silica hydrosol/polyethylene glycol was the purpose of the investigations described (1,2). Flame hydrolyzed and precipitated silica has been used to elucidate the conformation of adsorbed macromolecules at the interface (3,4,5). The flocculation of the silica hydrosols by the adsorption of polyethylene glycols (PEG) is reproducible provided the preparation and the pretreatment of the silica suspensions as well as the mixing procedure and conditions are controlled.

0097–6156/84/0240–0357$06.00/0

Suspensions of pyrogenic silica Aerosil 200 in water can be flocculated with PEG at high pH values (pH $\geq$ 4.7) without addition of electrolytes. Former measurements show that the adsorption of the polymer and the flocculated structure are dependent on the method of mixing the polymer solution with the Aerosil suspension. Therefore, the dependence of stability behaviour on the mixing conditions was systematically investigated. The mixing procedure leads to turbulent flow conditions in the mixing vessel. Thus, an orthokinetic flocculation mechanism, which influences the processes of polymer bridging and electrostatic interactions, has to be taken into consideration. This mechanism is based on particle collisions by fluid motion or shear stresses by stirring the suspension. Few investigations with respect to this point have been published by other authors (e.g.6,7,8,9).

In contrast to the behaviour of pyrogenic silica precipitated silica can only be flocculated with PEG by lowering the pH value below pH = 3.5 or by addition of an electrolyte.

Therefore, a systematic examination of the influences of pH and electrolyte concentration on the state of flocculation of both silica types seemed promising. For a quantitative examination of the state of flocculation a Laserphoto Sedimentometer was used to follow the turbidity and the sedimentation of the suspension as a function of time. This method was described in detail in our earlier work (1,10).

Materials

The pyrogenic flame hydrolyzed silica Aerosil 200, a commercial product from Degussa, was used as a dispersion in doubly distilled water (1). The precipitated silica was prepared by hydrolysis of orthosilicic acid tetraethylester in ammoniacal solution according to the method of Stober, Fink and Bohn (11). The prepared suspension was purified by repeated centrifugation, separation from solvent and redispersion of the sediment in fresh water. Finally, the water was evaporated and the wet silica dried at 150°C for about half an hour.

To obtain reproducible initial conditions the pyrogenic as well as the precipitated silicas were treated by ultrasonication for about 7 min. with 150 - 200 Watt, 20 KHz. Of the different dispersion methods tested the ultrasonication gave the most reproducible, standardized hydrosols (1). According to electron micrographs, ultracentrifugation-, diffusion-, viscosity- and density-measurements the pyrogenic silica consists of aggregated particles (1) whereas the precipitated silica probe contains relatively isolated monodisperse, spherical particles with an average diameter of about 100 nm.

Mixing Procedure

To obtain reproducible flocculation a standardized mixing procedure is necessary. By testing different possible mixing procedures inhomogenities in the polymer coverage of the particle and in the flocculated structure can be avoided if one uses a technique, whereby the sol and the polymer solution are separated by a pure water layer. Mixing is then accomplished using standardised shaking conditions (1). Using an alternative technique the silica suspension is put into a special vessel with an adjustable stirrer and the PEG solution is added continuously via a dosimate (Metrohm E 415). During the addition the mixture is stirred continuously. Only with the latter technique the influences of the time of addition, duration of stirring and the effect of different stirrer speeds can be quantitatively measured.

Adsorption Isotherms

The amount of polymer adsorbed in grams per gram Aerosil can be calculated from the mass balance, according

$$A = (c_E - c_L) / c_S$$

using the measured supernatant concentration, c_L, of nonadsorbed polymer, the known initial concentration, c_E, and the sol concentration, c_S. The supernatant polymer concentration, c_L, after centrifugation is measured using a turbidity method with tannic acid (12).

Determination of Colloidal Stability by measuring Turbidity and Sedimentation with a Laserphoto-Sedimentometer

The self-constructed Laserphoto Sedimentometer and the measuring procedures to obtain the transmission-height profiles and the characterizing parameters for the turbidity and the hindered sedimentation behaviour of the flocculated suspension are described in earlier publications (10,1). Thus only a summary of these parameters is given here:

a) $T (1') = U_1/U_0$ = relative transmission one minute after finishing the mixing, U_1 = transmission of the flocculated structure, U_0 = transmission of pure water.

b) $E_{rel}^o = \log (U_o/U)/\log(U_o/U_b)$ = relative absorbance in the supernatant liquid, U_b = transmission of the silica hydrosol, U = transmission of the supernatant liquid.

c) $h_{rel} = h/(h+\Delta h)$ = relative height of the boundary layer, h = height of the boundary layer of the sediment, $h + \Delta h$ = total height of the suspension

d) $E_{3/4} = -\log T_{3/4} = -\log(U_{3/4}/U_o)$, $U_{3/4}$ = transmission where the height is $3/4 (h+\Delta h)$; (supernatant liquid)

e) $E_{1/5} = -\log T_{1/5} = -\log (U_{1/5}/U_o)$, $U_{1/5}$ = transmission where the height is $1/5 (h +\Delta h)$; (sedimenting phase)

Results and Discussion; Adsorption Isotherms

The adsorption isotherms of PEG 6000 and 40,000 in fig. 1 show the typical high affinity character for precipitated and for pyrogenic silica with the following trends:

a) The amount adsorbed at saturation with PEG 40,000 is higher than with PEG 6000 for pH 5.5 and 4.7 as well as for pH 2.3.

b) The amount adsorbed for a given polymer is higher at pH 2.3 than at pH 5.5 (4,7).

c) The amount of sorbed PEG per square meter surface area on pyrogenic silica at pH 4.7 is higher than that on the precipitated silica.

d) With increasing stirring speed during mixing a very small decrease of the amount adsorbed is observed.

Colloidal Stability of the Pyrogenic Silica

To measure the influence of the mixing procedure on the sedimentation and turbidity (1) the stirrer speed, v_R {rpm}, (2) the time of polymer addition, t_Z[min], and (3) the time of stirring after addition of the polymer, t_N[min], were varied. Two polymer coverages, $\theta \sim 0.2$ and $\theta \sim 1.0$, at three pH-values, pH 4.7, pH 3.2 and pH 2.3 (the latter is close to the isoelectric point) were selected for the stability measurements. Fig. 2 shows the dependence of the three stability characterizing parameters T (1') E_{rel} (24h) and h_{rel} (24h) on the speed of stirring v_R, at pH 4.7 for $\theta \sim 0.2$ and $\theta \sim 1.0$. The addition of the polymer at very low v_R results in a lower transmission T (1'), of the dispersed system, in an increase of the relative adsorbance, E_{rel}, and in a low sedimentation volume, h_{rel}, after 24 hours. These results suggest a degree of aggregation of the silica particles without the formation of a boundary layer; only some flocs were formed. At higher stirring speeds ($v_R > 200$ rpm for $\theta \sim 1$, $v_R > 350$ rpm for $\theta \sim 0.2$) flocculation and the formation of a phase boundary were observed, the sedimentation volume, h_{rel} (24h), increased strongly and the adsorbance, E_{rel} (24h), and the transmission, T (1'), decreased. The sharp steplike phase boundary and the slowing down of the sedimentation velocity with increasing stirring speed (fig. 3) are evidence for the existence of a structured flocculation at both polymer coverages ($\theta = 0.2$ and 1.0). In the figures 4 to 9 it is shown that independent of the conditions (v_R, t_Z, c_E, c_S) an increasing time of stirring after mixing, t_N, leads to lower T (1') and E_{rel} (24h)-values and an increase in h_{rel} (24h). A concomitant sedimentation velocity decrease with increasing t_N is observed (figure 10). Fig. 4 shows the measured quantities T (1'), E_{rel} (24h) and h_{rel} (24h) as functions of t_N for different values of the stirrer speed v_R at particle coverage $\theta = 0.2$. Prolonging t_N and increasing v_R lead to decreases in T (1'), E_{rel} (24h) and an increase in h_{rel} (24h) (c.f. fig. 2). The figures 5 and 6 illustrate the influence of the time of addition of the polymer solution,

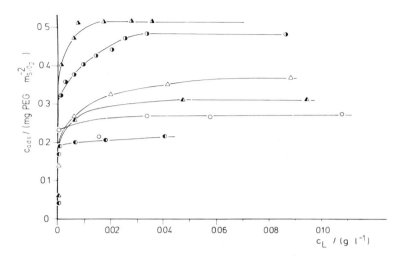

Fig. 1. Adsorption isotherms of PEG from water solution; pyrogenic silica: ▲ PEG 40 000, pH 4.7; ◑ PEG 6000, pH 4.7; precipitated silica:△ PEG 40 000, pH 2.3; ○ PEG 6000, pH 2.3; ▲ PEG 40 000, pH 5.5; ◐ PEG 6000, pH 5.5.

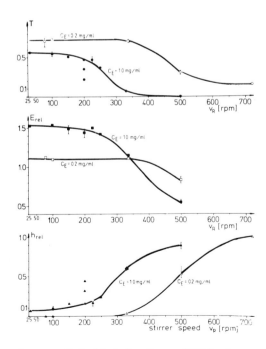

Fig. 2. Dependence of T (1min), E_{rel} (24h), h_{rel} (24h) on v_R; Aerosil 200, H_2O, PEG 40 000; T = 22°C; c_S = 0,01 g/ml; pH = 4.7; t_Z = 5 min, t_N = 5 min.

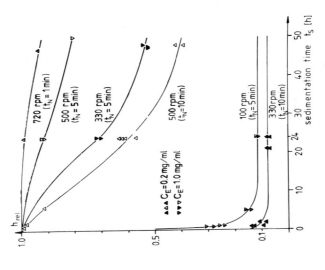

Fig. 4. Dependence of T (1min), E_{rel} (24h), h_{rel} (24h) on t_N; system as in fig. 2; c_E = 0.2 mg/mL; t_Z = 5 min.

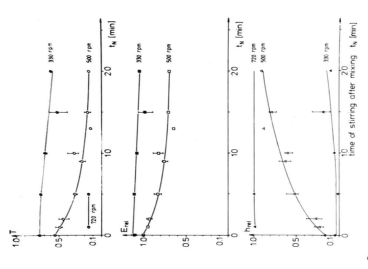

Fig. 3. Dependence of h_{rel} on the sedimentation time, t_S; system as in fig. 2.

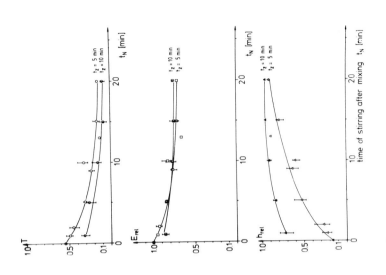

Fig. 6. Dependence of T (1min), E_{rel} (24h), h_{rel} (24h) on t_N; system as in fig. 2; v_R = 500 rpm.

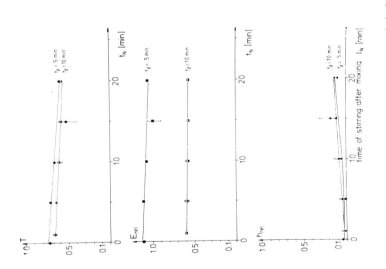

Fig. 5. Dependence of T (1min), E_{rel} (24h), h_{rel} (24h) on t_N; system as in fig. 2; v_R = 330 rpm.

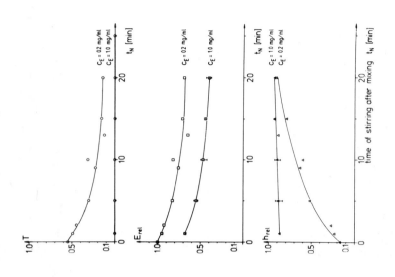

Fig. 8. Dependence of T (1min), E_{rel} (24h), h_{rel} (24h) on t_N; system as in fig. 2; v_R = 500 rpm; t_Z = 10 min.

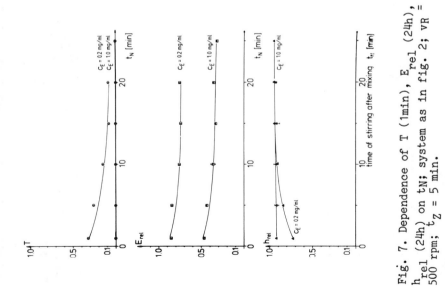

Fig. 7. Dependence of T (1min), E_{rel} (24h), h_{rel} (24h) on tN; system as in fig. 2; vR = 500 rpm; t_Z = 5 min.

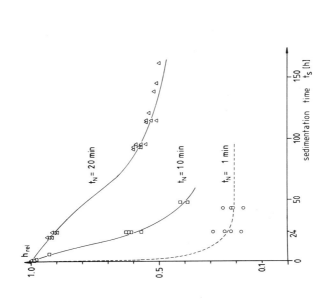

Fig. 10. Dependence of h_{rel} on sedimentation time, t_S; system as in fig. 2; t_Z = 5 min; v_R = 500 rpm; c_E = 0.2 mg/mL.

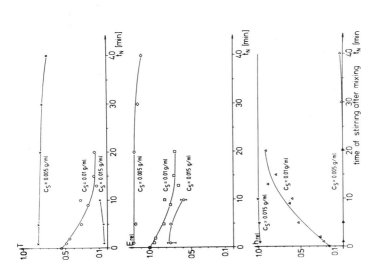

Fig. 9. Dependence of T (1min), E_{rel} (24h), h_{rel} (24h) on t_N; system as in fig. 2; t_Z = 5 min; v_R = 500 rpm; c_E = 0.2 mg/mL.

t_Z, on the flocculation behaviour at two different stirrer speeds. In both cases increasing the time of addition, t_Z, leads to a decrease in T (1') and E_{rel} (24h) (only where v_R = 330 rpm) and an increase in h_{rel} (24h). Additionally the sedimentation velocity levels off as the time of addition is increased (fig. 11).

Summarizing the described results one can conclude that for a given polymer concentration, c_E, by increasing the stirring speed, v_R, and times (t_Z, t_N) the extent of flocculation can be improved and the speed of sedimentation of the flocculate reduced. When v_R is low and t_N and t_Z are short little or no flocculation occurs and there is a tendency for the formation of granular flocs. This may be accounted for by the low bridging efficiency of the adsorbed polymer; the polymer forms single flocs rather than an extended network structure. A tendency to form granular flocs is also observed at very high shear intensities and very low stirring times. Under these conditions high and prolonged shear stresses and tensile stresses are existent and the flocculated structure can be disrupted. Between these two extreme states a region of moderate mixing conditions exists, under which structured flocculation with a sharp boundary layer dominates. As shown in figures 7 and 8 increasing the polymer concentration from 0.2 mg/ml to 1.0 mg/ml (corresponding to coverages $\theta = 0.2$ and θ = 1.0) results in a strong decrease of E_{rel} (24h) in the supernatant solution, in a decrease of the transmission T (1') corresponding to an increase in the turbidity of the suspension, and in an increase of h_{rel} (24h) to nearly h_{rel} = 1. All these characteristics indicate a very high flocculation efficiency.

Lowering the pH value of the suspension from pH 4.7 to pH 3.2 or pH 2.3 by adding an acid PEG-solution a totally different stability behaviour is observed. E_{rel} (24h) and T (1') are zero independent of the mixing parameters at both polymer concentrations. At low pH values h_{rel} (24h), a measure of the sedimentation volume, is slightly dependent on the stirrer speed, v_R, (see fig. 12). This behaviour demonstrates that no "critical" shear intensity is necessary for flocculation at pH 3.2 or 2.3. Thus, one may conclude that only at pH 4.7 is a kinetic energy necessary to overcome the electrostatic repulsion of the silica particles during flocculation.

The influence of the particle concentration on flocculation is shown in figure 9. At the lowest concentration, c_S = 0.005 g/ml, the T (1') and E_{rel} (24h) values decrease slightly with stirring time t_N; no flocculation was observed. At high stirring times, $t_N > 25$ min, some granular flocs are formed and a small stacking sedimentation is observed (h_{rel}). With the highest Aerosil concentration, c_S = 0.015 g/ml, despite the lowest polymer coverage, the flocculation is pronounced (T (1') < 0.1; $h_{rel} \simeq 1$). With increasing stirring time t_N the tendency to granular flocculation increases, especially at the highest particle concentration, and the sharp boundary layer becomes more diffuse. In this case the sediment loses its homogeneity showing structuring, volume regions

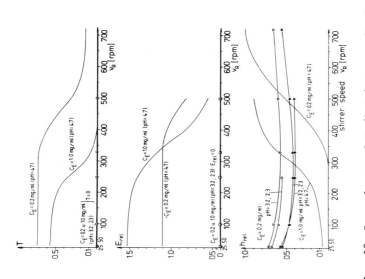

Fig. 12. Dependence of T (1min), E_{rel} (24h), h_{rel} (24h) on v_R; system as in fig. 2; $t_Z = 5$ min; $t_N = 5$ min.

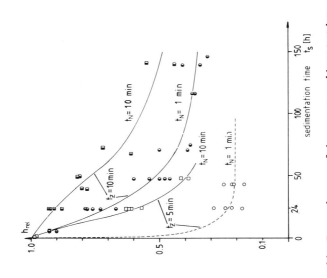

Fig. 11. Dependence of h_{rel} on sedimentation time, t_S; system as in fig. 2; $v_R = 500$ rpm; $c_E = 0.2$ mg/mL.

of low transmission alternate with regions of high transmission,
i.e. low particle concentration.

Colloidal Stability of Precipitated Silica

The pH value and the electrolyte concentration show decisive influences on the flocculation and the sedimentation behaviour of
precipitated silica. Precipitated silica could not be flocculated
at high pH values without the addition of an electrolyte. At
pH > 3.5 no change in the state of the suspension was observed,
e.g. the sedimentogramms of the suspensions with polymer addition
up to saturation ($\theta \sim 1$) have the same shapes as that of the sedi-
mentogram of the polymer free suspension. At pH 2.3 and even at
a very low polymer concentration ($c(40,000/PEG) \gtrsim 3 \cdot 10^{-5}$ mg/ml,
$\theta = 5 \cdot 10^{-4}$; $c(6000/PEG \gtrsim 5 \cdot 10^{-3}$ mg/ml, $\theta \sim 10^{-3}$) flocs were formed.
At higher coverages a sedimenting flocculated system was developed,
which produced a final boundary layer.

In the flocculated state for all suspensions, immediately
after mixing, no transmission of light could be detected through
the cuvette used and the sedimentation behaviour was different.
Thus, instead of the parameters used for the pyrogenic silica
systems we used the following characteristics for the precipitated silica mixtures to describe the flocculation and sedimentation behaviour:
(1) The relative absorbance $E_{3/4}$ to characterize the turbidity in
    the supernatant liquid.
(2) The relative absorbance $E_{1/5}$ to characterize the variation in
    the sedimenting flocculated dispersion.
(3) The relative height, h_{rel} (5 h), of the boundary layer at ab-
    sorbance $E = -\ln T = 0.5$ after 5 hours.

The major difference in the flocculation behaviour of PEG
40,000 at pH 5.3 and pH 2.3 is demonstrated by the absorbance in
the supernatant solution $E_{3/4}$ (fig. 13). At pH 2.3 a small addition of polymer leads to significant flocculation and therefore
a small absorbance, i.e. a high transparency of the supernatant
liquid. The time dependences of the absorbances with and without
polymer are shown for pH 5.3 and ca.pH 2 in fig. 14. Fig. 15
shows similar curves for a selection of salt concentrations. Similarly the time dependence of the absorbances $E_{1/5}$ with and without
polymer is illustrated for pH 5.3 and ca.pH 2 in fig. 16 and for
different salt concentrations in fig. 17.

The following conclusions can be drawn from these diagrams:
1) Without polymer all absorbances increase with decreasing pH
   and with increasing salt concentration. This behaviour can be
   explained by the increased aggregation of the particles at
   low pH and at high salt concentration leading to a more turbid
   suspension.
2) In salt free suspensions and in suspensions having low salt con-
   trations ($c_A < 0.005$) without polymer both absorbances $E_{1/5}$

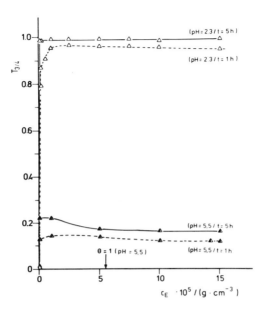

Fig. 13. Dependence of $T_{3/4}$ on polymer concentration, c_E; precipitated silica, $c_S \cong 0.36$ g/100 ml; H_2O; PEG 40 000.

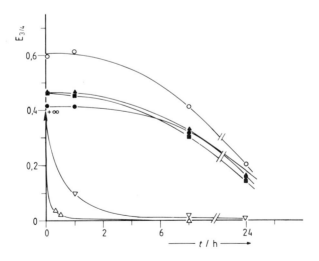

Fig. 14. Dependence of $E_{3/4}$ on time, t; system as in fig. 13; ● c_E = 0, pH 5.3; ○ c_E = 0, pH 1.9; ■ c_E = 0,01, pH 5,3 ▽ c_E = 0.1, pH 2.3; ▲ c_E = 5.0, pH 5.3; △ c_E = 5.0, pH = 2.2 (c_E in mg/100 ml).

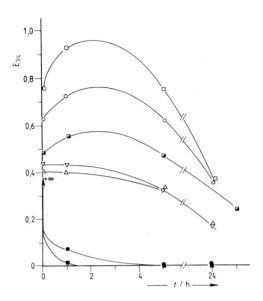

Fig. 15. Dependence of $E_{3/4}$ on time, t; system as in fig. 13; $c_E = 0$, c_{NaCl}: $\triangledown$ 0.001n, $\triangle$ 0.005 n, $\blacksquare$ 0.01 n, $\square$ 0,05 n, $\bigcirc$ 0.1 n; $\bullet$ $c_E = 0.1$, $c_{NACl} = 0.1n$, $\blacksquare$ $c_E = 1.0$, $c_{NaCl} = 0.1n$ (c_E in mg/100 ml).

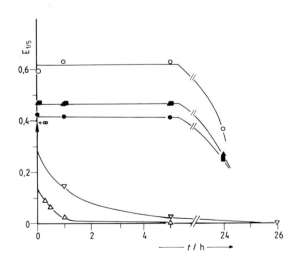

Fig. 16. Dependence of $E_{1/5}$ on time, t; systems and symbols as in fig. 14.

and $E_{3/4}$ decrease with time. At higher salt concentrations
the absorbances seem to go through a maximum (fig. 15). This
time dependence can be attributed to the aggregation and sedimentation of the particles which is more pronounced in the absorbance of the supernatant liquid at h_{rel} = 3/4.

3)   At pH 5.3 and at low salt concentrations polymer addition has
practically no influence on the aggregation and on the sedimentation behaviour. At pH 2.3 and at the highest salt concentration (0.1 m) the polymer addition results in infinite
absorbances immediately after mixing; these reduce to very
small absorbances $E_{3/4}$ and $E_{1/5}$ within a short time. This
behaviour is attributed to the significant flocculation and
the very fast sedimentation of the flocculated particles.

4)   In all these measurements the flocculated particles have a
granular structure and no structured flocculation appears.
This is especially seen in the non step-like hazy boundary
layer of the sedimenting phase.

The influences of pH and salt concentration as a function of polymer addition are more pronounced in the figures 18 to 22. The
absorbance $E_{1/5}$ in the suspension five hours after mixing is
plotted against pH in fig. 18 and against the logarithm of the
salt concentration in fig. 19. The height h/5 was chosen because
at this height the variations are very sensitive to aggregation,
flocculation and sedimentation. In fig. 20 the time dependence
of $T_{1/5}$ at pH 2.3 is demonstrated for different polymer concentrations. In addition, the relative height of the boundary layer
after five hours is illustrated as a function of the pH in fig.
21 and as a function of the salt concentration in fig. 22. The
diagrams 18, 21 clearly show that the pH value = 3.5 is a critical value. Without polymer and at lower pH an aggregation exists
leading to a higher absorbance. With polymer and at pH higher
than 3.5 no remarkable influence is demonstrated and all systems
show almost identical absorbance values. At pH lower than 3.5 in
contrast to the aggregation without polymer at higher concentrations the suspension flocculates in granular flocs. The latter
settle very rapidly and result in very low absorbances. Small
polymer additions up to c_{PEG} = 0.01 mg/ml result in a more and
more aggregated structure. This is seen in fig. 20 by the marked
decrease of $T_{1/5}$ with polymer concentration. At polymer concentration $c_{PEG} \sim 0.01$ mg/ml the formation of flocs and the measured
results are irreproducible. At higher polymer concentrations
$c_{PEG} \gtrsim 0.055$ mg/ml flocculation becomes more pronounced and the
transmission $T_{1/5}$ increases strongly due to the sedimentation of
the granular flocculated system. After a sedimentation time of
five hours very small sedimentation volumes are measured in contrast to the high volumes without flocculation (fig. 21).

Fig. 19 and also 22 show the existence of a critical salt
concentration for flocculation at high pH values (pH > 3.5). At
low salt concentrations $c_s \lesssim 10^{-2}$ mol/l no flocculation exists

372 POLYMER ADSORPTION AND DISPERSION STABILITY

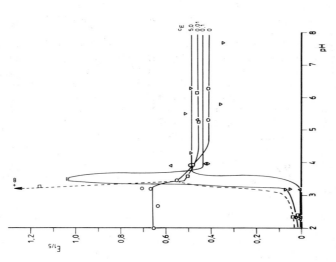

Fig. 18. Dependence of $E_{1/5}$ on pH; system as in fig. 13, $\bigcirc c_E = 0$; $\square c_E = 0.01$; $\triangledown c_E = 0.1$; $c_E = 5.0$ (c_E in mg/100 mL).

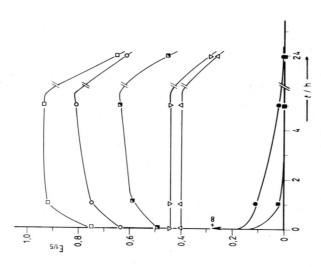

Fig. 17. Dependence of $E_{1/5}$ on time, t; systems and symbols as in fig. 15.

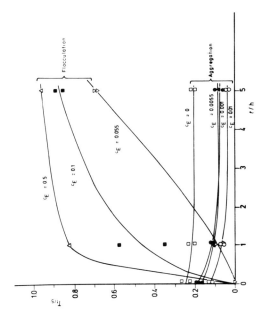

Fig. 20. Dependence of $T_{1/5}$ on time, t; system as in fig. 13; pH = 3.2; $\square c_E$ = 0; ● c_E = 0.001; ▲c_E = 0.0055; ○c_E = 0.01; ; ▽c_E = 0.055; ■ c_E = 0.1; △c_E = 0.5 (c_E in mg/100 mL).

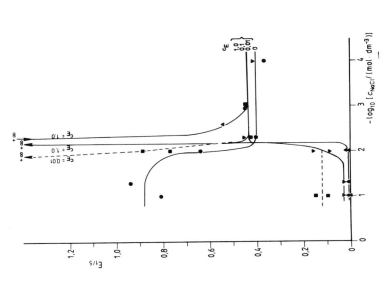

Fig. 19. Dependence of $E_{1/5}$ on $-\log cNaCl$ (mol/1); system as in fig. 13; ● c_E = 0; ■c_E = 0.01; ▼c_E = 0.1; ▲c_E = 1.0 (c_E in mg/100 mL).

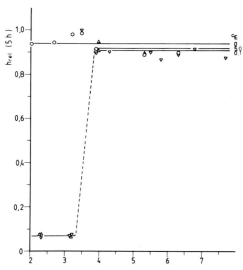

Fig. 21. Dependence of h_{rel} (5h) on pH; system and symbols as in fig. 18

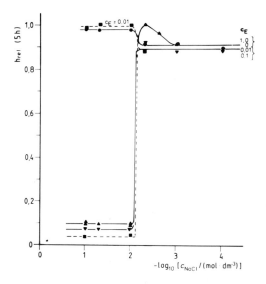

Fig. 22. Dependence of h_{rel} (5h) on $-\log c_{NaCl}$ (mol/1); system and symbols as in fig. 19.

with polymer addition and the same absorbance with or without polymer can be measured. At high salt concentration $c_s > 10^{-2}$ mol/l
the flocculation becomes more and more pronounced with increasing
polymer concentration. This results in E values which decrease
with the polymer coverage (fig. 15) and small sedimentation volumes h_{rel} which increase with the polymer concentration (fig.22).
At salt concentrations approximately equal to the critical concentration $c_s \sim 10^{-2}$ mol/l a zone comparable with the critical
pH region exists in which results are irreproducible.

The variation of the mixing procedure at pH 2.3 implies that
the critical concentration of the polymer necessary for flocculation is independent of the mixing parameters. This behaviour
differentiates the flocculation behaviour of precipitated silica from that of pyrogenic silica at pH 7. However, it should be
remembered that at low pH values the flocculation of pyrogenic
silica is also independent of mixing conditions.

Conclusions

The experimental results given above show that flocculation with
PEG is different for pyrogenic and precipitated silica. In contrast to pyrogenic silica precipitated silica is only flocculable
by decreasing the pH to below 3.5 or by the addition of salt to
a concentration greater than 10^{-2} mol/l. In this case the flocculation of precipitated silica can be induced with a very low concentration of polymer (reproducible for PEG 40,000 at $c_{PEG} \gtrsim 0.1$
mg/100 ml, $\theta \gtrsim 0.02$), whereas for pyrogenic silica higher polymer
concentrations are necessary. Increasing the polymer concentration or the coverage changes the structure of the flocculated
pyrogenic silica from granular flocs at very low coverage to
structured flocculation at high coverage. In contrast to this
behaviour granular flocs are formed from precipitated silica also
at high coverages of PEG.

The flocculation of the pyrogenic silica is strongly dependent on the mixing conditions, i.e. stirring intensity, duration
of stirring at high pH values and without salt. In contrast the
flocculation of precipitated and pyrogenic silica at pH $\lesssim$ 3.5
and at high salt concentrations is independent of mixing. The
reason for the different behaviour can be partially related to
the different shapes of the silica particles, i.e. monodisperse
spherical particles for the precipitated silica and highly aggregated structures for the pyrogenic silica. Because of the irreversible flocculated structures, measured here quantitatively, it
becomes understandable that different mixing procedures cause
different states of flocculation. The optimum method of mixing,
by slow   titration of the polymer solution into the suspension,
which we have used for this quantitative study, can also be approximately applied in practical cases to prevent inhomogeneities
during the mixing process. The mixing of the model system by
slowly titrating a polymer solution in a suspension, used here

to obtain quantitative results, can also be applied, albeit perhaps less precisely, to practical systems where inhomogeneities
must be prevented during mixing. The presented results using well
characterized model systems are thus expected to have validity
for real systems containing high molecular nonionic polymers.

Acknowledgments

We would like to thank the Deutsche Forschungsgemeinschaft and
the Arbeitsgemeinschaft Industrieller Forschungsvereinigungen e.V.
for financial support and the firms Degussa, Wolfgang for provision of Aerosil- and Hoechst, Gendorf for provision of PEG-samp-
les.

Literature Cited

1. Eisenlauer, J.; Killmann, E.; Korn, M. J. Coll. Interf. Sci.
   1980, 74, 108, 120.
2. Killmann, E.; Eisenlauer, J. in "The Effect of Polymers on
   Dispersion Properties", Tadros, Th. F., Ed.; Academic Press,
   London, 1982, p. 221.
3. Korn, M.; Killmann, E.; Eisenlauer, J. J. Coll. Interf. Sci.
   1980, 76, 7, 19.
4. Killmann, E.; Korn, M.; Bergmann, M. in "Adsorption from
   Solution", Ottewill, R.H.; Rochester, C.H.; Smith, A.L, Eds.;
   Academic Press, London, 1983, p. 259.
5. Killmann, E. Polymer 1976, 17, 864.
6. Ives, K.J. in "Scientific Basis of Flocculation", Ives, K.J.,
   Ed.; Nato Advanced Study Institutes Series, Sijthoff and
   Noordhoff, Alphen aan den Rijn, 1978, pp.37 and 165.
7. Gregory, J. "Scientific Basis of Flocculation", Ives, K.J.,
   Ed.; Nato Advanced Study Institutes Series, Sijthoff and
   Noordhoff, Alphen aan den Rijn, 1978, p. 101.
8. Gregory, J. in "The Effect of Polymers on Dispersion Properties", Tadros, Th.F., Ed.; Adacemic Press, London, 1981,
   p. 301.
9. Warren, L. Colloids and Surfaces 1982, 5, 301.
10. Killmann, E.; Eisenlauer, J. Progr. Coll. Polymer Sci. 1976,
    60, 147.
11. Stöber, W.; Fink, A.; Bohn, E. J. Colloid Interf. Sci. 1968,
    26, 62.
12. Attia, Y.A.; Rubio, J. Brit. Polymer J. 1975, 7, 135.

RECEIVED November 22, 1983

Colloidal Stability of Microcrystalline Cellulose in Aqueous Salt Solutions

PHILIP LUNER and T. CHOU[1]

Empire State Paper Research Institute, College of Environmental Science & Forestry, Syracuse, NY 13210

The coagulation of microcrystalline cellulose was re-investigated over a wider range of solids than previously reported. At solids less than 230 ppm only one CCC was found. As the solids concentration was increased to 410 ppm coagulation was followed by an apparent redispersion region. Further addition of salt led to coagulation. At higher solids ∼ 600 ppm, the CCC at the lower salt concentration was eliminated. The redispersion region coagulated at temperatures higher than 23°C, the extent varying with solids concentration. The flocs in this region differed considerably from that found at higher salt concentrations. While the system conforms to coagulation in a secondary minimum, the redispersion region is best accounted for in terms of gel formation originating from the rod-like shape of the particles and hydrated surface. During the final coagulation process additional attractive forces such as dipolar and hydrogen bonding form flocs which are irreversible and denser than those formed at a lower salt concentration.

In a number of recent publications (1, 2) microcrystalline cellulose dispersions (MCC) have been used as models to study different aspects of the papermaking process, especially with regard to its stability. One of the central points in the well established DLVO theory of colloidal stability is the critical coagulation concentration (CCC). In practice, it represents the minimum salt concentration that causes rapid coagulation of a dispersion and is an intimate part of the theoretical framework of the DLVO theory (3). Kratohvil et al (4) have studied this aspect of the DLVO theory with MCC and given values for the CCC for many salts, cationic

[1] Current address: The General Tire and Rubber Company, Akron, OH 44305.

surfactants and metal chelates. It was found that the MCC sol
behaved quite differently towards these destabilizing agents than
other more conventional sols, such as latex and AgI. In the
context of the present study suffice it to say that in the solids
range of 100 to 400 ppm the CCC did not vary and was 1.3×10^{-4}M
NaCl. In our previous studies, slightly higher values were found
which was attributed to either sample origin, preparation techniques, particle size or solids content.

In the course of further work on characterizing the MCC sols
it was found that the CCC of a variety of salts varied both with
the solids content and temperature. Investigation of these parameters forms the basis of the study. It will be shown that as a
result of particle shape, concentration and surface characteristics, coagulation leads to a gel-like structure. On further
addition of salt the coagulated gel-like structure aggregates into
flocs that are irreversible. In this paper, we outline the experimental parameters which lead to these phenomena and present some
possible explanations.

Experimental

Sol Preparation. Microcrystalline cellulose (Avicel PH 105) was
supplied by the FMC Corporation, Philadelphia, PA., as a white
powder. Twenty grams of Avicel PH 105 were mixed with 180 ml of
water in a Waring blender for 5 minutes. The thick slurry was then
transferred to a 1ℓ. volumetric flask and gradually diluted to 1ℓ.
under constant stirring. The diluted suspension was left undis-
turbed for 3 days. The supernatant with a volume of about 650 ml
was removed. This constituted the microcrystalline cellulose (MCC)
stock sol. The solids concentration of the sols were determined by
oven dry weighing and was about (1.2g/1). The unadjusted pH was
5.6. All the salts, hydrochloric acid and sodium hydroxide used
were certified A.C.S. grade from Fisher Scientific.

Stability Measurements. Stability experiments were performed by
the addition of electrolytes or HCl to the MCC sols. Two series of
graduated cylinders were prepared. One series contained 15 ml of
sol with the same solids concentration in each cylinder. The other
series of cylinders contained 15 ml of the electrolyte or HCl of
varying concentrations. Pairs of graduated cylinders (one from
each series) were combined by pouring the contents back and forth
between the cylinders several times to give a total combined volume
of 30 ml. HCl or NaOH was added to these mixtures when necessary
to adjust to the final pH value. These samples were left undis-
turbed for 2 hours. At the end of 2 hours, the upper 20 ml of the
supernatant was withdrawn with a long needle syringe for turbidity
measurement. The sol in water served as a blank. The turbidity
readings of all the samples were compared with the reading of the
blank, and this ratio, τ was used as the criterion for stability.
The turbidities were determined with a turbidimeter, Model DRT100,

obtained from HF Instruments, Fredonia, N.Y. The turbidities were expressed in Nephelometer Turbidity Unit (NTU).

In most experiments the smallest amount of electrolyte needed to coagulate the sols measured after 2 hours standing was chosen as the CCC. When using HCl, this point is the critical coagulation pH. A constant temperature water bath was used for temperature different than $23^{\circ}C$. The pH values were measured with a Beckman Model 96A pH meter and a Fisher combination electrode. The electrophoretic mobility measurements were made with a Laser Doppler Electrophoresis apparatus. These experiments were performed by Mr. J. Klein of the Chemistry Department, Syracuse University.

Filtration Test. The filtration test equipment consisted of a glass column, with a fritted disc 2 cm. diameter, fitted with a stopcock and a 25 ml graduated cylinder. After mixing the MCC sols with electrolyte solution, the mixture was immediately poured into the glass column with the stopcock closed. The time required to collect water (blank) and filtered sol between 5 to 25 mls in the graduated cylinder after 2 hrs. was determined. The fritted glass was backwashed with water thoroughly after each measurement and a new blank was established. The relative filtration time between sample and water was used to compare differences between samples.

Results

Effect of Particle Concentrations on the CCC. Figure 1 gives the plots of the relative turbidity, versus log NaCl concentration at different solid concentration at $23^{\circ}C$. At a solids concentration below 230 ppm (Figure 1A) the CCC increases somewhat with a decrease in solid concentration. However, when the solid concentration is between 300 ppm and 620 ppm, two CCC values are observed (Figure 1B). The minimum of the first unstable region gradually decreases as the solids concentration is increased until finally at about 670 ppm, only one CCC is observed at a higher electrolyte concentration (Figure 1C).

As the redispersion region may be the result of a charge reversal, the electrophoretic mobilities of the MCC sols as a function of NaCl concentration were determined. No charge reversal was detected and the mobility of the particles decreased from 3.5 to 2.6 mobility units in a linear manner with increasing salt concentration indicating that the redispersion region was not caused by charge reversal.

Three additional electrolytes, LiCl, $CaCl_2$ and $BaCl_2$ were used as destabilizing electrolytes and these coagulation curves are shown in Figure 2. Again, two CCC's are observed with all the electrolytes strongly indicating that this phenomenon does depend on electrolyte type. The coagulation concentrations of $BaCl_2$ and $CaCl_2$ are lower than those of LiCl and NaCl, which agrees with results of previous studies (4) and points to the fact that we are dealing with an electrostatic type of destabilization. Figure 2

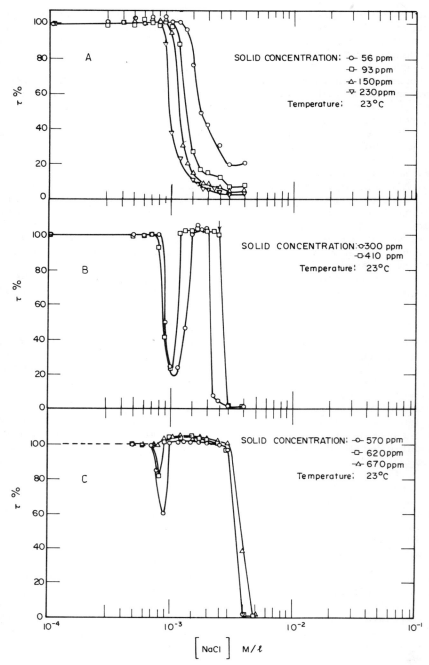

Figure 1. Relative Turbidity (τ%) versus NaCl concentration
for MCC sols at different solids concentration.

also shows that the CCC value of NaCl is lower than that of LiCl. Bohm and Luner (5) have observed by potentiometric titration that the order in the adsorption of counterions with oxidized MCC increases as follows:

$$Li^+ < Na^+ < K^+ < Mg^{2+} < Ca^{2+} < Ba^{2+}$$

Assuming that the same adsorption order would occur when these counterions are adsorbed onto the MCC sols used here, this coagulating sequence follows the adsorption order nicely.

Effect of Temperature on the Stability/Instability Regions. Figure 3 shows the effect of increasing temperature on the stability of the MCC sols. Two main features may be noted. First, while only one CCC is observed with the 670 ppm sols at 23°C, by increasing the temperature to 29°C creates an instability region at a salt concentration of $1 \times 10^{-3}M$ which increases with temperature. The second feature made apparent with increasing temperature is the systematic disappearance of the "restabilized zone". Indeed, the 670 ppm sol shows only one CCC at 44°C, and the 410 ppm sol shows only one CCC at 34°C. Similarly, the 410 ppm sol shows only one CCC at 17°C. An instability region appears at 23°C and $1 \times 10^{-3}M$ salt which increases progressively and the "restabilized" zone is eliminated at 45°, i.e., only one CCC is observed at a lower salt concentration (Figure 4).

The different stability regions are shown schematically in Figure 5 and in subsequent discussion reference will be made to the regions indicated in this Figure. These results show that the two CCC values are sensitive both to temperature and to particle concentration and there exist critical points of particle concentration and temperature where either region II could be stabilized or region III destabilized which finally results in only one CCC value.

In order to determine the critical temperature and solids concentration points, stability domain diagrams were constructed as a function of solids concentration and salt, (Figure 6) as well as a function of temperature and salt at fixed values of solids (Figure 7).

From the data given so far as well as data not reported, a two CCC domain diagram with temperature and solid concentration as coordinates was constructed and shown in Figure 8. The shaded area represents the two CCC domain.

Effect of pH on the CCC. It has been shown that the negative charge of MCC originates from the dissociation of carboxyl groups (6). A change in pH value of the MCC sol will lead to a change in the degree of dissociation of the carboxyl groups, resulting in a change of the surface potential of the MCC particles. Since surface potential is an important factor for the stability of the colloid system, the effect of pH on the stability of MCC sols was examined.

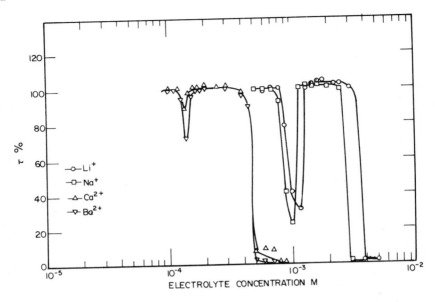

Figure 2. Relative Turbidity (τ%) versus salt concentration for MCC sols at 23°C and 410 ppm solids.

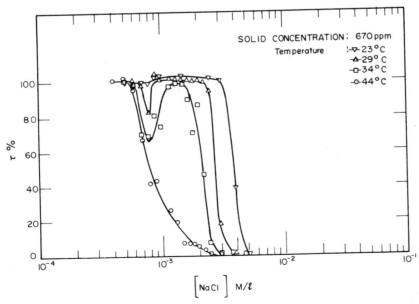

Figure 3. Relative Turbidity (τ%) versus NaCl concentration for MCC sols at 670 ppm solids at various temperatures.

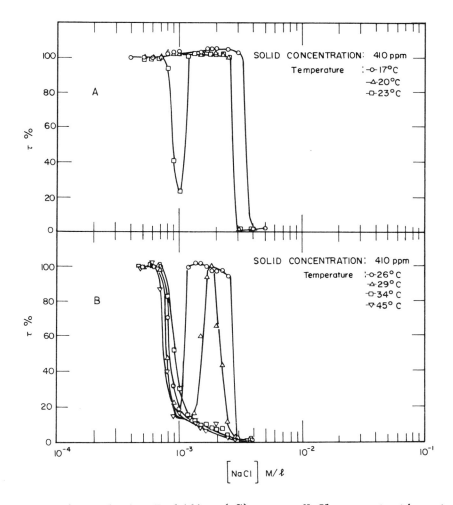

Figure 4.   Relative Turbidity (τ%) versus NaCl concentration at 410 ppm and at various temperatures.

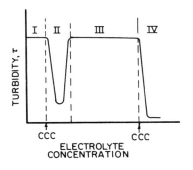

Figure 5.   Schematic representation of stability and instability regions.

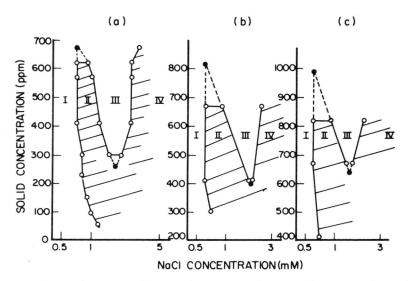

Figure 6. Stability domain diagrams of MCC sols, as a function of solid concentration. a) 23°C b) 29°C c) 34°C. The shaded areas represent coagulated and settled MCC sols.

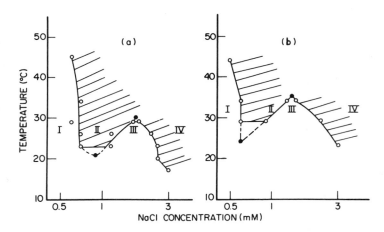

Figure 7. Stability domain diagrams of MCC sols as function of temperature and NaCl concentration at a solids concentration of a) 410 ppm, and b) 670 ppm. The shaded areas represent coagulated and settled MCC sols.

Figure 9A and 9B show the coagulation curves at pH 4.7 and 6.4 as well as the unadjusted one, pH 5.6, at 23°C with a solid content of 410 ppm. When comparing the coagulation curve for pH 5.6, it is seen that at pH 4.7, the whole curve was shifted in the direction of lower electrolyte concentration. At pH 6.4, only one CCC is observed at 23°C, but, on increasing the temperature to 29°C, two CCC's are observed.

Floc Reversibility by Changing NaCl Concentration. To evaluate more fully the nature of the coagulation process with increasing salt concentration a number of observations were made on the flocs. The solid concentration of MCC sol for this study was 410 ppm at 23°C. In region II, the NaCl concentration could be reduced by replacing the supernatant with water to make the final NaCl concentration the same as that in region I. After adjusting the concentration to region I the originally formed aggregates were redispersed by gently reversing the cylinders several times. The readjusted dispersion was stable and no visible flocs formed during two hours which indicated reversibility between region II and I. However, the flocs of region IV always reformed no matter which region they were diluted to. These results indicate that the type and extent of intermolecular forces vary with salt concentration.

Floc Reversibility by Changing Temperature. At 23°C with a solid concentration of 670 ppm, the MCC sol in region II was stable. On raising the temperature from 23°C to 34°C, the sol was destabilized and flocs formed. When the temperature was lowered again to 23°C (the cylinder reversed several times to redisperse the aggregates), the flocs were redispersed and the dispersion was stable. In another test, the MCC sol at 23°C and 410 ppm was unstable (region II). After decreasing the temperature to 20°C, the MCC sol was stabilized. If the temperature was raised back to 23°C, the MCC sol destabilized and flocs formed again. The flocs in region II seem to be temperature reversible.

    The reversibility of the MCC sols in region III was also studied at 410 ppm at 23°C. Three NaCl concentrations were chosen for this test, i.e., 1.33 x 10^{-3}M, which was close to the NaCl concentration of region II, 1.67 x 10^{-3}M, located in the middle of region III, and 2.25 x 10^{-3}M, was near the NaCl concentration of region IV. After two hours, all the sols were stable. Then when the temperature was raised from 23°C to 34°C, flocs formed in all three samples. After two hours, the temperature was lowered to 23°C. The sols with NaCl concentrations of 1.33 x 10^{-3}M and 1.67 x 10^{-3}M were restabilized, whereas the flocs formed in 2.25 x 10^{-3}M NaCl were irreversible.

Floc Sedimentation. Although flocs formed in both regions II and IV, their formation rate and sediment volume were different. The

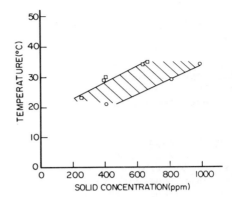

Figure 8. Two CCC domain diagrams of MCC as a function of temperature and solids concentration. The shaded area represents the two CCC domains.

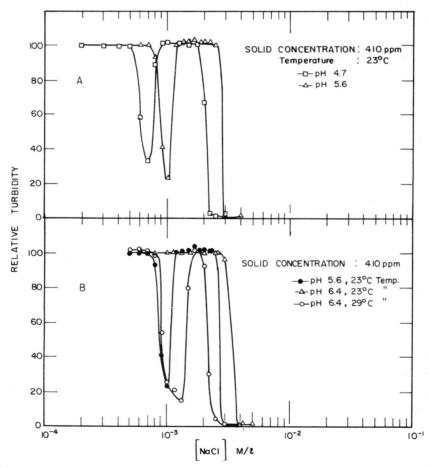

Figure 9. The effect of pH and temperature on the coagulation of MCC sols at a solid concentration of 410 ppm.

particles of region IV coagulated immediately after mixing the sol
with NaCl while the particles of region II did not coagulate until
an hour later or even longer after mixing.

Figure 10 shows the sedimentation results at 23°C and 410 ppm
in a total volume of 30 ml. For both regions, the initial volume
of subsidence could not be recorded because there was no clear
boundary between sediment and supernatant. From this figure, we
see that the sedimentation rate in region IV was higher than that
in region II, while the sedimentation volume in region II was twice
that of region IV.

Filtration Test. The sols in regions I and III appeared identical
by turbidity measurements at 23°C at a solids concentration of 410
ppm. However, the previous data showed that the sols in region III
coagulate at high temperatures or at lower solid concentrations,
while the sols in region I are stable under these conditions. One
possible explanation is that the particles in region III formed a
type of network (gel) structure. Such a structure immobilizes the
particles and gives the appearance of stable sols. One way to test
this possibility is to refilter samples from the different regions.
If a network structure is formed in region III, there ought to be
an extra resistance to filtration and leading to longer filtration times than those in region I. Table I gives the results

Table 1.   Relative Filtration Time of MCC Sols as a Function of
NaCl Concentration at 23°C

Solids ppm	0 Blank	5×10^{-4} Reg. I	9×10^{-4} Reg. II	1.33×10^{-3} Reg. III	1.67×10^{-3} Reg. III	2.25×10^{-3} Reg. III	4×10^{-3} Reg. IV
410	1.17	1.22	1.43	1.50	1.65	1.63	6.40
760	1.19	1.26	1.39	1.75	1.93	1.97	9.52

for the relative filtration time as a function of NaCl concentration. The results indicate that the different regions have different filterability indicating that the flocs have different structures.

Discussion

Figure 1A shows that the CCC decreases with increasing sol concentration in the range of 50 to 200 ppm. The variation of the CCC
with sol concentration is by no means an unexpected observation in
view of previous work with other systems (7). Recently Bensley and
Hunter (8) have investigated this aspect of colloidal stability
with latices and found that up to a volume fraction of 0.10 the CCC
was independent of the volume fraction. These authors also pointed
out the difficulties involved in measuring the stability of more

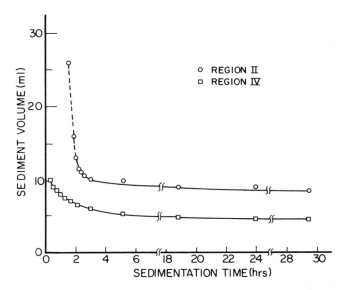

Figure 10.   Sediment volume (ml) versus settling time (hr) for MCC sols in region II and IV at 23°C and a solids concentration of 410 ppm.

concentrated dispersions and the importance of mixing during the coagulation process. In view of the rod-like shape of the MCC particles, their density (1.52), and wide size distribution, using the more rigorous optical techniques to determine the CCC would be a formidable task. Two more convenient but less accurate approaches were adopted; measuring the residual turbidity and sediment volume after settling for a finite time. While neither of these methods is absolute, they have proved convenient and informative.

The most straightforward explanation for the data in Figure 1A lies in the floc size formed on coagulation. As the sol concentration increases, larger flocs are formed which settle more quickly and give an apparent decrease in the CCC. Experiments made at longer standing times than two hours showed somewhat lower CCC values. As the sol concentration reaches 300 ppm, an apparent redispersion occurs which is followed by another CCC at a higher salt concentration. In all instances, the redispersion occurs over a very narrow range of salt concentration. Indeed, much of our preliminary work pointed to a very irreproducible system until this phenomenon was recognized as real. The electrophoretic results and the two CCC behavior with other mono and divalent salts seem to eliminate the specific adsorption of cations as an explanation for this phenomenon. When still higher sol concentrations are used (Figure 1C) only one CCC, at a higher salt concentration was observed.

The turbidity values indicate that region I and III are similar, i.e., both regions appear as a dispersed sol. To establish whether this is indeed the case, sols from the different stability zones were centrifuged at low speed. It was found that at a salt concentration greater than $1 \times 10^{-3}M$, i.e., between the two CCC values, the sols sedimented much more rapidly than at salt concentrations below $1 \times 10^{-3}M$ indicating that region III is composed of larger aggregates which did not settle on standing; thus, gelation may be occurring at a salt concentration $> 1 \times 10^{-3}M <$ 5×10^{-3} and at a sol particle concentration greater than 300 ppm. The refiltration data in Table 1 and the different equilibrium sediment values in regions II and IV seems to confirm that a different structure exists in these identifiable regions. Lastly, the lack of redispersibility of the sols coagulated at high concentration, in contrast to the redispersibility of the sols coagulated at $1 \times 10^{-3}M$, further shows that structural differences exist between flocs in regions II and IV.

DLVO Theory Applied to MCC Sols. In order to interpret the stability of MCC sols, several stability calculations were made. First, by using a spherical particle radius of 706Å, A = 2.6 kT, ψ_0 = 14 mV and T = 296°K at a salt concentration of $0.9 \times 10^{-3}M$ (region II), a secondary minimum was obtained at 500 Å, V_{max} = 4 kT at V_T = 0 at 14 Å. At higher salt concentrations, the DLVO plots showed nearly complete instability. Similar calculations were made using flat plate geometry with A = $2.94 \times 10^{-20}J$

(9, 10). It was found that $V_{max} \doteq 0.5 \times 10^{-10} J/m^2$ with a broad shallow secondary minimum of 600 Å.

Kratohvil et al (4) have accounted for the high sensitivity of MCC sol towards electrolyte based on a secondary minimum and indeed the calculations presented above make this a reasonable explanation. With this in mind, the first CCC < 200 ppm is a result of coagulation in a secondary minimum. However, given sufficient particles, 410 ppm, and a salt concentration greater than $1 \times 10^{-3} M$ the particles are brought still closer together and a three dimensional structure (gel) is formed. This gel imbibes sufficient water so as to prevent its sedimentation completely. Further addition of salt, (second CCC) breaks the gel structure and the flocs settle out. The temperature reversibility of flocs in regions II and III in contrast to those of region IV, as well as the difference in sediment volumes and refiltration time between the two regions, indicate that at the higher salt concentration, i.e., at the second CCC, the particles may indeed be at a primary minimum.

Observations such as those presented here have been reported previously for CeO_2 by Kruyt (11). Their results indicated that at $1.64 \times 10^{-2} M$ NaCl, the CeO_2 sol coagulates slowly while at $1.82 \times 10^{-1} M$ NaCl, the CeO_2 sol forms a gel and the particles do not settle. Similar gel-structure phenomenon have been observed for Al_2O_3 (12) and SiO_2 sols (13). Overbeek (14) has proposed that this type of gel was as a loose network structure formed by particle-particle interactions. This network structure immobilizes the particles as well as occluded liquid and prevents the particles from coagulating. Since the particles cannot coagulate, the system which forms a gel appears like a stable sol. Two recent reviews (15, 16) have recently focused attention on this type of coagulation and gelation phenomena, especially with rod-like particles. While considerable progress has been made, a complete explanation of these phenomena is still lacking. Much of the data are consistent with coagulation at secondary minimum, but two experimental results need further elaboration; the lower floc volume of region IV compared to region II and the temperature sensitivity of region III.

On the basis of viscosity and sedimentation analysis, Marchessault et al (17) have proposed a tactoid shape unit comprising about 20 microcrystals in dilute phosphate buffer. Other evidence (18) also suggests that cellulose microcrystals have a tendency to aggregate easily in a side-by-side fashion. It is our contention that region IV consists largely of tactoid type aggregates. Calculations show that the occluded volume fraction of the sol in the sediment in region IV is 0.16 while the occluded volume fraction of the original sol is 0.90. It would appear that the particles in this salt region are subjected to additional attractive forces. These may originate from dipole and/or hydrogen bonding forces (15) resulting in a more tightly packed floc.

As the gel is very dilute, the temperature sensitivity in this region is likely related to the increased Brownian motion which breaks the weakly bonded structure into discrete flocs. However, whether this occurs as a result of changes of particle charge and potential and/or dehydration of the dispersed phase is unknown at this time (19).

Concluding Remarks

This study has shown that MCC forms a gel-like structure at low solids concentration in the presence of salt. It has also been known for a considerable time (20) that MCC forms aqueous gels and pastes but at much higher solids concentration. It would appear that further studies with the MCC gel in dilute form may elucidate the mechanism of gelation more definitively.

Acknowledgments

We would like to acknowledge the helpful discussions with Dr. Robert Evans and Mr. A. Shrinath. Mr. Shrinath also contributed the experimental work dealing with the MCC sols. Contribution No. 167 Empire State Paper Research Institute.

Literature Cited

1. Sandell, L., and Luner, P., J. Appl Polymer Sci 18: 2075 (1974).
2. Goossens, J.W.S., and Luner, P., TAPPI 59 No. 2 89 (1976).
3. Verwey, E.J.W., and Overbeek, J.Th.G., "Theory of Stability of Lyopholic Colloids" Elsevier, Amsterdam, 1948.
4. Kratohvil, S., Janauer, G.E., and Matijevic, E., J. Colloid Interface Sci 29 187 (1969).
5. Bohm, J., and Luner, P. unpublished results.
6. Edelson, M.R., and Hermans, J. Jr., J. Polymer Sci Part C No. 2 145 (1963).
7. "Colloid Science", H.R. Kruyt, ed. Vol. 1, p. 321, Elsevier, Amsterdam, 1952.
8. Bensley, C.N., and Hunter, R., J. Colloid Interface Sci 88, No. 2 546 (1983).
9. Visser, J., Adv. Colloid Interface Sci. 3 331 (1972).
10. Visser, J., J. Colloid Interface Sci 34 26 (1970).
11. Kruyt, H.R., and van der Made, J.E.M., Rec. Trav. Chem. 42, 277 (1923).
12. Gann, J.A., Kolloid Chem. Beihefte 8 64 (1916).
13. Kruyt, H.R., and Postma, J., Rec. Trav. Chem. 44 765 (1925).
14. See Ref. 7, p. 335.
15. I.F. Efremov in "Surface and Colloid Science"; Matijevic, E., Ed., Wiley Interscience: 1976 Vol. 8 p. 85.
16. W. Heller in "Polymer Colloids II"; Fitch, R.M., Ed., Plenum Press, 1980; p. 153.

17. Marchessault, J. Jr., Koch, M.J., and Yang, J.T., _J. Colloid Sci_ 16 345 (1961).
18. Hermans, J. Jr., _J. Polymer Sci_ Part C, No. 2, 129 (1963).
19. Baran, A.A., Solomentseva, I.M., and Kurilenko, O.D., _Kolloidnyi Zhurnal_ 37 No. 2 p. 219 (1975).
20. Battista, O.A., Cruz, M.M., and Ferraro, C.F., in "Surface and Colloid Science; Matijevic, E., Ed., Wiley Interscience 1971 Vol. 3 p. 241.

RECEIVED October 7, 1983

Adsorption of Polyacrylamides on Kaolinite and Its Flocculation and Stabilization

P. SOMASUNDARAN, Y. H. CHIA, and R. GORELIK

Henry Krumb School of Mines, Columbia University, New York, NY 10027

Adsorption of nonionic and anionic polyacrylamides on kaolinite clay is studied together with various flocculation properties (settling rate, sediment volume, supernatant clarity and suspension viscosity) under controlled conditions of pH, ionic strength and agitation. Adsorption and flocculation data obtained simultaneously for selected systems were correlated to obtain information on the dependence of flocculation on the surface coverage. Interestingly, optimum polymer concentration and type vary depending upon the flocculation response that is monitored. This is discussed in terms of the different properties of the flocs and the floc network that control different flocculation responses. Flocculation itself is examined as the cumulative result of many subprocesses that can depend differently on system properties.

The nature of the flocculation of fines obtained in polymer solutions is dependent upon a number of factors including polymer characteristics, solid and solvent properties as well as the hydrodynamic conditions used during the flocculation and preflocculation stages. Understanding the role of factors is important for achieving the desired flocculation state of fines, particularly of mineral dispersions which are not easily processed (1,2). It is noted here that different properties of the flocculated systems can be the determining criterion in different processes. For example, whereas supernatant clarity will be important when water is to be recycled, it can be the sediment volume or the settling rate that will be important in effluent treatment. Different polymers can have different effects on the above-named properties of a flocculating system, and a simultaneous study of these effects can provide useful information about the mechanism of interaction between polymers and particles as

0097–6156/84/0240–0393$06.00/0
© 1984 American Chemical Society

well as between the polymer-coated particles. In this study,
the effect of polymer properties, such as charge density, on
selected flocculation parameters, such as settling rate, sediment
volume, and supernatant clarity, is studied for kaolinite fines.
     The flocculation of kaolinite has been studied extensively
in the past (3-9). However, the results have been contradictory,
for example, in the case of the polymer charge density required
for optimum flocculation. While the discrepancies might be
owing partly to the different methods used to measure flocculation,
they also could have resulted from uncertainties in the measured
properties of kaolinite caused by aging or ion exchange, in the
properties of polymer due to the use of different commercial
samples, or in the properties of the solution owing to variations
in pH, ionic strength etc. An accurate understanding of the
flocculation and dispersion of clays is, however, of much importance since clays are universally present in ore deposits, oil
reservoirs, and marine and agricultural systems and markedly
influence various processes involving them.
     Flocculation is indeed dependent on polymer adsorption, and
there are hypotheses correlating the two phenomena, but often
these have been put forth without detailed measurement of the
two phenomena simultaneously (10-13). In this paper, flocculation
is investigated as a function of polymer and solution properties
and hydrodynamic conditions by measuring different properties
of the system, including adsorption, using well characterized
kaolinite and polymer samples prepared specifically for this
purpose. Also, the role of concentration and charge density of
polyacrylamide and polyacrylamide-polyacrylic acid co-polymers
in determining kaolinite flocculation is examined under controlled
hydrodynamic conditions.

Experimental

Materials. Na-Kaolinite: A homoionic sample of kaolinite was
prepared from a well-crystallized sample purchased from Source
Clays, University of Missouri, using a standardized technique (14)
which involved repeated washing with distilled water and by
treatment with NaCl solutions to remove exchangeable ions such as
Ca, and freeze-drying of the final product. Nitrogen specific
surface area of this kaolinite was estimated to be $9.4m^2/g$ and
X-ray analysis showed the characteristic pattern of kaolinite.
     Polymers: Polyacrylamide and hydrolyzed polyacrylamide were
prepared by the American Cyanamid Company specifically for this
project, starting with ^{14}C labelled monomer. The radioactivity
level of the monomer was kept below 0.20 mC_i/g in order to avoid
significant spontaneous polymerization, utilizing a copper inhibitor. The homopolymer was synthesized by free radical solution
polymerization in water at 40°C, using monomer recrystallized from
chloroform, an ammonium persulfate-sodium metabisulfite catalyst
system, and isopropanol as a chain transfer agent. Sodium

ethylene diamine tetraacetate was included in the recipe to seques-
ter any residual copper inhibitor in the labelled monomer. In order to avoid broadening the molecular weight distribution, the polymerization reaction was not carried to completion. Residual monomer was extracted with methanol-water mixtures and with methanol until it was less than 0.5 wt. % of the polymer. The final product
was stored as the freeze-dried material. Polyacrylamides of different anionicities were prepared by hydrolyzing dilute aqueous solutions of the homopolymer to the desired level with sodium hydroxide
at 43°-46°C, in the presence of 2 wt. % isopropanol. These products also were stored as freeze-dried materials.

The intrinsic viscosity of the homopolymer was found to be
1.8 dl/g in 1 M NaCl at 30°C, using a #75 Cannon-Ubbelhode viscometer. Using the Mark-Houink equation ($\eta = KM^a$) with K = 3.73 x
10^{-4} and a = 0.66, the viscosity average molecular weight is
estimated to be 0.4 x 10^6 daltons (15). The carboxyl levels of
the hydrolyzed polyacrylamides were analyzed by infrared absorption
spectroscopy, and were reported to be 9 ± 2, 21 ± 2, and 33 ± 2
mole %. The polyacrylamides are designated as PAM or as HPAM to
indicate the homopolymer or a hydrolyzed product. Two numbers are
added after the letters, the first indicating the molecular weight
in units of a million, and the second the extent of hydrolysis (e.g.,
HPAM 0.4-33 has a molecular weight of 0.4 x 10^6 daltons and is
hydrolyzed to the extent of 33 mole %).

Procedure. For each test, a 5 gram sample of Na-kaolinite was
first conditioned in 150 ml of 3 x 10^{-2} kmol/m^3 NaCl solution in
teflon bottles for two hours using a wrist-action shaker set for
maximum agitation of the suspension. It was then stirred for desired intervals using a 1" propeller (three 2.54cm diameter blades
at 45° inclination) at 1200 rpm in a 250 ml 6.3 cm diameter beaker
fitted with four 0.63 cm wide baffle plates (16) with 50 ml of polymer solution added in the beginning while the suspension was being
stirred. Time of conditioning of the suspension with the polymer
is indicated in each figure. Samples were then removed from this
for various measurements.

Percent solid settled: In tests where adsorption and flocculation were determined simultaneously, the 200 ml sample was allowed
to settle for 30 seconds and then 100 ml of the supernatant was removed using a suction device and after centrifugation analyzed for
residual polymer concentration. The minimum level of detection was
at 0.5 to 1 ppm and the reproducibility of the adsorption measurements was 2-3%. The settled 100 ml portion was analyzed for solid
content. Flocculation due to polymer addition is measured by
noting % solid settled as a function of polymer concentration.

Settling rate: For determing the settling rate, the 200 ml
sample was transferred to a 250 ml flat bottomed graduated cylinder
and 4 ml of supernatant was used for polymer analysis. The original
solution was made up with an equal volume of electrolyte solution
and then remixed manually end over end. The settling rate was determined by measuring the descent of the solid/solution interface as a
function of time and by estimating the slope of the linear region.

Sediment volume: The sample used for measurements of settling rate was allowed to subside overnight for 16 to 24 hours and the sediment volume was read on the graduated cylinder.

Supernatant clarity: After subsidence, the sample was remixed manually and allowed to settle for 3 minutes. Supernatant clarity was measured using a Brinkman probe colorimeter PC 1600 by dipping the probe to just below the surface of the liquid.

Viscosity: A 16 ml sample of the suspension removed after remixing was used for torque measurements using a Brookfield viscometer (Model: LVTD) with a UL adapter. Initial torque readings were used for estimating viscosity in order to avoid problems arising from any settling of the kaolinite in the viscometer during the measurements.

Results

Simultaneous Adsorption/Flocculation Tests. Results obtained for adsorption and flocculation (as measured by the amount of solid settled) for the same samples are given as a function of concentration of the nonionic polyacrylamide in Figure 1 and the 33% hydrolyzed polymer in Figure 2. Flocculation as measured by settling rate is given in Figure 3 for the case of the nonionic polyacrylamide. In these tests both polymers were completely depleted from solution up to about 100 mg/kg addition. As far as flocculation is concerned, the nonionic polymer is found to increase both the percent solid settled and the settling rate which go through maxima at about 25 mg/kg addition. While polymer addition had no measurable effect on percent solid settled even at higher polymer concentrations, at all levels of addition, the settling rate is higher than that obtained in the absence of the polymer. It is clear from a comparison of the polymer effect on these two flocculation responses that a single parameter cannot be used to characterize flocculation. Even though the settling rate is often a more sensitive parameter, as in the present case, it is often necessary--particularly in the case of selective flocculation--to also measure percent solid settled to a given level and to analyze the settled mass for mineralogical composition. It is noted that while the nonionic polymer enhanced the amount of solid settled, the anionic polymer had no measurable effect on this response even though its adsorption was comparable to that of the former. More important is the observed lack of the proposed correlations between the extent of polymer coverage and flocculation. This is further seen when the effect of time of stirring of the mineral with the polymer solution is examined (see Figure 4). While adsorption reached its maximum value within 2 minutes, flocculation decreased for at least 20 minutes upon continued stirring. Evidently the amount of polymer adsorbed cannot be considered to be the sole factor governing the flocculation.

Polymer Concentration. The effect of polymer dosage on additional flocculation responses was measured together with adsorption

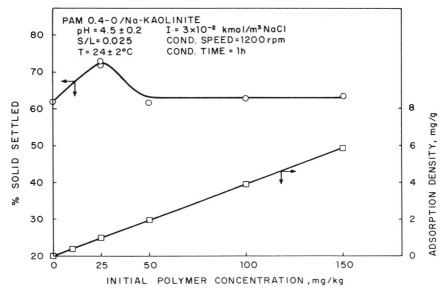

Figure 1.   Adsorption and flocculation obtained with Na-kaolinite at pH 4.5 as a function of dosage of polyacrylamide (PAM 0.4-0).

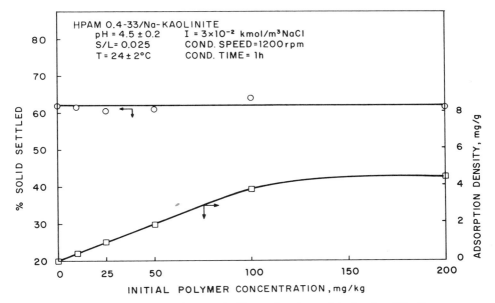

Figure 2.   Adsorption and flocculation obtained with Na-kaolinite at pH 4.5 as a function of dosage of 33% hydrolyzed polyacrylamide (HPAM 0.4-33).

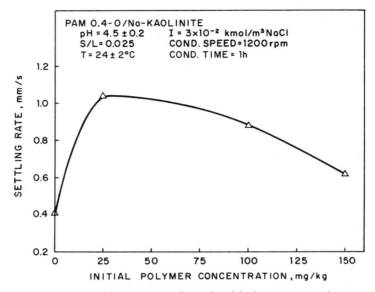

Figure 3. Settling rate of Na-kaolinite suspension at pH 4.5 as a function of polyacrylamide (PAM 0.4-0)dosage.

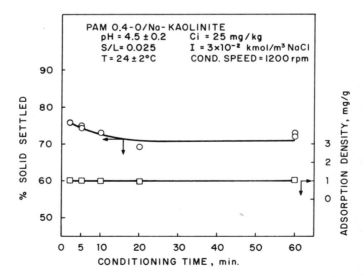

Figure 4. Diagram illustrating kinetics of adsorption and flocculation for Na-kaolinite/polyacrylamide (PAM 0.4-0) system.

for both the nonionic and the anionic polymer. Conditioning was
done in these tests at 1200 rpm for 10 minutes. On the basis of
the results given in Figure 4, adsorption can be considered to
have attained equilibrium during this time for these systems.

Results obtained for various flocculation responses are
given in Figures 5 and 6 for the nonionic and the anionic polymer respectively. It is seen from Figure 5 that while the
settling rate goes through a maximum as a function of PAM concentration, the transmittance of the supernatant increases from
38% at 0 mg/kg to 80% at 25 mg/kg and then remains at that level
till at least 50 mg/kg. The sediment volume does not vary to
any significant extent. Adsorption of the polymer on the other
hand is found to increase continuously in the complete concentration range of 0 to 100 mg/kg. In contrast, with the 33%
hydrolyzed polyacrylamide, while the adsorption reaches its
maximum value at about 50 mg/kg, both the settling rate and
the supernatant transmittance are found to go through a maximum
in the 10-25 mg/kg ranges. Also in this case the sediment volume
is affected by the polymer addition. It is to be noted that the
maximum effect is seen at different polymer concentrations for
different responses. Viscosity of the suspension also responds
to the PAMA addition, but again the polymer concentration required for this effect is different from those for changes in
other responses.

These differences in the effect of polymers on various
flocculation responses have important theoretical and practical
implications and can be explained in terms of various characteristics of flocs and floc-aggregates. Polymer adsorption or attachment of particles to polymer can occur in any number of configurations, and as a result the aggregation of particles also can take
place in many ways, leading to different floc and suspension
structures which will respond differently to different tests.
Thus, a wide size distribution of floc can yield both a turbid
supernatant and a relatively high settling rate. Viscosity and
sediment volume will also depend on floc structure, but more
importantly on possible interfloc aggregation to form network
structures (17-19). They also can be directly affected if the
polymer adsorbs with long loops and tails and by alterations
in the structure of the fluid medium in the vicinity of the
adsorbed species. Indeed, such alterations in the fluid structure
and attachments of ultrafines and colloids to the polymer can be
expected to depend on the charges of both the particle and the
polymer. Thus, at 50 mg/kg polymer addition, even though both
types of polymer adsorb to the same extent, the sample containing
the nonionic polymer is in a flocculated state with a clear
supernatant whereas the one containing the anionic polymer is
dispersed and the supernatant is totally turbid. The anionic
polymer has adsorbed to saturation at this level of addition, but
under these conditions aggregation between the particles can
be prevented by the electrostatic repulsion between them. However,

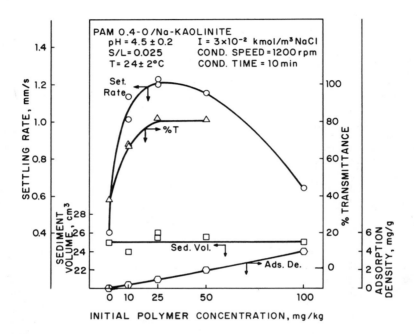

Figure 5.   Various flocculation responses together with adsorption obtained with Na-kaolinite at pH 4.5 as a function
of polyacrylamide (PAM 0.4-0) dosage.

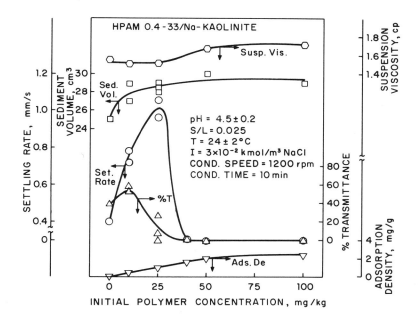

Figure 6.   Various flocculation responses together with adsorption obtained with Na-kaolinite at pH 4.5 as a function of 33% hydrolyzed polyacrylamide (HPAM 0.4-33) dosage.

while particle/polymer-polymer/particle aggregation will be
prevented by such repulsion, particle/polymer-particle aggregation conceivably could occur since the particles are not completely covered by the anionic polymer under such conditions (the
nonionic polymer adsorbs to a greater extent than the anionic
polymer at polymer additions higher than 50 mg/kg, and there
is no apparent reason for a larger surface coverage per molecule
by the anionic polymer). Evidently the electrostatic repulsion
is sufficient to prevent even particle/polymer-particle aggregation. Whether or not the entropy changes in this system are
sufficient to produce such stabilization of the suspension is not
clear at present.

Polymer Charge Density. The effect of polymer charge density is
illustrated in detail in Figure 7. For reference purposes,
values obtained in the absence of the polymer are 0.4 mm/s, 38%,
25 cm^3 and 1.56 cp for settling rate, supernatant transmittance,
sediment volume and viscosity, respectively. While all the
responses are sensitive to the polymer charge density, it is
clearly seen that a maximum effect is obtained at different levels
of anionicity for different responses. Settling rate and sediment
volume are sensitive in the 0 to 20% hydrolysis range, whereas
viscosity and supernatant transmittance become sensitive at
higher anionicities. Discrepancies in the literature regarding
the optimum charge density for flocculation might partly be
the result of use of different techniques to monitor flocculation.
It is to be noted that the values obtained for the optimum charge
density can be dependent on the polymer dosage, solution proper-
ties--such as pH and ionic strength--and hydrodynamic conditions.

Discussion

The results of this study clearly show the complex dependence
of the flocculation process on polymer dosage and charge density.
It is seen that the form of dependence varies markedly among the
responses monitored. In addition to the factors studied here,
it can also be expected to depend upon several other physicochemical conditions of the system, including the type of mixing.
The final state of flocculation achieved by a mineral/polymer
system will depend upon many interactions in the system as
determined by various chemical and hydrodynamic properties of
the particles, polymer, dissolved organics and the fluids.
These include electrostatic interaction between the particles and
interaction of particles with the fluid governed by their wet-
tability, morphology and density (17-19); the extent of adsorption
of the polymer and its influence on the interaction of particles,
the orientation or configuration of the adsorbed polymers (and
surfactant when it is present) and resultant interaction of
adsorbed layers; the hydrodynamic state of the system and its influence on the interaction of flocs themselves.

POLYACRYLAMIDE (MW ~ 0.4×10⁶)/Na-KAOLINITE

Ci = 10 mg/kg   I = 3×10⁻² kmol/m³ NaCl
pH = 4.5±0.2   COND. SPEED = 1200 rpm
S/L = 0.025   COND. TIME = 10 min
T = 24±2°C

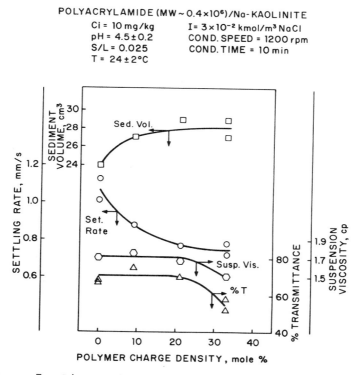

Figure 7. Diagram illustrating the effect of polymer charge density on various flocculation responses of Na-kaolinite at pH 4.5.

Among the properties measured here, the settling rate is mainly a measure of the size of the flocs and in later stages the compressibility of flocs and floc networks, and the supernatant clarity is a measure of the size distribution of flocs and size dependent capture of the particles and flocs by the polymer. The sediment volume and the pulp viscosity on the other hand, are direct measures, not only of floc size and structure but also of adsorbed polymer layers. It is to be noted in this regard that it is this latter aspect which makes it possible to estimate the thickness of adsorbed polymer layers by measuring the viscosity of the medium and the suspension in the presence of polymers (20,21). This combination of effects is another reason one cannot always expect correlation between various flocculation responses.

In order to generate information on the mechanism of flocculation by polymers it is, however, necessary to correlate flocculation with various system properties, particularly adsorption. Thus, if particle/polymer-polymer/particle contact is the aggregation mechanism, the flocculation responses should be expected to continuously increase with surface coverage. On the other hand, if particle/polymer-particle contact is predominant and if the polymer adsorption is essentially irreversible, maximum flocculation might be expected under submonolayer conditions. In order to determine the nature of this relationship for the present systems, selected flocculation responses are plotted in Figures 8 and 9 as a function of surface coverage for the nonionic and the anionic polymer respectively. The assumptions involved in the computation of the surface coverage are to be noted at this point:
1. Saturation adsorption corresponds to monolayer formation;
2. Configuration of the adsorbed species remains unaltered from low to high concentrations. Indeed, these assumptions cannot be considered valid for polymer adsorption particularly if it is possible for the adsorbed polymer to move from a flat configuration to one with loops and trains (22,23). In spite of these difficulties, it can be safely stated that the flocculation response exhibits a maximum with respect to surface coverage, the optimum surface coverage being about 0.1 for the nonionic polymer and 0.1 to 0.2 for the anionic, depending on the flocculation response measured. It is seen from Figure 9 that full surface coverage leads to dispersion, suggesting that particle/polymer-polymer/particle aggregation is not the predominant mechanism in this case. Also, the 0.5 coverage criterion proposed in the past (13) appears not to be valid for the present system under the tested conditions. Evidently, in this case, flocculation is favored when a major fraction of the surface remains bare and available for aggregation by bridging. Indeed, such bridging should be influenced both by the electrostatic properties of the polymer and the mineral and by the polymer configuration, which in turn will depend upon molecular weight, charge density, pH and ionic strength. While the nonionic polyacrylamide can be

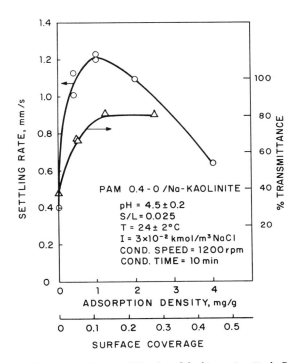

Figure 8. Flocculation of Na-kaolinite at pH 4.5 as measured by settling rate and supernatant clarity as a function of particle surface coverage by polyacrylamide (PAM 0.4-0).

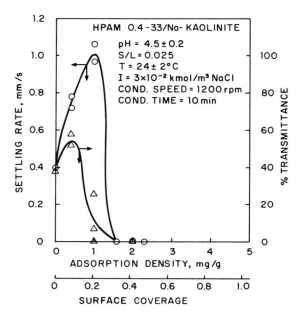

Figure 9.   Flocculation of Na-kaolinite at pH 4.5 as measured by the settling rate and the supernatant clarity as a function of particle surface coverage by 33% hydrolyzed polyacrylamide (HPAM 0.4-33).

expected to be in a coiled form, the 33% hydrolyzed polymer will
be more extended at pH 4.5 since about half of the carboxylate
groups will be in dissociated anionic carboxylate form. The
higher viscosity obtained for the anionic polymers supports the
above consideration. Such expansion of the polymer due to charge
repulsion can facilitate bridging due to increased polymer length
but can also retard it via electrostatic repulsion between
the polymer and the similarly charged faces of the kaolinite
particle. The net effect of these competing phenomena will
actually determine the flocculation power of the hydrolyzed polyacrylamide. In the present study, reduced flocculation was
obtained upon increasing the charge density of the polyacrylamide,
suggesting the predominating contribution of the electrostatic
repulsion. The higher sediment volume obtained with hydrolyzed
polyacrylamides can also be attributed to such changes in configuration of the polymer upon hydrolysis: The charged polymer
can produce voluminous flocs due to both its expanded configuration and to longer loops owing to the fewer contact points expected between the similarly charged polymer and mineral particles. Indeed some additional contacts can occur between the polymer and the edges of the kaolinite particles.

The presence of excess salt, particularly of bivalent inor-
ganics can reduce the electrostatic repulsion between the anionic
polymer and the kaolinite particles and enhance flocculation
(24,25). The optimum flocculation of fine coal and coal refuse
(which contained 13 to 65% clays) obtained by Lewellyn and Wang(24)
with hydrolyzed polyacrylamide containing 70% acrylate in fact
might have resulted from the use of recycled water which contained 55 ppm Ca and 30 ppm Mg. Other works in literature have
reported maximum flocculation of kaolinite to occur with 30%
hydrolyzed polyacrylamide (5,6,10,26,27). Such differences in
reported results could easily result from variations in water
chemistry, originating either with the water used or with dissolved organics released by the mineral itself.

Summary

Flocculation using polyacrylamide and hydrolyzed polyacrylamides
was investigated by studying a number of flocculation responses
of Na-kaolinite under controlled chemical and hydrodynamic conditions.

The flocculation responses studied are settling rate, percent
solid settled, supernatant clarity, sediment volume and slurry
viscosity. The polymer concentration and polymer anionicity
required for maximum flocculation were seen clearly to depend
on the response studied. Both the settling rate and the supernatant clarity with the nonionic polyacrylamide flocculent showed
at pH 4.5 a marked increase to a maximum at about 25 mg/kg,
whereas with the anionic polymer settling rate and supernatant
clarity showed maxima at 10-25 mg/kg, but the system was totally

dispersed at higher concentrations. Sediment volume did not
show any measurable change over the entire concentration range
of nonionic polymer. In contrast, with the anionic polyacrylamide
(33% hydrolyzed) both the sediment volume and the slurry viscosity
showed increases with polymer concentration in the 0 to 50 and
25 to 50 mg/kg ranges respectively. Viscosity and sediment volume,
however, remained at the highest levels up to the highest tested
concentrations of anionic polymer. The different effects of
polymers on the above responses are discussed in terms of
various characteristics of flocs and floc-aggregates. While
settling rate and percent solid settled can be expected to be
governed essentially by the coarser region of the particle size
distribution, by the density and compressive strength of the flocs,
and by the structure of any three dimensional networks that can
trap the fluid, the supernatant clarity will depend on any
shift in the fine region of the size distribution and on the
ability of the polymers and the network to capture the ultrafines and colloids. Sediment volume and slurry viscosity on the
other hand can depend on, in addition to the floc size distribution and the compressive strength of the flocs, also the thickness of the adsorbed layers of the polymer on the particles.

All the measured responses were sensitive to the anionicity
of the polymer used as the flocculent. Settling rate showed a
maximum with 0% hydrolysis and the supernatant clarity exhibited a maximum in the 0 - 20% hydrolysis range. While
the anionicity did not have a significant effect on the viscosity
in the 0-20% range, further increases in anionicity produced a
measurable decrease in viscosity. These effects are accounted
for in terms of electrostatic interactions between the polymer
layers on the particles and alterations in the configuration of
the adsorbed polymers due to the presence of the charged groups.

Flocculation was correlated with both adsorption density
and estimated surface coverage for the nonionic and 33% hydrolyzed
polyacrylamides. Maximum settling rate was obtained with the
nonionic flocculent at 0.1 and with the hydrolyzed sample at
0.2 surface coverage. Supernatant clarity showed a maximum
at a surface coverage of Na-kaolinite by the hydrolyzed
polyacrylamide of 0.1. At higher surface coverages (such as
0.5) considered in the past to be optimum for flocculation,
complete dispersion was obtained with both the nonionic and the
anionic polymer.

Acknowledgments

The authors wish to acknowledge the particulate and multiphase
processing program of the National Science Foundation (CPE-80-
11013) for support of this work and Dr. F. Halverson of American
Cyanamid for polymer syntheses and helpful discussions.

Literature Cited

1. Somasundaran, P., in "Research Needs in Mineral Processing"; Somasundaran, P.; Fuerstenau, D.W., eds.; NSF Workshops Rep. 1976.
2. Read, A.D.; Hollick, C.T., Minerals Sci. Eng. 1976, 8, 202.
3. Gardner, W.M.; Montemayer, L.W., B.S. Thesis, M.I.T. 1953.
4. Michaels, A.S., Ind. Eng. Chem. 1954, 46, 1485.
5. Michaels, A.S.; Morelos, O., Ind. Eng. Chem. 1955, 47, 1801.
6. Dollimore, D.; Harridge, T.A., Trans. J. Brit. Ceram. Soc. 1971, 70, 191 (b) Water Res. 1972 (c) J. Colloid Interf. Sci. 1973, 42, 581.
7. Roberts, K.; Kowalewska, J.; Friberg, S., J. Colloid Interf. Sci. 1974, 48, 361.
8. Halverson, F., Proc. 10th Annual Meeting, Canadian Mineral Processors Ottawa, Canada 1978.
9. Solomchenko, N.Y.; Kochetkova, E.I.; Sokolova, N.P., Colloid J. USSR 1981, 43, 310.
10. Smellie, R.H., Jr.; La Mer, V.K., J. Colloid Sci. 1958, 13, 589.
11. Linke, W.F.; Booth, R.B., Trans. AIME 1960, 217, 364.
12. Kuzkin, S.F.; Nebera, W.P.; Zolin, S.N., Proc. 7th Int. Miner. Process Congress New York, 1964.
13. La Mer, V.K.; Healy, T.W., J. Phys. Chem. 1963, 67, 2417.
14. Hollander, A.F.; Somasundaran, P.; Gryte, C.C., Adsorption from Aqueous Solutions"; Tewari, P.H., ed.; Plenum, 1981.
15. American Cyanamid Technical Bulletin, "Cyanamer^{TM} Polyacrylamides", 1967.
16. Wang, Y.C., Carrier Flotation of Anatase from Clay and its Physicochemical Mechanisms, D.E.Sc. Thesis, Columbia University, New York, 1980.
17. Somasundaran, P.; Smith, E.L., Jr.; Harris, C.C., "Proceedings of the First International Conference in Particle Technology", IITRI, Chicago, 1973, 144-150.
18. Harris, C.C.; Somasundaran, P.; Jensen, R.R., Powder Technology, 1975, 11, 75-84.
19. Nagaraj, D.R.; McAllister, L.; Somasundaran, P., Int. J. Miner. Process. 1977, 4, 111-129.
20. Doroszkowski, A.; Lambourne, R., J. Colloid Interf. Sci. 1968, 26, 214.
21. Sato, T.; Ruch, R., Stabilization of Colloidal Dispersion by Polymer Adsorption, Marcel Dekker, Inc., NY, 1980.
22. Theng, B.K.G., Formation and Properties of Clay-Polymer Complexes, Elsevier Scientific Publishing Company, N.Y., 1979.
23. Strombert, R.R., in "Treatise on Adhesion and Adhesives"; Patrick, R.L., ed.; Marcel Dekker, NY, 1967; Vol. 1.
24. Lewellyn, M.E.; Wang, S.S., presented at 183rd ACS National Meeting, New York, 1981.
25. O'Gorman, J.V.; Kitchener, J.A., Int. J. Miner. Process. 1973, 1, 33.

26. Werneke, M.F., presented at 108th AIME Meeting, New Orleans, LA, 1979.
27. Pearse, M.J.; Barnett, J., Filtr. Sep. 1980. 17, 460.

RECEIVED October 7, 1983

Rheological Studies of Aqueous Concentrated Polystyrene Latex Dispersions with Adsorbed Poly(vinyl alcohol) Layers

TH. F. TADROS

I.C.I. Plant Protection Division, Jealott's Hill Research Station, Bracknell, Berkshire RG12 6EY, England

The viscoelastic behavior of concentrated (20% w/w) aqueous polystryene latex dispersions (particle radius 92nm), in the presence of physically adsorbed poly(vinyl alcohol), has been investigated as a function of surface coverage by the polymer using creep measurements. From the creep curves both the instantaneous shear modulus, G_o, and residual viscosity, η_o, were calculated. The yield value, τ_β, was also measured as a function of surface coverage. All the rheological parameters decreased with increasing surface coverage. This was related to the reduction in particle interaction with increase of polymer adsorption. At full coverage the residual G_o, η_o and τ_β values were attributed to the combined action of long-range electrostatic repulsion and steric interaction due to the presence of long, dangling tails.

Rheological measurements were also carried out on flocculating, concentrated (25% w/w) aqueous polystyrene latex dispersions (particle radius 115nm). The flocculation was produced either by addition of Na_2SO_4 or raising the temperature of the dispersion at constant Na_2SO_4 concentration. Both the yield value and shear modulus were measured and the results obtained analyzed using two models, namely the floc rupture and elastic floc models proposed by Hunter and coworkers. Good agreement between the experimental yield values and those calculated using the elastic floc model was obtained, thus confirming its applicability to the case of flocculating, sterically-stabilized dispersions.

0097–6156/84/0240–0411$06.00/0
© 1984 American Chemical Society

Investigations of the rheological properties of disperse systems
are very important both from the fundamental and applied points
of view (1-5). For example, the non-Newtonian and viscoelastic
behaviour of concentrated dispersions may be related to the interaction forces between the dispersed particles (6-9). On the
other hand, such studies are of vital practical importance,
as, for example, in the assessment and prediction of the long-
term physical stability of suspensions (5).

Any fundamental study of the rheology of concentrated
suspensions necessitates the use of simple systems of well-
defined geometry and where the surface characteristics of the
particles are well established. For that purpose well-
characterized polymer particles of narrow size distribution are
used in aqueous or non-aqueous systems. For interpretation of
the rheological results, the inter-particle pair-potential must
be well-defined and theories must be available for its
calculation. The simplest system to consider is that where the
pair potential may be represented by a hard sphere model. This,
for example, is the case for polystyrene latex dispersions in
organic solvents such as benzyl alcohol or cresol, whereby
electrostatic interactions are well screened (1). Concentrated
dispersions in non-polar media in which the particles are
stabilized by a "built-in" stabilizer layer, may also be used,
since the pair-potential can be represented by a hard-sphere
interaction, where the hard sphere radius is given by the
particles radius plus the adsorbed layer thickness. Systems of
this type have been recently studied by Croucher and coworkers.
(10,11) and Strivens (12).

Fairly recently the viscoelastic properties of aqueous,
electrostatically stabilized polystyrene latex dispersions have
been investigated by Russel and Benzig (6,7) and by Buscall et al.
(8,9). These perhaps constitute one of the first studies whereby
an attempt has been made to relate rheological parameters to the
interaction forces between the particles. Although such
studies are of fundamental importance, their application to
practical disperse systems of the aqueous type is not straightforward since,in most practical cases, adsorbed polymer layers
are used for stabilization of such suspensions. Only a few
investigations have been reported on the rheology of these
relatively more complex systems. For example, Hunter et al
(13,14) have investigated the flow behaviour of aqueous poly
(methyl methacrylate) (PMMA) latices stabilized by a block
copolymer of poly(ethylene oxide-b-methylacrylate) which
was adsorbed onto the surface of the PMMA spheres by the smaller
PMMA anchor groups of the copolymer. The authors used a simplified rheological approach, whereby the energy dissipation in
a flocculating system was assumed to arise mainly from the
rupture between doublets in a shearing field. Using this
approach the authors were able to investigate the interaction

properties of the flocculating dispersions. Interaction energies
of the order of 5 kT (where k is the Boltzmann constant and T
the absolute termperature) were obtained for the PMMA system
stabilized by adsorbed poly(ethylene oxide).

In this paper we report some rheological studies of aqueous
concentrated polystyrene latex dispersions, in the presence of
physically adsorbed poly(vinyl alcohol). This system has been
chosen in view of its relevance to many practical systems and
since many of the parameters needed for interpretation of the
rheological results are available (15-18). The viscoelastic
properties of a 20% w/w latex dispersion were investigated as a
function of polymer coverage, using creep measurements.
Moreover, rheological studies were carried out on a dispersion
(25% w/w) which was flocculated either by addition of sufficient
electrolyte (Na_2SO_4) or by raising the temperature at a
constant electrolyte concentration.

Experimental

Materials Water was doubly-distilled from all glass apparatus.
All other materials were analytical grade and used as received.
Poly(vinyl alcohol) (Alcotex 88/10, supplied by Revertex Ltd.,
London) was the same sample used previously in this laboratory
(15-18); it has a weight average molecular weight M_W, of
45,000 and 12% acetate groups.

Two 50 l batches of polystyrene latex were prepared using
the method described by Goodwin et al (19); these will be
referred to as latex A and B, respectively. Both latices were
dialyzed against distilled water until there was no further
change in the conductivity of the dialyzate. Two procedures
were used to concentrate the latices. Latex A (which was 3.32%
w/w) was concentrated in two stages. In the first stage, the
latex was placed in Visking tubing and suspended in a refrigera-
tor for one week at 5°C to evaporate as much water as possible.
The latex was then transferred to 28 mm diameter Visking
tubing and a weight of approximately 4kg was placed on the top
of the tubing which was immersed in distilled water. After four
weeks the volume of the latex was reduced reaching a concentration
of 46% w/w. Latex B (which was 4% w/w) was concentrated by rotary
evaporation to 28.3% w.w.

The particle size of the two latices was determined using
electron microscopy and a "Quantimet" image analyzer. Latex A
had an average radius of 92±3nm and latex B 115±2nm.

Adsorption Isotherm The details of the technique used have
been described before (15). Basically, 0.5 g of the dilute latex
was added to poly(vinyl alcohol)(PVA) solutions covering the
range 50-1000 ppm. These were then rotated end-over-end for
24 hours at room temperature (22±2°C) for equilibration.

The particles were then separated by centrifugation and the
supernatant was analyzed for PVA using the colorimetric technique described previously (15).

Critical Flocculation Electrolyte Concentration   The critical
flocculation electrolyte (Na_2SO_4) concentration was determined
by following the average particle size of the dilute dispersion
(where the particles were coated with PVA corresponding to the
plateau adsorption) as a function of Na_2SO_4 concentration, using
a Coulters Nanosizer (Coulters Electronics Ltd) as described
before (20).

Rheological Measurements   Three types of rheological measurements have been carried out.   In the first type, transient
(creep) measurements were performed on a 20% w/w dispersion of
latex A, as a function of coverage by PVA.   These experiments
were carried out using a "Deer" rheometer (PDR 81, Integrated
Petronic Systems, London) fitted with a stainless steel con-
centric cylinder.   The procedures used have been described in
detail before (21,22).

Secondly, steady state measurements were carried out to
obtain shear stress-shear rate curves and the Bingham yield
value.   Two methods were used.   In the first method the viscosity was measured as a function of shear rate (using the
Deer rheometer) by applying a series of torsional forces and
recording each time the angular velocity.   These experiments were
performed on a 20% latex A, as a function of PVA coverage.   The
Deer rheometer was also used to determine the yield value for
these latex dispersions, by applying a series of stress values
of equal increments and recording the response until flow
occurred.   In the second method, shear stress-shear rate curves
were obtained using a Haake "Rotovisko" (model RV100 fitted with
an M 150 measuring head) as described before (21,22).   From the
shear stress-shear rate curves, the plastic viscosity, η_{PL}, was
calculated from the slope of the linear portion of the curve.
The Bingham yield value, τ_β, was obtained by extrapolating the
linear portion of the curve to zero shear rate.   In these
experiments, a 25% w/w latex B was used, where the particles
were fully coated with PVA, and results were obtained as a
function of Na_2SO_4 concentration at constant temperature
(20±1°C) or as a function of temperature at a constant Na_2SO_4
(0.2 or 0.25 mol dm^{-3}) concentration.

Finally, the shear modulus, G_o, was measured using a pulse
shearometer (Rank Bros, Bottisham, Cambridge) as described
before (21,22). G_o was measured as a function of Na_2SO_4 concentration for 25% w/w latex B with the particles fully-
coated with PVA.

Results

Adsorption Isotherm The adsorption isotherm of PVA on polystyrene latex was of the high affinity type, as previously found (15). The saturation adsorption (plateau) was found to be 4.26 mg m^{-2}, which is in close agreement with the value obtained before (18) for the same PVA sample on a similar latex.

Influence of surface coverage of PVA on rheological parameters
Figure 1 shows creep curves for 20% w/w latex A at three different concentrations of PVA for 20% w/w latex A(0.05, 0.15 and 0.30g PVA per 20g dispersion) corresponding to adsorption amounts of 0.87, 2.56 and 4.76 mg m^{-2}, i.e. roughly at the point where the isotherm leaves the y-axis, half coverage and full coverage, respectively. All the creep curves show the behaviour to be expected with a viscoelastic system. They consist of three regions: (a) directly after the application of the stress a rapid elastic deformation occurs, resulting in an instantaneous compliance J_o (instantaneous shear modulus $G_o = \tau / \gamma_o = 1/J_o$, where τ is the applied stress); (b) a slow elastic deformation, i.e. mixed viscoelastic region. In this region bonds are broken and reformed at various rates resulting in a spectrum of i retarded elastic compliances; (c) a region of viscous deformation, whereby the strain varies linearly with time. In this region individual units flow past each other, since the time required to restore bonds is larger than the test period.
    Since the stress applied was fairly small(0.015 Nm^{-2}) it is highly likely that the measurements fall within the linear region. Moreover, since this was the smallest stress that could be applied whereby a response was obtained, the viscosity calculated from the linear portion of the curve is very close to the limiting (residual) viscosity η_o. The latter is more accurately obtained by applying a series of reducing stresses, establishing the creep curve in each case and plotting η at each stress τ versus τ. Usually η increases with decreasing τ, but reaches a limiting (Newtonian) value over a range of sufficiently small stresses. This limiting value is usually referred to as the residual viscosity η_o. However, since creep measurements are time consuming, the creep curves were only obtained at one shear stress. The latter was the smallest value that could be applied to produce a measurable creep curve. Thus, strictly speaking, the viscosity calculated from these creep curves may not be identical to the residual viscosity, but it does correspond to the viscosity at some very low shear rate. However, for the sake of comparison, we shall still refer to this viscosity as η_o. Both G_o and η_o have been calculated from the creep curves shown in figure 1 and plotted versus surface coverage, as shown in figure 2. The yield value, τ_β,obtained using the procedure of applying a series of successive torsional stresses, is also shown as a function of surface

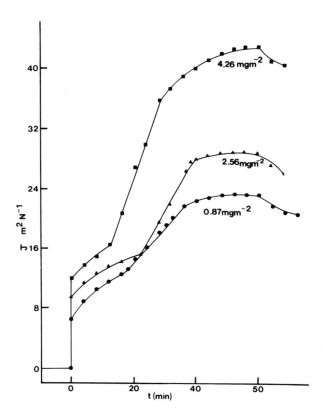

Figure 1   Creep Curves at three concentrations of PVA

coverage in the same figure. All the rheological parameters
show the same trend, namely a continuous decrease with increase
of surface coverage by the polymer.

Figure 3 shows plots of η versus shear rate at three different temperatures for the same latex (20% w/w latex A) at
full coverage with PVA. These curves are typical of a pseudoplastic system showing a reduction of η with increasing shear
rate, $\dot{\gamma}$; η reaches a limiting value at $\dot{\gamma} > 50$ s^{-1}. It is also
clear from fig. 3 that at $\dot{\gamma} < 10$ s^{-1}, η increases rapidly
with reduction in γ. Comparison with η_o values obtained
from the creep curves would indicate the η should increase very
steeply with reduction of γ, in the low shear rate region (η_o
is the limit of η as $\dot{\gamma} \rightarrow 0$).

Influence of addition of Na$_2$SO$_4$ and increase of temperature
on rheological parameters   As mentioned in the Experimental
Section, these experiments were carried out using 25% w/w latex
B at full PVA coverage. For C (Na$_2$SO$_4$ concentration)
< 0.2 mol dm^{-3}, the dispersions were virtually Newtonian
showing no yield value or hysteresis in the shear stress-shear
rate curves. For C > 0.2 mol dm^{-3}, the flow curves were
typical of a thixotropic system, showing a yield value and a
hysteresis loop which increased in magnitude with increase of C.
Figure 4 shows the variation of the extrapolated yield value,
τ_β (obtained from extrapolation of the ascending part of the
flow curve) as a function of C. The shear modulus, G_o,
measured using the pulse shearometer, is also shown as a
function of C in the same figure. A measurable τ_β and G_o is
obtained above a critical value of C, which in both cases is
~0.22 mol dm^{-3}. As we will see later, this electrolyte
concentration should be taken as the critical flocculation
concentration (CFC) for the concentrated dispersion. Above the
CFC, τ_β increases rapidly with increasing C whereas G
initially increases gradually with increasing C until C = 0.3
mol dm^{-3}, above which there is a more rapid increase of G_o.
The CFC obtained with the dilute dispersion (~10^{-2}%) using the
Nanosizer was ~0.28 mol dm^{-3}, i.e. significantly larger than
that for the concentrated dispersion.

Figure 5 shows the variation of τ_β with temperature at
two C values (0.20 and 0.25 mol dm^{-3}). In both cases τ_β is
essentially zero until a critical termperature is reached, above
which τ_β increases rapidly with increasing temperature reaching a maximum above which there is a tendency for τ_β to fall
again with further increase in temperature. The critical
temperature corresponding to the abrupt increase in τ_β is 20
and 25°C for C equal to 0.25 and 0.20 mol dm^{-3}, respectively
This temperature may be identified with the critical flocculation temperature (CFT) of the concentrated dispersion.

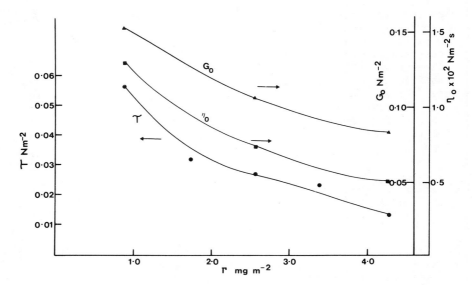

Figure 2   Variation of G_o, η_o and τ_β with surface coverage
            by PVA

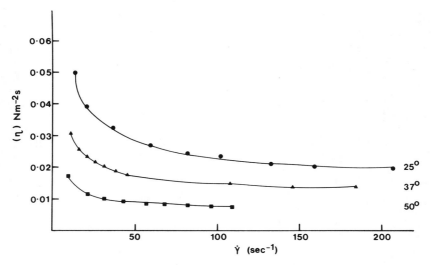

Figure 3   Viscosity – shear rate curves at three different
            temperatures

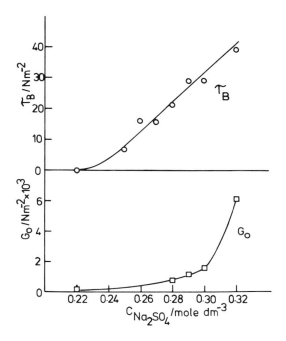

Figure 4   Variation of extrapolated yield with Na_2SO_4 con-
            centration

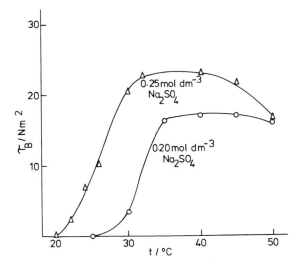

Figure 5   Variation of τ_β with temperature at two Na_2SO_4
            concentrations

Discussion

Viscoelastic Properties   The viscoelastic behaviour of the polystyrene latex dispersions, in which the particles carry physically adsorbed poly(vinyl alcohol) layers, is the result of interaction of the polymer chains, which are close to each other in
concentrated dispersions.   For PVA with an average molecular
weight of 45,000, the adsorbed layer thickness at full coverage is of the order of 47 nm (17).   Such thick adsorbed layers
are due to the presence of long dangling tails (23-25).   For a
latex dispersion with a particle volume fraction, ϕ_s, of 0.2 and
an average radius of 92 nm, the effective volume fraction of the
particles plus adsorbed layer, ϕ_{eff}, is ~0.69 ($\phi_{eff}=\phi_s[1+(\delta/a)]^3$
(10,11).   At such a high volume fraction (which is close to
the packing fraction for hexagonal close packing) interaction
between the polymer tails is strong.   Such interaction accounts,
at least in part, for the viscoelastic behaviour observed at
full coverage.   In the present system, when no electrolyte was
added, there must be a contribution from the interaction of the
double layers.   The presence of extended double layers leads to
viscoelastic behaviour in concentrated dispersions (7-10).
Evidence for the electrostatic contribution with sterically
stabilized dispersions has been recently obtained (21) from a
study of the effect of the addition of NaCl to a latex dispersion containing adsorbed PVA layers.   The results showed a
progressive reduction in residual viscosity, shear modulus and
Bingham yield value with increasing electrolyte concentration.
The fact that there was a measurable η_o and G_o at a NaCl
concentration of 10^{-1}mol dm^{-3} (where double layer effects
are negligible) also indicates a contribution from steric
interactions.   With dispersions where the interaction is purely
electrostatic, such as those investigated by Russell and Benzig
(7,8) and Buscall et al. (9,10), G_o tends to zero at high
electrolyte (>10^{-2}mol dm^{-3}) concentrations.   Thus, the
residual modulus, yield value and η_o values obtained at full
coverage in the present system with adsorbed PVA are due to the
combined action of long-range electrostatic repulsion and steric
interaction resulting from the presence of long dangling tails.
It should be mentioned, however, that the electrostatic
repulsion is significantly modified due to the effect of the
adsorbed polymer layer on the distribution of ions in the
electrical double layer.
    The increase in the rheological parameters, η_o, G_o and
τ_β with reduction in surface coverage points towards an increase in particle interaction.   This could be the result of
either flocculation by polymer "bridging" (which is favourable
at coverages <0.5) or as a result of coagulation due to the van
der Waals attraction between the "bare" patches on the particles.
In the absence of any quantitative relationship between
interaction forces and rheology, it is clearly difficult

to distinguish between these two effects. Hence quantitative interpretation of the creep curve is also not possible at present. The basic problem is to relate the pair-potential to the rheological moduli. With the system of physically adsorbed polymer on polystyrene latex, the pair-potential should take into account all the contributions, i.e from electrostatic, van der Waals and steric forces. In addition to it being difficult to calculate these interactions, in view of the many assumptions that need to be made, the pair-wise additivity approximation is far from being satisfactory with concentrated dispersions.

<u>Influence of Addition of Electrolyte and Increase of Temperature</u>
Addition of electrolyte or increase of temperature at a given electrolyte concentration to a sterically stabilized dispersion may result in its flocculation at a critical concentration or temperature, which in many cases coincides with the theta point for the stabilizing chain. At the theta point the mixing term in the steric interaction is zero and any yield value measured should correspond to the residual van der Waals attraction. The energy arising from van der Waals attraction may be calculated from the following approximate relationship,

$$G_A = - \frac{(A_1^{1/2} - A_2^{1/2})^2 \, a}{12 \, H_o} \tag{1}$$

where a is the particle radius, H_o is the particle separation, A_1 is the Hamaker constant of the particle and A_2 that of the adsorbed polymer layer, which is given by,

$$A_2 = [\phi_p A_p^{1/2} + \phi_m A_m^{1/2}]^2 \tag{2}$$

where ϕ_p is the volume fraction of polymer in the adsorbed layer, ϕ_m that of the medium, A_p and A_m are the Hamaker constants of the polymer and medium (solvent) respectively. Using the following values, A_1=19 kT, A_p = 16.6 kT, A_m = 9 kT and ϕ_p = 0.067 (17), G_A was calculated at a particle separation of 2δ (i.e. 94 nm), which is the point at which the adsorbed layers touch . This gave a value for G_A of 0.17 kT, which would correspond to a yield value of 0.024 Nm^{-2} (see below). This is certainly a very small and unmeasurable value. Hence, the electrolyte concentration at which a measurable value of τ_β is obtained (0.22 mol dm^{-3} Na$_2$SO$_4$) is very close to the concentration corresponding to the CFC. Beyond that point the measured yield value is mainly due to the attraction arising from the mixing term which is negative about the θ-point. Any contribution from the van der Waals attraction is relatively small at the distances of interpenetration of chains considered (see below).

The difference observed between the CFC for the concentrated and dilute dispersions (0.22 and 0.28 mol dm03, respectively) may be accounted for if one considers the actual electrolyte concentration in bulk solution. With dilute dispersions ($\phi_s \sim 10^{-4}$) there is no difference between the nominal and actual electrolyte concentration since the particle volume fraction is very small. With the concentrated dispersion ($\phi_s = 0.25$) the electrolyte concentration was adjusted to the value required on the basis of the volume fraction of the medium (0.75) assuming the same electrolyte concentration in the adsorbed polymer layers. With a layer of volume fraction $\phi_p = 0.067$ this is possible provided the segments are uniformly distributed within the total volume. Clearly a uniform density distribution is an unlikely situation with adsorbed polymers. Recent studies using neutron scattering (26,27) have shown that with PVA on polystyrene latex, the segment density shows two distinct regions, a very high density region close to the surface due to trains and loops, followed by a slow decay due to the presence of tails which extends to the hydrodynamic thickness. If the assumption is made that electrolyte is excluded from the more "dense" region of the adsorbed layer, i.e. the region of the trains and loops, then the actual concentration of Na_2SO_4 would be higher than the adjusted concentration due to this effect. Alternatively, the difference between the CFC for concentrated and dilute dispersions may be accounted for in terms of the balance between the energy and entropy terms in the flocculation process. As pointed out by Vincent et al, (28), the free energy of flocculation, ΔG_f may be split into two contributions, i.e.,

$$\Delta G_f = \Delta G_i + \Delta G_{hs} \qquad (3)$$

where ΔG_{hs} (= $-T\Delta S_{hs}$) is the entropic contribution associated with the aggregation of hard spheres in the presence of other interparticle interactions. ΔS_{hs} per particle is negative, decreasing in magnitude with increasing volume fraction of particles ϕ_s. ΔG_i is the interaction free energy term which is a function of floc structure and depth of energy minimum, G_{min}, in the free energy-particle separation curves. Since ΔS_{hs} is reduced in concentrated dispersions, the flocculation of the dispersion occurs at relatively lower G_{min} than that observed with dilute dispersions. Thus, this effect would result in a reduction of the CFC for concentrated dispersions. However, the net result of reduction of CFC may be due to a combination of this effect and depletion of electrolyte from the dense region of the adsorbed layers.

Two models may be used to interpret the rheological results of the present flocculating system. Both models have been introduced by Hunter and his coworkers (13,14,29-32).

(i) Floc Rupture Model (13, 14)

This model was introduced by Neville and Hunter (13,14) for the case of sterically stabilized dispersions which have undergone reversible flocculation. It is assumed that the major contribution to the excess energy dissipation in such pseudoplastic systems comes from the need to provide energy from the shear field to separate contacting particles. Under these conditions, the extrapolated yield value is given by the expression (13,32,33),

$$\tau_\beta = \frac{3 \phi_H^2}{\pi^2 (a+\delta)^3} E_S \qquad (4)$$

where ϕ_H is the hydrodynamic volume fraction of the particles ($\phi_H = \phi_S[1+(\delta/a)]^3$), $(a+\delta)$ is the interaction radius of the particle and E_S is the energy needed to separate a doublet which is the sum of the van der Waals and steric interactions,

$$E_S = (Aa/12H_0) + G_S \qquad (5)$$

As discussed above, the contribution from G_S to the attraction will be significantly larger than the van der Waals attraction. Thus, E_S may be equated to G_S. Equation (4) may be used to calculate E_S from the measured τ_β values for the flocculating dispersions. The results are summarized in tables I and II . A comparison between the E_S values listed in tables I and II with theoretical G_S values is not possible at present, since for calculation of G_S one needs to know the polymer-solvent interaction parameter as a function of Na_2SO_4 concentration. Moreover, an assumption must be made about the segment distribution of the adsorbed layer. In the absence of such information, it is not possible to calculate G_S. However, the values of E_S obtained from rheology (tables I and II) are reasonable, considering the approximation made and the crude model used for calculating E_S.

The floc rupture model may also be used to explain the maximum observed in τ_β versus temperature (figure 5). According to equation (4) $\tau_\beta = f(\phi^2_H) E_S$, where $f(\phi^2_H)$ is the collision frequency term. Although E_S increases with increase of temperature, $f(\phi^2_H)$ is a decreasing function of temperature as a result of decrease of solvency of the dispersing medium which leads to the contraction of the adsorbed layer (13). The increase of E_S with increase of temperature initially outweighs any reduction of $f(\phi^2_H)$, but at higher temperatures, the reduction in $f(\phi^2_H)$ as a result of chain contraction may exceed the increase in E_S and this results in reduction in the measured τ_β.

Table I. E_s for a flocculated dispersion produced by an
                increase of Na_2SO_4 concentration

$C/(mol\ dm^{-3})$	$\tau_\beta/(Nm^{-2})$	E_s/kt
0.25	6.8	47.7
0.26	16.1	113.8
0.27	15.8	111.5
0.28	21.3	150.2
0.29	29.0	204.9
0.30	29.0	204.9
0.32	39.0	275.4

Table II. E_s for a flocculated dispersion produced by an
                increase of temperature

(a) 0.20 mol dm^{-3} Na_2SO_4

$t/°C$	$\tau_\beta/(Nm^{-2})$	E_s/kT
30	3.5	24.8
35	16.4	116.0
40	17.2	121.6
45	17.2	121.6
50	16.2	114.5

(b) 0.25 mol dm^{-3} Na_2SO_4

22	2.5	15.5
24	7.1	50.2
26	10.3	72.8
30	20.6	145.6
32	22.8	161.2
40	23.3	164.7
45	21.8	154.1
50	16.8	118.8

(ii) Elastic floc model (29-32)

In the elastic floc model, the structural units (which persist at high shear rates) are assumed to be small flocs of particles (called floccules) which are characterized by the extent to which the particle structure is able to trap some of the dispersion medium. The degree to which liquid is trapped in the floc is measured by the floc volume ratio, C_{FP}, given by,

$$C_{FP} = \phi_F/\phi_S \tag{6}$$

where ϕ_F is the volume fraction of the floc and ϕ_S is that of the particle. ϕ_F may be evaluated from the plastic viscosity using the Mooney equation (34),

$$\eta_{PL} = \eta_S \exp\left(\frac{2.5\phi_F}{1-k'\phi_F}\right) \tag{7}$$

where η_S is the viscosity of the medium and k' is the so-called "crowding factor" which may be taken as 1.4, so that η_{PL} becomes infinitely large as ϕ_S approaches the closepacking value (35). The values of C_{FP} calculated using equations (6) and (7) are given in table III.

Table III.   The elastic floc model

C (mol/dm^{-3})	$\eta_{PL} \times 10^3$ (Nm^{-2}s)	$(\tau_\beta)_{expt}$ (Nm^{-2})	C_{FP}	$n_c \times 10^{-13}$	γ_0 (s^{-1})
0.25	10.8	6.8	1.63	1.79	152
0.28	32.7	21.4	1.84	1.16	211
0.29	33.8	29.0	1.90	1.15	352
0.30	33.0	29.0	1.89	1.16	421
0.31	31.6	–	1.88	1.17	–

C (mol/dm^{-3})	$F_M/N \times 10^{-17}$	$n_F \times 10^{-8}$	$F/N \times 10^{-22}$	a_{floc} (µm)	$(\tau_\beta)_{theor.}$ (Nm^{-2})
0.25	1.7	4.4	4.2	24.3	6.6
0.28	5.2	1.71	7.6	39.2	25.9
0.29	5.3	1.99	8.2	36.2	33.8
0.30	5.2	3.41	15.2	27.7	36.5
0.31	5.0	4.19	17.9	25.0	–

For the intepretation of the rheological results, using the elastic floc model, it is necessary to have a model for the flocculated structure. For the present case, flocculation probably takes place by interpenetration of PVA tails under worse than θ- conditions for the chain. A typical floc may be assumed to consist of strings of particles linked together in a more-or-less three-dimensional network. The compactness of the floc (as measured by C_{FP}) is related to its strength by the number of chains, n_c, which pass through unit cross sectional area of the floc (29,31). n_c can be calculated from the total number of bonds per floc (36), i.e.

$$n_c = \frac{(C_{FP} + 0.7)}{b\, C_{FP}(C_{FP}-1)a^2} \qquad (8)$$

where b is a constant of order 10 which can be estimated from the close-packed structure. Values of n_c calculated using equation (8) are given in table III.

The elastic floc model also suggests that

$$C_{FP} = 1.5 + (F_M/b\eta_s a^2) \qquad (9)$$

where F_M is the maximum force of attraction between the particles. Values of F_M calculated using equation (9) are also given in table III.

The critical shear rate, $\dot{\gamma}_o$, above which the τ-$\dot{\gamma}$ curve becomes linear, is related to the number of floc-floc bonds, n_F, by the relation,

$$\dot{\gamma}_o = \frac{n_F\, F_M}{5\eta_s} \qquad (10)$$

Values of n_F are also included in table III.

The force required to break a floc doublet is then given by,

$$F = (n_F/n_c)\, F_M \qquad (11)$$

Values of F are also included in table III.

From n_F, the floc radius a_{floc} can be calculated using the equation (31),

$$a_{floc} = (1.22\pi n_F)^{-1/2} \qquad (12)$$

Values of a_{floc} are also included in table III.

The yield value τ_β is given by (30),

$$\tau_\beta = \beta\lambda\eta_s\dot{\gamma}(a_{floc})^2\, \Delta\phi_s^2\, C_{FP}/a^3 \qquad (13)$$

where β is a constant (= 27/5) and λ is the orthokinetic capture efficiency which depends weakly on shear rate γ ($\lambda \propto \dot{\gamma}^{-0.18}$)and Δ is the distance through which bonds are stretched inside the floc by the shearing process. Thus, τ_β can be calculated using Equation (13) provided reasonable values are used for $\dot{\gamma}$ and Δ. γ may be taken to be equal to γ_o, and a reasonable value of Δ would be 0.5 nm. In this manner, a comparison between τ_β calculated from Equation (13) and the experimental τ_β may be made. The results are also given in table III. Given all the approximations made, it is clear that the agreement between the experimental and theoretical values of τ_β is quite good, confirming the validity of the elastic floc model for flocculating, sterically- stabilized dispersions.

Acknowledgments

Most of the experimental work described in this paper was carried out by Mr. R. Rajaram and Miss Sheila Spence (Brunel University) during a six month industrial training period at Jealott's Hill. I am grateful to Dr. B. Vincent for many valuable comments. I am also grateful to Mr. D. Heath for preparing the latex and supervising part of the experimental work. Permission by the Management to publish this work is also appreciated.

Literature Cited

1. Krieger, I.M. Adv. Colloid Interface Sci., 3, 111 (1972).
2. Mewis, J. Adv. Colloid Interface Sci., 6, 173 (1979).
3. Goodwin, J.W. "Colloid Sci." Ed. D.H. Everett, Specialists Periodical Reports, Vol 2, Chem. Soc. London (1975).
4. Russel, W.B. J. Rheol., 24, 287 (1980).
5. Tadros, Th.F. Adv. Colloid Interface Sci. 12, 141 (1980).
6. Russel, W.B. and Benzig, D.W. J. Colloid Interface Sci. 83, 163 (1981).
7. Benzig, D.W. and Russel, W.B. J. Colloid Interface Sci. 83, 178 (1981).
8. Buscall, R., Goodwin, J.W., Hawkins M.W. and Ottewill, R.H. J. Chem. Soc. Faraday Trans I, 78, 2873 (1982).
9. Buscall, R., Goodwin, J.W., Hawkins M.W. and Ottewill, R.H. J. Chem. Soc. Faraday Trans I, 78, 2889 (1982).
10. Croucher, M.D. and Milkie, T.H., in "The Effect of Polymers on Dispersion Properties" Editor Th.F.Tadros, Academic Press London (1982) p. 101.
11. Milkie, T.H., Lok K. and Croucher. D. Colloid and Polymer Sci. 260, 531 (1982).
12. Strivens, T. A. Colloid and Polymer Sci., 261, 74 (1981).
13. Neville, P. and Hunter, R.J. J. Colloid Interface Sci., 49, 204, (1974).
14. Frith, B.A., Neville P.C. and Hunter, R.J. J. Colloid Interface Sci. 49, 214 (1974).

15. Garvey, M.J., Tadros Th.F. and Vincent, B. J. Colloid Interface Sci. 49, 57 (1974).
16. Garvey, M.J., Tadros Th.F. and Vincent, B. J. Colloid Interface Sci. 55 440 (1976).
17. van den Boomgaard, Th., King, T.A., Tadros, Th.F., Tang, H. and Vincent, B. J. Colloid Interface Sci. 61, 68 (1978).
18. Tadros,Th.F and Vincent, B. J. Colloid Interface Sci. 72, 505 (1972).
19. Goodwin, J.W., Hearn, J., Ho C.C. and Ottewill, R.H. Colloid and Polymer Sci. 252, 464 (1974).
20. Tadros,Th.F and Vincent,B. J. Phys. Chem., 84, 1575 (1980).
21. Luckham, P.F., Vincent,B. and Tadros, Th.F. Colloids and Surfaces, 6, 101 (1983).
22. Heath,D. and Tadros, Th.F. Disc. Faraday Soc. in press (1983).
23. Van Vliet,T. and Lyklema, J. Disc. Faraday Soc. 65, 25 (1978).
24. Cain, F.W., Ottewill, R.H. and Smitham, J.B. Disc. Faraday Soc. 65, (1978).
25. Sonntag, H., Emke, B., Miller R. and Knapschinsky, L. in "The Effect of Polymers on Dispersion Properties" Editor Tadros, Th.F. Academic Press, London (1982) p. 207.
26. Barnett, K., Cosgrove, T., Crowley, T.L., Tadros, Th.F. and Vincent, B. in "The Effect of Polymers on Dispersion Properties: Editor Tadros, Th.F. Academic Press, London (1982) p. 183.
27. Cosgrove, T., Crowley, T.L., Vincent., B., Barnett, K.G. and Tadros, Th.F. J. Chem. Soc. Faraday Symp. 1981, 16, 101.
28. Vincent, B., Luckham P.F. and Waite, F.A. J. Colloid Interface Sci. 73, 508 (1980).
29. Frith, B.A. and Hunter, R.J. J. Colloid Interface Sci. 57, 266, (1976).
30. van den Ven, T.G.M. and Hunter, R.J. J. Colloid Interface Sci. 68, 135 (1979).
31. Hunter, R.J. Advances Colloid Interface Sci. 17, 197 (1982).
32 Friend, J.P. and Hunter, R.J. J. Colloid Interface Sci. 37 548 (1971).
33. Michael, A.J. and Bolger, J.C. Ind. Eng. Chem. Fundament. 1, 153 (1962).
34. Mooney, M. J. Colloid Sci. 6, 162 (1951).
35. Hunter, R.J., Matarase R. and Napper, D.H. Colloids and Surfaces, 7, 1, (1983).
36. van den Ven T.G.M. and Hunter, R. J. Rheol. Acta, 16, 534 (1977).

RECEIVED November 15, 1983

Polymer Adsorption and Particle Flocculation in Turbulent Flow

ANDERS L. WIGSTEN[1] and ROBERT A. STRATTON

The Institute of Paper Chemistry, Appleton, WI 54912

Simultaneous polymer adsorption and particle flocculation rates were measured for a dilute colloidal
system in turbulent pipe flow. The particles were
negatively charged polystyrene latex, diameter 1.07
μm, and the polymer was a linear high molecular
weight cationic polyamine. The charge degree of the
polymer was varied from 95% at pH 3 to 3% at pH 10.
Reaction times ranged from 0.16 to 2.4 seconds.
Flocculation rates were compared with rates obtained
by destabilizing the suspension with a simple
electrolyte. Polymer-induced flocculation was considerably slower. Concentrations of unadsorbed
polymer measured at the end of the pipe were rarely
below 75% of the initial dose. This indicates that
polymer adsorption was the rate-determining step in
the overall flocculation process in this system.
The results are discussed in terms of collision rate
theories where the shear rate in the system and the
hydrodynamic sizes of the particles and the polymer
molecules are considered.

The two major theories of flocculation, the bridging model
(1) and the electrostatic patch model (2,3), provide the concep-
tual framework for the understanding of polymer-aided flocculation, but they do not directly address the kinetics of the
process. Smellie and La Mer (4) incorporated the bridging concept into a kinetic model of flocculation. They proposed that
the collision efficiency in the flocculation process should be
a function of the fractional surface coverage, Θ. Using a
modified Smoluchowski equation, they wrote for the initial flocculation rate

[1] Current address: Westvaco Research Center, Covington, VA 24426

where n_o = initial number concentration, m^{-3}
      t = time, s
      k = flocculation rate constant, m^3/s
      θ = fractional surface coverage, dimensionless

   This approach is based on the assumption that polymer
adsorption is fast ("instantaneous") compared with flocculation.
In other words the surface coverage is taken to be constant
during the flocculation process. Equation (1) states that the
flocculation rate tends to zero when θ tends to 0 or 1. The
maximum rate occurs at θ = 0.5, i.e., at 50% surface coverage.
   Equation (1) implies that flocculation is slower than
coagulation (destabilization with a simple electrolyte),
assuming that the rate constant, k, is the same in both cases.
However, the opposite result is generally found for perikinetic
flocculation (Brownian motion dominating); i.e., flocculation is
faster than coagulation. This has been observed for the case,
in which the polymer is of opposite charge to the particles
(3,5,6) and the rate increase was assumed to be caused by
electrostatic attractive forces between polymer-free and
polymer-covered patches on colliding particles. Increased flocculation rates have also been found for nonionic polymers (7)
and polymers of like charge to the particles (8). These results
were explained as the effect of reduced viscous interactions
between particles and increased collision radii due to adsorbed
polymer. It is thus clear that a polymeric flocculant can
increase particle collision efficiencies. Furthermore, the
adsorption step appears not to be rate limiting in perikinetic
flocculation, although these results do not necessarily mean
that the polymer adsorption rate is extremely fast compared with
the particle collision frequency.
   Studies on orthokinetic flocculation (shear flow dominating
over Brownian motion) show a more ambiguous picture. Both rate
increases (9,10) and decreases (11,12) compared with orthokinetic coagulation have been observed. Gregory (12) treated
polymer adsorption as a collision process and used Smoluchowski
theory to predict that the adsorption step may become rate
limiting in orthokinetic flocculation. Qualitative evidence to
this effect was found for flocculation of polystyrene latex,
particle diameter 1.68 µm, in laminar tube flow. Furthermore,
pretreatment of half of the latex with polymer resulted in
collision efficiencies that were more than twice as high as for
coagulation.
   The flocculation rate dependency on the fractional surface
coverage θ in Equation (1) has been qualitatively confirmed (13,
14), although the maximum rate appears to occur for a surface
coverage of less than 50%. The adsorption rate is also a function of θ, and it has been shown (15) for adsorption onto a
smooth solid surface that the rate is proportional to the fraction of polymer-free surface area, $1-\theta$. This approach has not

previously been experimentally tested for adsorption in
dispersed systems.

In summary, polymeric flocculants generally increase perikinetic flocculation rates compared with perikinetic coagulation
rates. This is not necessarily true for orthokinetic flocculation, and experimental results in the literature are seemingly
in conflict. Collision rate theory predicts that the polymer
adsorption step may become rate limiting in orthokinetic flocculation. The present study was designed to elucidate the relationship between polymer adsorption rates and particle
flocculation rates under orthokinetic conditions.

Experimental

Polystyrene latex particles (Dow) with a radius of 0.535 µm were
flocculated with polyvinylamine (Dynapol) of two molecular
weights, $1.3 \cdot 10^5$ and $1 \cdot 10^6$. The experiments were carried
out at pH 3 and pH 10, where the polymer is 95% and 3% charged,
respectively, (16). Latex concentrations, after mixing with the
polymer, ranged from 1.0 to 4.5 g/L. The experimental apparatus
consisted of two containers, one for the latex particles and one
for the polymer, connected to the flocculation tube via a mixing
tee. The inner diameter of the flocculation tube was 4.8 mm
(3/16 inch), and the length was variable. Flowrates between 0.7
and 2.6 m/s were obtained by gravity or nitrogen pressure.
Samples were collected in a cationic surfactant solution to
quench the flocculation and adsorption processes. The latex was
removed from the samples by filtration, using 0.4-µm polycar-
bonate filters (Nuclepore), and the free polymer concentrations
were determined spectrophotometrically with a method based on
the colloid titration principle (17). Floc size distributions
were measured on a Coulter Counter Model TAII using a 30-µm
aperture.

Flocculation experiments were also performed with half of
the latex pretreated with polymer to ensure complete surface
coverage. Coagulation rates were determined using aluminum
chloride at pH 3.

Theory

The coagulation, flocculation, and adsorption processes were
modeled mathematically using classical coagulation theory as a
starting point. The Smoluchowski equation for orthokinetic
coagulation in laminar flow is written (18)

$$dn_k/dt = 0.5 \sum_{\substack{i=1 \\ j=k-i}}^{i=k-1} (4G/3)(a_i+a_j)^3 n_i n_j - \sum_{i=1}^{\infty} (4G/3)(a_i+a_k)^3 n_i n_k \qquad (2)$$

where n_k = number concentration of flocs containing k primary
          particles (singlets), m^{-3}

    G = shear rate, s^{-1}

    a_i = floc radius, m

    k = i + j

The first term on the right-hand side of Equation (2)
describes the formation rate of k-flocs, and the second term is
the disappearance rate. In the present study the flow was turbulent, and an effective shear rate was calculated as $(\varepsilon/\nu)^{1/2}$
(19), where ε is the energy dissipation, W/kg, and ν is the
kinematic viscosity, m^2/s. Equation (2) was also extended to
include a collision efficiency factor, α, defined as

$$\alpha = J/J_s \qquad (3)$$

where J = observed rate

    J_s = rate according to Smoluchowski,
          Equation (2)

Theoretical collision efficiencies as a function of shear
rate and particle size were based on theory derived for spherical particles in simple shear (20,21). Effective floc size
radii (22) were calculated according to

$$a_i = i^m a_1 \qquad (4)$$

where m = 0.476, exponent determining the radius of gyration of
          a floc containing i singlets.

It was also assumed that a successful collision in flocculation can only occur if a polymer-free area on one floc hits
a polymer-covered area on another floc or vice versa. The
complete dimensionless flocculation rate equation is given by
Equation (5) below

$$dN_k/d\tau = \sum_{\substack{i=1 \\ j=k-i}}^{i=k-1} \alpha_F[(1-\theta_i)\theta_j + \theta_i(1-\theta_j)]\sigma_{ij}N_iN_j -$$

$$-2\sum_{i=1}^{\infty} \alpha_F[(1-\theta_i)\theta_k + \theta_i(1-\theta_k)]\sigma_{ik}N_iN_k \qquad (5)$$

where $N_k = n_k/n_o$

    $\tau = t/t_{1/2}$

    $t_{1/2} = 3/(16n_oGa_1^3)$, s

    θ_i = effective fractional surface coverage

    $\sigma_{ij} = (1/8)(i^m + j^m)^3$

Polymer adsorption was also modeled as a collision process, with the effective radius of a polymer molecule being equal to its radius of gyration, Equation (6).

$$dP/d\tau = -2\sum_{i=1}^{\infty}\alpha_A(1-\theta_i)\sigma_{ip}N_i P \qquad (6)$$

where P = p/p_o, dimensionless concentration of unadsorbed
  polymer
 p_o = initial polymer concentration
 σ_{ip} = $(1/8)(i^m + r)^3$
  r = a_p/a_1
  a_p = effective radius of a polymer molecule

The rate of change of surface coverage was calculated using Equation (7).

$$d\theta_k/d\tau = (2s\theta_e/k)\alpha_A(1-\theta_k)\sigma_{kp}P + (1/N_k)(dN_k/d\tau)_f(\theta_k^f-\theta_k) \qquad (7)$$

where s = total initial number concentration if all flocs
  are broken down to singlets, divided by n_o
 $(dN_k/d\tau)_f$ = formation rate of k-flocs
  θ_e = initial polymer dose divided by dose required
  to give 100% effective surface coverage
  θ_k = average effective surface coverage of k-flocs
  at time τ
  θ_k^f = average effective surface coverage of k-flocs
  formed by collisions between i- and j-flocs
  during the time interval $d\tau$

The first term on the right-hand side of Equation (7) is due to adsorption, and the second term is due to flocculation. It has been assumed that the total surface area of a floc is proportional to the number of singlets in that floc, a reasonable assumption for small flocs and open floc structures. The effective fractional surface coverage, θ_k, is not necessarily equal to the fractional surface coverage at equilibrium for a given amount of adsorbed polymer. This will be discussed in some detail below.
    Particle collision frequency due to Brownian motion was estimated to be less than 1% of the collision frequency due to shear. The effects of Brownian motion could therefore be neglected in the flocculation rate calculations. However, for the smallest molecular size, radius of gyration 14 nm (see Table I), the effect of Brownian motion on the particle-polymer collision efficiency was of the same order of magnitude as the effect of shear. These two contributions were assumed to be additive in the adsorption rate calculations. Additivity is not fundamentally justified (23) but can be used as an interpolating

technique in the transition region from Brownian motion to shear
flow domination (24). The coupled set of rate Equations (5),
(6) and (7), including corresponding perikinetic adsorption rate
equations, was solved numerically on a Burroughs B6900 computer.

Results

Flocculation with a high charge density polymer. The flocculation results for a molecular weight of $1 \cdot 10^6$ and a charge
density of 95% are shown in Fig. 1. The theoretical curves
represent the best fit between the mathematical model and the
experimental data. The initial dose in OFC units is given
beside each flocculation curve. One OFC unit is equivalent to
the amount of polymer needed to give maximum extent of flocculation under quiescent equilibrium conditions, 0.4 mg/L for a
polystyrene latex concentration of 1.5 g/L. The initial particle size distribution was 91% singlets, 6% doublets, and 3%
triplets and larger flocs.

It is seen that the flocculation rates are generally considerably lower than the coagulation rate. A "pseudo" optimum
flocculation concentration of ~ 6 OFC units is found for short
flocculation times, but for longer times it is clear that the
suspension is stabilized and no further flocculation occurs. At
higher initial doses restabilization becomes even more pronounced.

The amount of adsorbed polymer rarely exceeded one OFC
unit, although the degree of adsorption was sufficient to sta-
bilize the suspension. The equilibrium and nonequilibrium
isotherms are shown in Fig. 2. Maximum adsorption at
equilibrium was 3.5 times higher than what was achieved under
nonequilibrium conditions. Figure 3 shows the adsorption
results as polymer concentration vs. time. The theoretical
curves represent the best fit between the model and the experimental data. Only 25% of an initial dose of 1.4 OFC units is
adsorbed at the end of the experimental time range shown in Fig.
3. Based on the adsorption data, the model predicts an effective surface coverage of singlets of only 30% at the longer
adsorption time; see the dashed curve in Fig. 3. According to
the flocculation model, the maximum flocculation rate should
occur at 50% surface coverage. Conditions are obviously far
from optimum for efficient flocculation during the experimental
time range. It is concluded that the flocculation process is
adsorption rate limited. This was further confirmed by an
experiment where clean polystyrene latex was flocculated with an
equal amount of polymer-treated latex. The observed flocculation rate was about 50% higher than anticipated, assuming
that collisions between particles of like charge are elastic and
that the collision efficiency for particles of opposite charge
is the same as the collision efficiency for coagulation. This
flocculation rate increase is interpreted as an enhanced

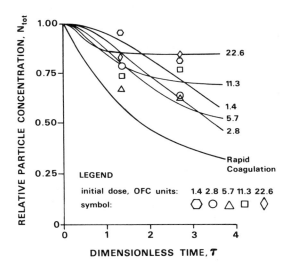

Figure 1. Flocculation. Experimental and theoretical particle concentration vs. time. Initial dose in OFC units beside curves. Molecular weight 1×10^6, charge density 95%. Shear rate 1800 s^{-1}.

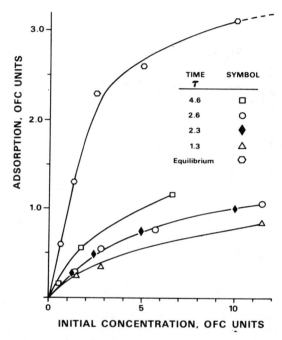

Figure 2. Adsorption isotherms for equilibrium (top curve) and nonequilibrium conditions. Molecular weight $1x10^6$, charge density 95%. Nonequilibrium, open symbols $G = 1800$ s^{-1}, closed symbol $G = 8000$ s^{-1}.

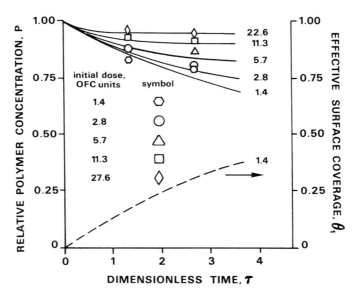

Figure 3. Adsorption. Experimental and theoretical
polymer concentration vs. time, solid lines. Theoretical
effective surface coverage of singlets, θ_1, vs. time,
dashed line. Initial dose in OFC units beside curves.
Molecular weight 1×10^6, charge density 95%. Shear rate
1800 s^{-1}.

collision efficiency due to electrostatic attraction between
polymer-covered and polymer-free particles. A similar experiment was performed by Gregory (12), who found an increase in
collision efficiency, compared with coagulation, of more than
100%.

Adsorption rates were not significantly affected by molecular weight, but flocculation was about 25% faster for the high
molecular weight polymer. Two shear rate levels were tested
1800 s^{-1} and 8000 s^{-1}. The absolute adsorption and flocculation rates increased with shear rate as expected. The
"pseudo" OFC appeared to be shifted to a higher value for the
higher shear rate. Collision efficiencies were affected by both
molecular weight and shear rate, as discussed below.

Flocculation with a low charge density polymer. The low charge
density case, 3% charged, also resulted in flocculation which
was adsorption rate limited and considerably slower than coagulation. It also appeared that floc breakup occurred, since the
extent of flocculation was rather insensitive to the flocculation time after an initial drop in particle concentration.
The adsorption rate was lower than at pH 3 (high charge
density), which is expected since the low charge density polymer
has a smaller radius of gyration and a lower energy of interaction with the particles. Re-stabilization did also occur
despite a maximum adsorption of less than one OFC unit. The
adsorption rate of the low molecular weight polymer was about a
factor of 2.5 slower than the adsorption rate of the high molecular weight polymer. The absolute adsorption rates increased
with shear rate, but particle-polymer collision efficiencies did
not change. Molecular weight and shear rate did not appear to
have a significant effect on the flocculation rate. This observation can possibly be attributed to floc breakup.

Discussion

The difference between the high and low molecular weight is a
factor of 7.7; however, the difference in radius of gyration is
only a factor of 3.8 in the high charge density case and a factor of 2.7 in the low charge density case; see Table I. The
polymer radius appears as the fraction, r, of the singlet radius
in the collision radius factor (1+r) in the adsorption rate,
Equation (6). This results in a predicted difference in adsorption rate between the two molecular weights of a factor of 2.0
in the high charge density case and a factor of 1.2 in the low
charge density case (neglecting the effect of Brownian motion).
This explains why no drastic differences in flocculation and
adsorption rates were observed for the two molecular weights.
The experimental results showed no significant difference in
adsorption rate with respect to molecular weight for the high
charge density case. However, at low charge density the

adsorption rate of the high molecular weight polymer was about
2.5 times faster than that of the low molecular weight polymer.
The reason for this discrepancy between theory and experiment
may be explained by different collision efficiencies for
particle-polymer interactions depending on molecular weight and
charge density (see below).

Collision efficiency. The collision efficiency for floc-
culation, α_F in Equation (5), and for adsorption, α_A in Equation
(6), were estimated by fitting the mathematical model to the
experimental data. The results are presented in Table I as
relative collision efficiencies, α_F/α_C and α_A/α_C, where α_C is
the singlet collision efficiency for coagulation. (Since floc-
culation did not proceed very far, particle collision efficiencies were taken to be equal to the singlet collision
efficiency.) The experimental values of α_C are 0.33 and 0.20
for shear rates of 1800 s^{-1} and 8000 s^{-1}, respectively. The
corresponding theoretical values are 0.20 and 0.16 (20). The
flocculation efficiency for the high charge density polymer is
about the same or higher than the coagulation efficiency, but
the low charge density polymer gives a lower flocculation efficiency, which is presumably due to a lower interaction energy
and floc breakup. The adsorption efficiency is generally lower
than the singlet coagulation efficiency, which is expected
because an increasing difference in size between colliding enti-
ties results in a decreasing collision efficiency (21). On the
other hand, particle-polymer collision (i.e., adsorption) efficiencies are much higher than collision efficiencies for polystyrene latex particles of dissimilar size. For example,
particles with a size ratio of 0.535/0.200 would theoretically
have a collision efficiency 10-15% lower than the collision
efficiency for particles of equal size and a radius of 0.535 µm,
$\alpha_C = 0.20$. The collision efficiency drops rapidly with
increasing difference in particle size and for a ratio of
0.535/0.053 theory predicts $\alpha_C < 10^{-3}$ (21). This drastic drop
is not seen experimentally for particle-polymer collisions,
Table I. This is probably due to electrostatic attraction between polymer and particle and to the porous and flexible nature
of the polymer molecule.

Fractional surface coverage. It is concluded that the effective
degree of surface coverage for a given amount of adsorbed
polymer is higher under nonequilibrium conditions than at
equilibrium, since restabilization occurred during the dynamic
flocculation experiments despite adsorption levels that were
equal to or less than one OFC unit. Another support for this
conclusion was that the restabilization trend could not be
modeled mathematically unless a higher degree of nonequilibrium
surface coverage was assumed. This phenomenon is due to a
finite polymer reconformation rate, i.e., the rate of attaining

equilibrium after the first polymer segment has attached to a
particle surface. It is likely that after initial adsorption,
many of the segments of the polymer molecules are dangling out
into solution, sweeping across areas which become inaccessible
to other polymer molecules. Very little is known about polymer
reconformation rates. Gregory and Sheiham (5) estimated a
reconformation time of 1-4 seconds based on flocculation experiments with high charge density polymers. However, the reconformation time could be considerably longer (25). By assuming the
reconformation rate to be negligible on the time scale of the
experiments, 0.16 to 2.40 seconds, a ratio of effective nonequilibrium surface coverage to equilibrium surface coverage
could be estimated for the high charge density polymer from the
best fit between experiment and theory; see Table I. Because of
probable floc breakup, a reliable value of this ratio could not
be obtained for the low charge density polymer. However, indications are that the ratio is higher than unity, maybe as much
as a factor of 2, but lower than the value for the high charge
density case, about 3.5.

Table I.   Relative Collision Efficiencies Estimated from Fitting
           the Mathematical Model to Experimental Data

Molecular Weight	pH	Radius of Gyration, nm	G s^{-1}	θ_e/θ_∞[a]	Relative Collision Efficiency[b]	
					Flocculation	Adsorption
1.3×10^5	3	53	1800	3.9	0.9	0.9
			8000	3.5	1.3	0.9
1×10^6	3	200	1800	3.5	1.1	0.5
			8000	3.1	1.7	0.5
1.3×10^5	10	14	--[c]		0.6	0.2
1×10^6	10	38	--[c]		0.6	0.3

[a]Ratio between effective surface coverage under nonequilibrium
and equilibrium conditions for a given amount of adsorbed
polymer.
[b]Collision efficiency divided by collision efficiency for
coagulation; α_C (1800 s^{-1}) = 0.33, α_C (8000 s^{-1}) = 0.20.
[c]No shear rate dependence.

      The theoretical flocculation trends as a function of ini-
tial polymer dose, shown in Fig. 1, are correct, but the experimental concentrations are generally lower at short times and
higher at long times compared with the theoretical predictions.
This indicates that the reconformation time may in fact be of
the same order of magnitude as the experimental time range (2.4
seconds), which agrees with the estimate in (5).

Flocculation rate limitation. The adsorption step was rate
limiting for the overall flocculation process in this system.
Polymer adsorption rate measurements for dispersed systems
reported in the literature ($\underline{2},\underline{26}$) do not lend themselves to
direct comparisons with the present work due to lack of infor-
mation on shear rates, flocculation rates, and particle and
polymer sizes. Gregory ($\underline{12}$) proposed that the adsorption and
coagulation halftimes, t_A and t_C, respectively, should be good
indications of whether or not the adsorption step is expected to
be rate limiting. The halftimes, t_A and t_C, are defined as the
times required to halve the initial concentrations of polymer
and particles, respectively. Adsorption should not limit the
flocculation rate if

$$t_A \ll t_C \tag{8}$$

For orthokinetic conditions the ratio of adsorption halftime to coagulation halftime can be calculated by integrating
the adsorption Equation (6) and the coagulation Equation (2).
The perikinetic halftimes can be derived analogously.

The ratio of perikinetic adsorption halftime to perikinetic
coagulation halftime is given by

$$t_{Ap}/t_{Cp} = (\alpha_{Cp}/\alpha_{Ap})4r\ln2/(1+r)^2 \tag{9}$$

$$t_{Ap} < 0.7t_{Cp} \text{ if } \alpha_{Ap} = \alpha_{Cp} \tag{10}$$

It is reasonable to assume, at least for oppositely charged
polymers and particles, that $\alpha_A > \alpha_C$, which means that the
adsorption time is always expected to be shorter than the coagulation time under perikinetic conditions. Consequently, perikinetic flocculation rates are very likely not to be adsorption
rate limited. The ratio of orthokinetic adsorption time to
orthokinetic coagulation time is

$$t_{Ao}/t_{Co} = (\alpha_{Co}/\alpha_{Ao})8\ln2/(1+r)^3 \tag{11}$$

$$t_{Ao} < t_{Co} \text{ if } r > 0.8 \text{ and } \alpha_{Ao} = \alpha_{Co} \tag{12}$$

The polymer radius has to be larger than 80% of the particle radius to avoid adsorption limitation under orthokinetic
conditions. As a rule of thumb a particle diameter of about 1
µm marks the transition between perikinetic and orthokinetic
coagulation (and flocculation). The effective size of a polymeric flocculant must clearly be very large to avoid adsorption
limitation. However, if the polymer is sufficiently small, the
Brownian diffusion rate may be fast enough to prevent adsorption
limitation. For example, if the particle radius is 0.535 µm and
the shear rate is 1800 s^{-1}, then t_{Ap} due to Brownian motion will
be shorter than t_{Co} for r $\leqslant$ 0.001, i.e., for a polymer with a

radius of gyration of 0.5 nm or less (it has been assumed that
$\alpha_A = \alpha_C$).
        Table II lists experimental halftimes obtained by
extrapolation to 50% of initial concentration; cf. Fig. 1 and 3.
The values within parentheses in Table II are calculated by
integrating Equations (2) and (6) for initial, monodisperse conditions assuming $\alpha_A = \alpha_C = 0.20$. It is clear that the adsorption halftime is considerably longer than the coagulation
halftime, which results in a relatively long flocculation halftime. It is also seen that the integration method is a useful
approximation to estimate halftimes.
        Literature reports on increased perikinetic flocculation
rates compared with coagulation are in agreement with the
discussion presented here. Reported cases on improved orthokinetic flocculation rates can presumably be explained by
increased particle collision efficiencies or increased particle
radii due to polymer adsorption. Franco and Stratton (9) flocculated TiO_2 particles, average diameter 0.15 μm, in turbulent
pipe flow and found increased rates compared with coagulation.
The most effective flocculant was a high molecular weight, low
charge density polymer. They explained the observed increase in
flocculation rate as being caused by an increased effective particle radius due to adsorbed polymer. This appears to be a
reasonable explanation, because of the high value of r (= 2.4).
The adsorption halftime is in this case expected to be shorter
than the coagulation halftime, cf. Equation (12). Furthermore,
a low charge density polymer is assumed to adsorb in a bulky
state similar to its solution conformation, which would in this
case result in a substantial increase in the effective particle
radius (maximum, a factor of 5.7).
        Graham (10) flocculated porous silica particles, diameter
7.6 μm, in a paddle-stirred vessel with an average shear rate of
100 s^{-1}. The highest flocculation rate using an oppositely
charged polymer was about 30 times higher than the coagulation
rate. Contrary to this result, Equation (11) indicates that the
adsorption step should be rate limiting, assuming $\alpha_A = \alpha_C$ and r
< 0.8. However, if $\alpha_C = 0.017$, as found experimentally by
Graham, and α_A is taken to be unity, then Equation (11) gives t_A
< 0.1 t_C. Thus, it is quite possible that adsorption is not
rate limiting. Furthermore, adsorbed polymer is likely to
increase the particle collision efficiency by electrostatic
attraction and reduced hydrodynamic interactions. The effect of
increased particle diameter due to polymer adsorption is probably of secondary importance in this case.
        Finally, as pointed out in the results of the present
study, there is a possibility of determining a "pseudo" OFC in
an orthokinetic experiment if the extent of flocculation is not
taken to its equilibrium value. This may erroneously lead to
the conclusion that the polymer adsorption step is not rate
limiting for the overall flocculation process.

Table II. Halftimes for Coagulation, t_C, Adsorption, t_A, and Flocculation, t_F. $G = 1800$ s^{-1}, $n_o = 2\times10^{15}$ m^{-3}, Molecular Weight = 1×10^6, Initial Polymer Concentration = OFC

Charge Density, %	Halftimes in Seconds			
	t_C	t_F	t_A	t_A/t_C
95	0.6(0.7)	1.4	2.0(1.6)	3.3(2.1)
3	0.6(0.7)	3.1	3.2(3.4)	5.3(4.5)

Conclusions

The polymer adsorption step was rate limiting for the ortho-kinetic flocculation process in this study. This was shown by comparing coagulation and flocculation rates and by measuring polymer adsorption rates in the flocculating system. The experimental results could, at least qualitatively, be predicted with a mathematical model based on modified coagulation rate theory. The adsorption step is likely to become rate limiting in orthokinetic flocculation, but this may not happen if the polymer is larger than the particles or if the adsorbed polymer substantially increases the particle collision efficiency.

Acknowledgments

A. L. Wigsten wishes to acknowledge the financial support provided by The Institute of Paper Chemistry and Mr. Gunnar Nicholson, New York.

Portions of this work were used by one of the authors (ALW) as partial fulfillment of the requirements for the Ph.D. degree at The Institute of Paper Chemistry.

Literature Cited

1. La Mer, V.K.; Healy, T.W., Rev. Pure Appl. Chem. 1963, 13, 112.
2. Kasper, D.R., Ph.D. Thesis, California Institute of Technology, Pasadena, California, 1971.
3. Gregory, J., J. Colloid Interface Sci. 1973, 42, 448.
4. Smellie, R.H.; La Mer, V.K., J. Colloid Sci. 1958, 13, 589.
5. Gregory, J.; Sheiham, J., Br. Polym. J. 1974, 6, 47.
6. Gregory, J., J. Colloid Interface Sci. 1976, 55, 35.
7. Fleer, G.J., Ph.D. Thesis, Agricultural University, Wageningen, The Netherlands, 1971.
8. van der Scheer, A.; Tanke, M.A.; Smolders, C.A., Faraday Discuss. Chem. Soc. 1978, 65, 264.
9. Franco, R.P.; Stratton, R.A., Unpublished work, The Institute of Paper Chemistry, Appleton, Wisconsin, 1978.
10. Graham, N.J.D., Colloids and Surfaces 1981, 3, 61.
11. Birkner, F.B.; Morgan, J.J., J. AWWA 1968, 60, 175.

12. Gregory, J., in "The Effect of Polymers on Dispersion Properties"; Tadros, Th.F., Ed.; Academic: New York, 1982; p.301.
13. Uriarte, F.A., Ph.D. Thesis, Carnegie-Mellon University, Pittsburgh, Pennsylvania, 1971.
14. Singer, J.M.; Vekemans, F.C.A.; Lichtenbelt, J.W.Th., Hesselink, F.Th.; Wiersema, P.H., J. Colloid Interface Sci. 1973, 45, 608.
15. Petersen, C.; Kwei, T.K., J. Phys. Chem. 1961, 65, 1330.
16. Sikora, M. D.; Stratton, R. A., Tappi 1981, 64, 97.
17. Wigsten, A.L., Ph.D. Thesis, The Institute of Paper Chemistry, Appleton, Wisconsin, 1983.
18. Kruyt, H.R., "Colloid Science Vol. 1."; Elsevier: New York, 1949; 389p.
19. Camp, T.R.; Stein, P.C., J. Boston Soc. Civ. Eng. 1943, 30, 219.
20. van de Ven, T.H.M.; Mason, S.G., Colloid and Polymer Sci. 1977, 256, 468.
21. Higashitani, K.; Ogawa, R.; Hosokawa, G., J. Chem. Eng. Japan 1982, 15, 299.
22. Tambo, N.; Watanabe, Y., Water Research 1979, 13, 409.
23. van de Ven, T.G.M., Adv. Colloid Interface Sci. 1982, 17, 105.
24. Guzy, C.J.; Bonano, E.J.; Davis, E.J., J. Colloid Interface Sci., to be published.
25. Clayfield, E.J.; Lumb, E.C., J. Colloid Interface Sci. 1974, 47, 6.
26. Black, A.P.; Birkner, F.B.; Morgan, J.J., J. AWWA 1965, 57, 1547.

RECEIVED October 7, 1983

Filtrability of Polymer-Flocculated Suspensions

J. GREGORY and A. E. L. DE MOOR

Department of Civil Engineering, University College, London WC IE 6BT, England

The filtrability of suspensions can be a useful
means of assessing the performance of polymeric
flocculants. A newly-developed technique involves
filtration at constant pressure, continuous
monitoring of filtration rate and on-line data
processing to give the specific resistance to
filtration. The flocculation of kaolin
suspensions by various cationic polymers has been
studied using this method. Optimum polymer
dosages are clearly established and show good
agreement with those from other techniques.
Filtrability seems not to be greatly dependent
on floc size.

Polymer flocculants are now used in a wide range of
applications (1). Early interest in these materials was
largely based on their ability to improve the dewatering rates
(i.e. to increase the permeability) of suspensions.
Applications as soil conditioners (2) and in the dewatering of
phosphate slimes (3) were among the first successful uses of
synthetic polymeric flocculants. For this reason, several test
methods based on permeability have been developed, including the
re-filtration rate method of La Mer (3).
    Even in applications other than dewatering, permeability
methods are quite often used to assess the performance of
polymeric flocculants, since, in principle, they can give a very
sensitive indication of the state of aggregation of particles
and are useful in locating optimum polymer concentrations.
    Traditional permeability tests are time-consuming and
subject to some uncertainties (4). In the present paper, we
describe an automated technique for determining the filtrability
of fairly dilute suspensions, which can give useful information.
on the behaviour of polymeric flocculants.

0097–6156/84/0240–0445$06.00/0

Permeability and Specific Resistance

Laminar flow through a porous medium is described by Darcy's laws

$$v = (K/\eta)(\Delta P/L) \tag{1}$$

where v is the approach velocity of the fluid ($m\ s^{-1}$), K is the permeability of the medium (m^2), η is the fluid viscosity (Pa s), ΔP is the pressure difference (Pa) and L the depth of the medium (m).

The permeability, K, is characteristic of the medium and can be related to measurable properties by the Carman-Kozeny equation:

$$K = \varepsilon^3/5S^2(1-\varepsilon)^2 \tag{2}$$

where ε is the porosity of the medium (void volume/total volume) and S is the specific surface (i.e. the surface area per unit volume of particles) (m^{-1}).

Strictly, the value 5 in the Carman-Kozeny equation should be treated as an empirical constant, which has to be determined experimentally. However, for many systems of interest, the value is very close to 5.

When a suspension is filtered by a straining mechanism, the permeability of the resulting filter cake can be interpreted by means of Equation 2. There should be a strong dependence of permeability on the state of aggregation of the particles, since aggregates have a smaller effective surface area than the individual particles and may pack less efficiently, giving a higher porosity. Both of these effects should lead to an increased permeability, although their relative importance does not appear to have been clearly established. One complicating factor is that flocculated suspensions often give compressible filter cakes (5), so that porosity and specific surface may change during filtration and may vary through the depth of the filter cake.

The re-filtration technique of La Mer (3) involves filtering the flocculated suspension and then passing the filtrate once more through this pre-formed filter cake. The second filtration is carried out under a constant pressure difference (normally by applying suction) and the time to filter a known volume is noted. This re-filtration time is directly related to the permeability of the filter cake and can be greatly reduced by flocculation.

Although the re-filtration rate can be a sensitive indicator of flocculation, the mathematical treatment by Smellie and La Mer (6) and the interpretation of the results has been the subject of some criticism (4). There are practical difficulties, too, such as the disproportionate effect of a small amount of 'fines' (unflocculated particles). For these reasons, the re-filtration method is not much used in flocculation studies.

Essentially equivalent information can be obtained during the formation of the filter cake, without the need for a second filtration. During filtration, particles are deposited as a layer of increasing thickness, so that the resistance to filtration increases. The resistance, $R(m^{-1})$, is inversely related to permeability and is defined in terms of the volume flow rate:

$$dV/dt = F\Delta P/\eta R \tag{3}$$

where F is the area of the filter (m^2) and V is the volume of filtrate (m^3) produced in a time t (s).

The resistance has two components: the resistance of the support medium, R_m, and the filter cake resistance, R_c. If R_m remains constant and all particles are removed to give a uniform filter cake, then:

$$R = R_m + \alpha cV/F \tag{4}$$

where c is the concentration of the suspension (kg m^{-3}) and α is the <u>specific</u> <u>resistance</u> to filtration (m kg^{-1}).

The specific resistance should depend only on the nature of the suspended particles (size, shape and density) and on their state of aggregation. It is related to the permeability, K, by:

$$\alpha = 1/K \rho(1-\varepsilon) \tag{5}$$

where ρ is the density of the particles (kg m^{-3}).

Substituting the value of R from Equation 4 into Equation 3 and integrating (with ΔP constant) gives the well-known parabolic filtration equation:

$$t = (\eta/F\Delta P)(R_m V + \alpha cV^2/2F) \tag{6}$$

Dividing throughout by V gives the linearized version of Equation 6:

$$t/V = \eta R_m/F\Delta P + (\eta\alpha c/2F^2 \Delta P)V \tag{7}$$

If the volume of filtrate is measured as a function of time, under constant pressure, then a plot of t/V against V should give a straight line, the slope of which can be used to calculate the specific resistance.

Equation 7 is based on a number of assumptions and may not apply in all cases, especially if the filter cake is compressible. A rigorous treatment of cake filtration has been given by Willis and Tosun (7).

Experiments to determine specific resistance, based on
Equation 7, have usually been carried out by some form of vacuum
filtration. These methods are time-consuming and subject to
error. More rapid techniques such as the measurement of
capillary suction time (CST) can be used (8), although these do
not give absolute values of specific resistance. Nevertheless,
the CST method is very useful for rapidly obtaining comparative
data on the flocculation of fairly concentrated suspensions by
polymers (9). In the present work, specific resistance has
been determined by an automated technique, which will be
described below.

Automated Filtrability Determination

The new technique (10) is based on the apparatus shown in
Figure 1. A 50 ml Hamilton glass syringe, with a Teflon-coated
piston, is connected via a three-way tap to a Swinnex filter
holder, which is fitted with a suitable membrane filter (0.45 μm
or 0.22 μm Millipore filters in the present work). The syringe
piston has been modified by fitting a circular platform, on which
one or more ring-shaped weights can be placed. The total load
(typically 3 kg) is chosen to give a reasonable filtration rate
and serves to maintain a constant pressure during the fitration
process.

Rather than measuring the filtrate volume directly, the
movement of the syringe piston is monitored by a displacement
transducer, which gives a voltage output proportional to the
piston displacement and hence to the filtrate volume. The
output of the transucer is digitized and fed to the user port of
a Commodore PET microcomputer, so that, during a filtration
experiment, a series of time and displacement data can be stored.
After the syringe has been filled with the suspension under test
and the load applied, the required data can be obtained with no
further attention being needed.

Figure 2 shows the form of the displacement vs. time results
for different suspension concentrations. For particle-free
water (c = 0), the line is straight, since the resistance is just
that of the membrane filter, which remains constant.
For suspensions of particles larger than the pores in the membrane,
the formation of a filter cake leads to progressively increasing
resistance and a declining filtration rate. The higher the
suspension concentration, the more rapidly does the rate decline.

By analogy with Equation 7, the displacement-time data can
be linearized, giving:

$$t/D = \text{constant} + bD \tag{8}$$

where D is the displacement of the piston at time T. The slope
of the line, b, is given by:

$$b = \eta \alpha c A^2 / 2F^2 \Delta P \tag{9}$$

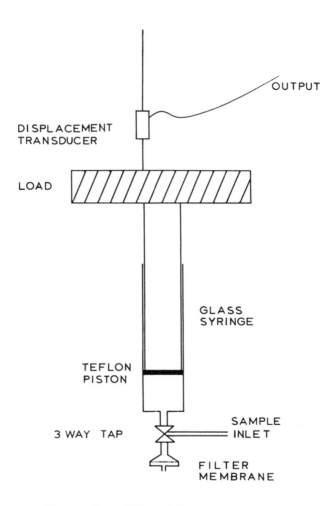

Figure 1.   Filtrability apparatus.

where A is the cross-sectional area of the syringe.

In the present method, t/D values are computed and displayed during a filtration experiment. At the end of a run a plot of t/D vs. D is drawn on a Bryans 50000 digital plotter. Such a plot is shown in Figure 3 for a suspension of kaolin particles at a concentration of 35 mg/l. After a brief initial phase, when the pores of the membrane filter are being blocked and the first layers of particles deposited, the plot shows good linear behaviour, indicating a uniform filter cake and the absence of significant compressibility effects. The slope of the line is determined automatically by a linear regression routine and the specific resistance is calculated from the slope (and other necessary data, which are entered initially). The entire sequence of operations, from the start of the filtration to the computation of specific resistance is carried out automatically under microcomputer control.

This technique has been thoroughly evaluated for a range of dilute suspensions and shown to give consistent results (10). The specific resistances obtained are independent of applied load, suspension concentration and membrane type, as expected for non-compressible filter cakes. Tests with uniform latex particles have given permeabilities in very good agreement with Equation 2, using a value of 5 for the Carman-Kozeny constant.

The method is better suited to dilute, rather than concentrated suspensions, since the data can be obtained in a short time (a few minutes at most) and only thin filter cakes are formed. With higher concentrations, much longer filtration times are needed and the thicker filter cakes are more likely to show compressibility effects and non-linear behaviour.

Effect of Flocculation on Filtrability

Some preliminary experiments have been conducted using the new technique, with kaolin suspensions and cationic polymers. The kaolin was from BDH Ltd. and was dispersed by high-speed stirring at around neutral pH. The resulting suspension was allowed to stand overnight and the sedimented material was rejected. The remaining suspension contained particles up to about 2 μm in size. Final suspensions for the flocculation experiments were made up in 10^{-3}M NaCl, to control the ionic strength.

The cationic polymers used were as follows:

A. Poly(dimethylaminoethyl methacrylate), with a molecular weight of about 5000, fully quaternized with dimethyl sulfate.

B. As A, but with a molecular weight of about 150,000.

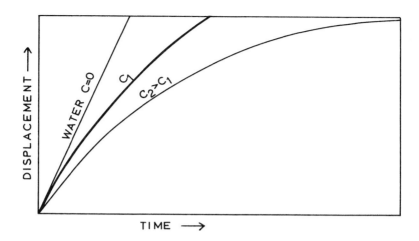

Figure 2.   Form of displacement vs. time curves for different suspension concentrations.

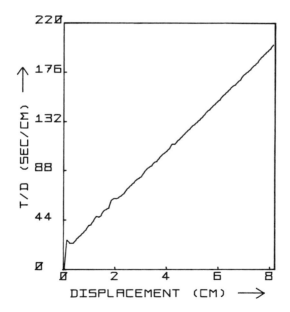

Figure 3.   Linearized plot for an unflocculated 35 mg/l kaolin suspension.

C.   Poly(1-ethyl 2 methyl 5 vinyl pridinium bromide) with a
     molecular weight of about 1 million.
     These materials have been used previously (11).

Procedure.   Initially, the flocculation procedure adopted was to
add polymer to the clay suspension, stir rapidly for 15 seconds
to ensure good mixing and then to flow the treated suspension
through a 3 m length of coiled 1 mm diameter tubing. Tube flow
is known to be an effective method of applying shear to a
suspension and hence promoting orthokinetic flocculation (12).
The flocculated suspension was then transferred to the syringe
and the specific resistance was determined as described
previously. Results are shown in Figure 4 for three different
kaolin concentrations, flocculated with polymer A. The polymer
concentration is shown as a percentage of the clay concentration.
In all cases, plots of t/D vs. D were linear.
     The specific resistance of the unflocculated kaolin is about
12×10^{12} m/kg and falls to about 1×10^{12} m/kg at the optimum
flocculant concentration. It is clear that the amount of
polymer required to give the minimum specific resistance is about
0.5% of the clay concentration in all cases. This
proportionality indicates that the polymer is strongly adsorbed
and probably acts by a charge neutralization, rather than a
bridging mechanism. The amount of cationic polymer required to
neutralize the negative charge of clay particles must be
proportional to the clay concentration. Restabilization of the
kaolin occurs at excess polymer doses because the particles
become positively charged. The more pronounced restabilization
observed for the highest clay concentration in Figure 4 may be a
result of the more rapid polymer adsorption under these
conditions.
     The procedure used to obtain the results in Figure 3 is not
entirely satisfactory, since transfer of the flocculated
suspension to the syringe inevitably causes some break-up of
flocs which may affect the filtration behaviour. In order to
investigate this point, two different procedures were adopted:
a) The suspension was transferred to the syringe after adding
the polymer and stirring rapidly for 15 seconds, but without
tube flow. In this case, no visible flocs had formed so that
no significant break-up would be expected. The suspension was
filtered immediately after transfer. Since the filtration of
the samples is quite rapid, there is very little opportunity for
flocculation in the syringe.
b) After polymer addition and 15 seconds of rapid mixing, the
suspension was transferred to the syringe and then subjected to
10 minutes of slow sitrring in situ, using a small magnetic bar.
This resulted in quite large flocs, which could be filtered
without disturbance.

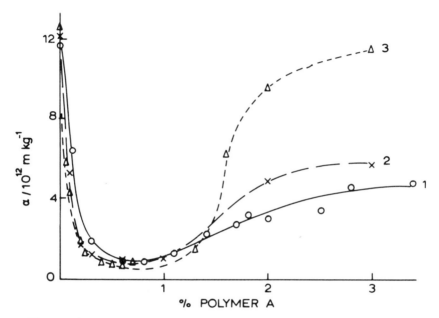

Figure 4.   Specific resistance of kaolin suspensions treated with different amounts of polymer A. Kaolin concentrations: 1) 70 mg/1, 2) 140 mg/1, 3) 280 mg/1. Polymer concentration expressed as a percentage of kaolin concentration.

The results in Figure 5 compare these procedures and the previous one (rapid mix and tube flow) for a kaolin concentration of 140 mg/l. In this and subsequent Figures, specific resistances are plotted as percentages of the original value (i.e. for the unflocculated kaolin). Evidently, the procedure makes little difference to the results and essentially the same 'optimum' polymer concentration would be chosen in each case. The results at high polymer concentrations show different behaviour, depending on the procedure employed, but no satisfactory explanation seems apparent.

In view of the nature of the results in Figure 5, comparison of the effects of different polymers was carried out using the simplest technique, i.e. filtration immediately after rapid mixing.

Behaviour of Different Polymers. The effects of polymers A, B and C, on the specific resistance of a 140 mg/l kaolin suspension are shown in Figure 6. The results are remarkably similar, bearing in mind the very different molecular weights of these materials. Again, there is a strong indication that charge neutralization is the predominant effect and that polymer bridging plays a minor role, if any. The less pronounced restabilization with the higher molecular weight polymers may be a result of a slower adsorption or of a non-uniform charge distribution (11).

It is worth noting that the specific resistances obtained by flocculation with cationic polymers are much less than those achieved by simple salts. For instance, when the kaolin suspension is completely destabilized by the addition of a calcium salt, the specific resistance is only reduced by a factor of about two. A ten-fold reduction can easily be achieved by cationic polymers.

The flocculation and restabilization behaviour indicated by the filtrability results is well matched by other test methods, including simple settling tests and a newly-developed optical monitoring technique (13). All of these methods give essentially the same optimum polymer concentration.

Effect of Stirring. The rather small effect of tube flow and slow stirring on the specific resistance results in Figure 5 was unexpected and has been checked by a series of trials in which a kaolin suspension was subjected to various periods of slow stirring, following polymer addition and rapid mixing. For this purpose, 500 ml of a 140 mg/l kaolin suspension was treated with an amount of polymer A corresponding to 0.5% of the clay concentration (i.e. the optimum dose). After 15 seconds of rapid mixing, the suspension was subjected to slow (30 r.p.m.) stirring, using a paddle stirrer. Samples were withdrawn at different intervals directly into the syringe and a filtrability determination was carried out.

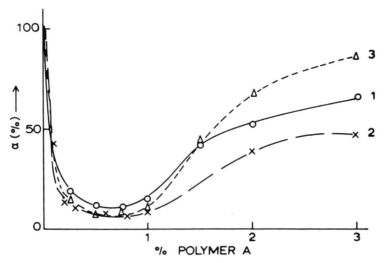

Figure 5.   Effect of different flocculation procedures, using polymer A and a kaolin concentration of 140 mg/l. Procedures: 1) Rapid mixing only, 2) Rapid mixing and tube flow (as in Figure 1); 3) Rapid mixing and slow stirring in syringe. Specific resistance shown as percentage of original value.

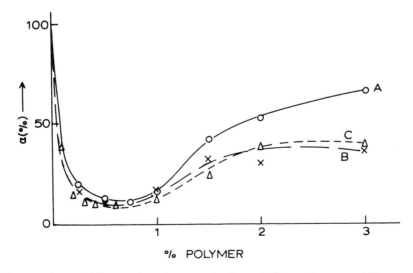

Figure 6.   Effect of polymers A, B and C on the specific resistance of kaolin. Rapid mixing only.

In this procedure, visible flocs became apparent after about 5 minutes of slow stirring and the floc size continued to increase up to about 30 minutes. After long stirring times, flocs appeared to be quite strong and survived transfer to the syringe without much break-up.

Figure 7 shows the specific resistance of the flocculated samples immediately after rapid mixing and after increasing times of slow stirring. The major reduction in specific resistance (about 85%) has already occurred during the rapid mixing phase. Further prolonged slow stirring, during which the flocs grow considerably in size, produces only a relatively minor reduction. Practically all of the reduction in specific resistance has occurred after 15 minutes.

One possible explanation of this behaviour is in terms of a model for floc structure postulated by Michaels and Bolger (14) and elaborated by van de Ven and Hunter (15). Flocs are regarded as aggregates, not of individual particles, but of 'micro-flocs' or 'flocculi'. Micro-flocs would be formed during the rapid mixing period and their size would depend on the shear conditions. During the slow stirring period floc growth is by collision and aggregation of the micro-flocs. The implication of the present results is that the formation of micro-flocs gives the major improvement in filtrability, most likely by an effective reduction in the surface area of the particles. Aggregates of micro-flocs might still be quite permeable, so that most of the remaining particle surface would be accessible to the flowing liquid and the resistance to flow would not be much less than that of the micro-flocs.

However, during the formation of a filter cake, flocs must be subject to considerable disruptive forces and large aggregates may not survive. Scanning electron micrographs of filter cakes formed after various periods of slow stirring have shown no obvious differences.

Conclusions

The method described here provides a convenient means of determining the specific filtration resistance of fairly dilute suspensions. Results for clay suspensions flocculated by cationic polymers show that the specific resistance gives a sensitive indication of flocculation and is a useful guide in the selection of optimum flocculant concentrations. In a series of trials not reported here, it has been shown that the specific resistance results are very well matched by re-filtration rate data, as expected. The results also agree well with other, unrelated techniques. For more concentrated suspensions, some discrepancies have been found between permeability methods and other measures of flocculation (4).

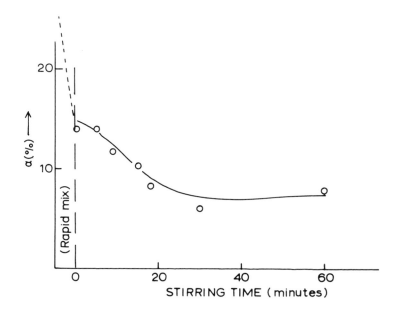

Figure 7.   Effect of slow stirring period on specific
resistance of flocculated kaolin (0.5% polymer A).

There is a problem with the present technique, which has
not so far been mentioned. Attempts to study flocculation by
high molecular weight anionic polymers have proved largely
unsuccessful and the reason was found to be blockage of pores in
the membrane filter by the polymer. Similar effects were
found for the highest molecular weight cationic polymer (C), but
only at concentrations rather higher than those used in this work.
This problem could be overcome by using a support medium with
larger pores, but then primary (unflocculated) particles would
not be efficiently retained. Membrane filtration of polymer
solutions using a method like that described here might provide
a simple means of estimating molecular weights.
      Even though the new technique is largely automated, it is
still a rather lengthy procedure, compared to some other
methods of flocculation testing (13), and would probably not be
used simply to find optimum flocculant concentrations.
However, as a means of studying the filtrability of suspensions
and the effect of particle aggregation, either in fundamental
work or in practical applications, it could prove to be useful.

Acknowledgment

This work was supported by a grant from the Science and
Engineering Research Council.

Literature Cited

1. Halverson, F.; Panzer, H.P. in Kirk-Othmer:Enclclopedia of
   Chemical Technology; John Wiley: New York, 1980; Vol. 10,
   pp. 489-523.
2. Ruehrwein, R.A.; Ward, A. Soil Sci. 1952, 73, 485-492.
3. La Mer, V.K. Disc. Faraday Soc. 1966, 42, 248-254.
4. Slater, R.W.; Kitchener, J.A. Disc. Faraday Soc. 1966, 42,
   267-275.
5. Grace, H.P. Chem. Eng. Prog. 1953, 49, 303-318.
6. Smellie, R.H.; La Mer, V.K. J. Coll. Sci. 1958, 23. 589-599.
7. Willis, M.S.; Tosun, I. Chem. Eng. Sci. 1980, 35, 2427-2438.
8. Gale, R.S.; Baskerville, R.C. Water Pollution Control 1968,
   67, 233-241.
9. O'Gorman, J.V.; Kitchener, J.A. Intl. J. Miner Proc. 1974, 1,
   33-49.
10. de Moor, A.E.L.; Gregory, J. Proc. Water Filtration Symposium,
    KVIV Antwerp, 1982.
11. Gregory, J.J. Coll. Interface. Sci. 1976, 55, 35-44.
12. Gregory, J. Chem. Eng. Sci. 1981, 36, 1789-1794.
13. Gregory, J.; Nelson, D.W. in "Advances in Solid-Liquid
    Separation"; Gregory, J., Ed; Ellis-Horwood: Chichester, 1984.
14. Michaels, A.S.; Bolger, J.C. Ind. Eng. Chem. Fundam. 1962, 1.
    153-162.
15. van de Ven, T.G.M.; Hunter, R.J. Rheol. Acta 1977, 16, 534-543.

RECEIVED October 7, 1983

Author Index

Subject Index

Production by Frances Reed
Index by Susan Robinson
Jacket design by Anne G. Bigler

Elements typeset by Hot Type Ltd., Washington, D.C.
Printed and bound by Maple Press Co., York, Pa.

RECENT ACS BOOKS

"Assessment and Management of Chemical Risks"
Edited by Joseph V. Rodricks and Robert C. Tardiff
ACS SYMPOSIUM SERIES 239; 192 pp; ISBN 0-8412-0821-2

"Chemical and Biological Controls in Forestry"
Edited by Willa Y. Garner and John Harvey, Jr.
ACS SYMPOSIUM SERIES 238; 406 pp; ISBN 0-8412-0818-2

"Chemical and Catalytic Reactor Modeling"
Edited by Milorad P. Dudukovic and Patrick L. Mills
ACS SYMPOSIUM SERIES 237; 240 pp; ISBN 0-8412-0815-8

"Multichannel Image Detectors Volume 2"
Edited by Yair Talmi
ACS SYMPOSIUM SERIES 236; 333 pp; ISBN 0-8412-0814-X

"Efficiency and Costing: Second Law Analysis of Processes"
Edited by Richard Gaggioli
ACS SYMPOSIUM SERIES 235; 262 pp; ISBN 0-8412-0811-5

"Xenobiotics in Foods and Feeds"
Edited by John W. Finley and Daniel E. Schwass
ACS SYMPOSIUM SERIES 234; 432 pp.; ISBN 0-8412-0809-3

"Nonlinear Optical Properties of Organic and Polymeric Materials"
Edited by David J. Williams
ACS SYMPOSIUM SERIES 233; 244 pp.; ISBN 0-8412-0802-6

"Rings, Clusters, and Polymers of the Main Group Elements"
Edited by Alan H. Cowley
ACS SYMPOSIUM SERIES 232; 182 pp.; ISBN 0-8412-0801-8

"Bacterial Lipopolysaccharides: Structure, Synthesis, and Activities"
Edited by Laurens Anderson and Frank M. Unger
ACS SYMPOSIUM SERIES 231; 326 pp.; ISBN 0-8412-0800-X

"Geochemistry and Chemistry of Oil Shales"
Edited by Francis P. Miknis and John F. McKay
ACS SYMPOSIUM SERIES 230; 557 pp.; ISBN 0-8412-0799-2

"Molecular-Based Study of Fluids"
Edited by J. M. Haile and G. A. Mansoori
ADVANCES IN CHEMISTRY 204; 524 pp.; ISBN 0-8412-0720-8

"Polymer Characterization--Spectroscopic,
Chromatographic and Physical Instrumental Methods"
Edited by Clara D. Craver
ADVANCES IN CHEMISTRY 203; 792 pp.; ISBN 0-8412-0700-3